Military

During a military assignment to a small, embassy-attached organization in Belgium, all of its members essentially became a family. My wife Ruth and Mae were especially close.

The two of them led a group of thirty of the European Commonwealth-connected wives on a tour that was of historical proportions.

The group had their own Sabena Jet, led by the famous Dakaks of Jerusalem, Jordan. They traveled through Lebanon to Baalabek, one of the world's most historical cities, throughout the Holy sites of Jordan, and the fantastic civilization of ancient Egypt. Such a trip would be difficult to top.

However, they managed this feat! Their plane with their group aboard was the first to land in Athens, Greece, after the great coup attempt of 1967. They dined at the first restaurant to open in post-war Athens to the delight of the local Greeks. This was a restaurant kept open especially for this American group!

William Woodyard, B/G, USAF
Former Dean of Faculty, USAF Academy

Political

I have known Kip since we were both learning to walk. We were always more closely knit than brothers. When he brought Edna Mae Gentry to Massillon for a summer vacation at his mother's home, I was astounded.

Edna Mae was so beautiful one could hardly look directly at her. She came with a wonderful physic, coal-black hair, perfect complexion, sparkling brown eyes, and a quick, enquiring mind. I knew Kip had found a perfect companion who would make an impression on our world.

Warren Wefler, Esquire
Ohio Land Baron and Real Estate Developer

Sports

I am largely a product of World War II as a B-17 Wing Commander. Mine was the only B-17 to survive a raid on the Ploestie oil fields. I tend to judge events against that background.

Mae is a competitor. She has been golf club champion twenty times. Mae is beautiful, athletic, and is always self-composed. She is quietly determined, and any golfer, including the men, must do their best to stay with her.

Mae is the type of person we all strive to be.

Marlen Reber, Colonel, USAF
Its Youngest Full Colonel
Service #8455A

Family

I was there when Mae was born. I shared her march through schooldom and attended her marriage at West Point.

I was involved with and kept abreast of all her simply unbelievable involvement in military, political and civil activities all over our world.

I watched amazed as Mae successfully raised three sons and at the same time had major impacts on our Earth's events. What a niece!

Vada Gentry, Forty-Years Executive Secretary
Review and Herald Publishing Company, Washington, D.C.

American Princess

American Princess
Dancing among the Stars

A biography of
Edna Mae Gentry Kipfer

Colonel Don Kipfer

MaeDon Publishing

ISBN: 0-9614549-2-X
Library of Congress Control Number: 2003107594
Manufactured in the United States of America

By the author:
Punta Gorda
Color U. S. Yellow
To Save Our World
Of Thee I Sing

MaeDon Publishing
825 Via Formia
Punta Gorda, FL 33950

Contents

Introduction

All of the history's great immigration of human beings seems to be for the benefit of some individual seeking power for himself. In the nineteenth century a new style of immigration began and became a torrent of tortured human beings. They streamed from Europe to the New World to find personal freedom, economic opportunity and self-esteem.

Never before in the history of mankind had a government, such as that visualized by the Continental Congress of the future United States of America, been implemented. God had certainly touched men such as Washington, Jefferson, Adams, and the other members of this optimistic Continental Congress. They visualized a country governed by the people, of the people, and for the people with equality for all.

Men, such as Charlemagne, Paladin, Ceasar, and the Egyptian pharaohs, and women, such as Queen Victoria and Queen Elizabeth, were born to exercise absolute rule by whim. In the United States it was hoped and planned that leaders would be freely elected by the people. When George Washington was urged to accept the position of emperor in this infant state in the New World, he declined, saying that this new country was to issue into the progress of mankind a government that would serve the people.

In this new government many of its presidents came from well-to-do families. However, many, such as Lincoln, Grant, and Eisenhower, rose to the top position of leadership from humble backgrounds.

During the nineteenth century women were notably absent from high public office. Nevertheless, they played a vital role in the country's development. They bore copious numbers of sons and daughters. They ran the homes and worked with dynamic fervor alongside their men. They counseled and supported their husbands in their efforts to provide increasingly affluent lives.

But beginning with the twentieth century, the women of the United States became emancipated. They led drives to improve their own political positions and began to appear in positions of responsibility. This biography is about a woman, Edna Mae Gentry Kipfer, who in her quiet way, like millions of other American women, led a transition to the true equality for women. No longer were women to be placed upon a pedestal only for their sexuality.

Since it was they who produced the men and women of the future, they intended to have a powerful voice in the direction their country was steered. They also intended to stop the virtual slavery of the hapless women in many other countries.

This biography is intended to examine the influence that produced such a woman. It is intended to set into the record the unbelievably constructive life of a modern American woman, Edna Mae Gentry Kipfer!

Preface

A species' eternity and well-being depend upon its female's ability to produce and nurture outstanding offspring. A civilization's continuity depends upon its ability to satisfy its peoples' needs.

Into man's twentieth century civilization strode a woman who, in addition to birthing and raising her own children, encouraged and assisted innumerable of her fellow women to give their best effort to their walk. Across North and South America, Europe, Asia and Africa, Australia and New Zealand, she strode, presenting herself as a role model for all of Earth's people.

Called by her grandfather a princess, and her mother, an angel, born in a country devoid of nobility, she must be regarded nevertheless as an American Princess.

American Princess is the true story of an American heroine. It is based on the observations of an eyewitness, detailed logs, and photographs that portray every incident included.

Historical characters, political positions, and military exercises are not necessarily the positions of the author. Rather, they are an interpolated version expounded by many different historians.

1

1800–1900: Immigrants, The Quest for Personal Freedom

The Gentrys

David Gentry and his wife, Jaley, were married in 1808 in England. He had no way of knowing nor even fully understanding the Berlin, Warsaw and Milan Decree by Napoleon to bring Britain to its knees by prohibiting British produce from entering Europe. Nor had he any concept of the intricacies of arrangements between European countries decreed by Napoleon. He certainly did not know of Napoleon's retreat from the French campaign in Russia that left Napoleon's *grande armée* as a mere remnant, which had lost a half million men. And David Gentry did not understand that the French principles of liberty, equality, and fraternity were becoming a bit tattered.

But David was a clever, hard-working man who was relegated to a minor clerical position in a small business. "I will never," he complained to Jaley, "rise above this station." And for reasons that he could not identify he knew his company's export business was in trouble. "We, my lass, are sailing for America."

He did not know nor care that James Madison was president of the United States and that the United States was at war with Britain in the War of 1812. Nor did he care that Tecumseh, the fabled Shawnee Indian chief had been killed at the Battle of the Thames, fighting for Great Britain.

The David Gentrys took thirty-four days on a sailing ship to reach Virginia. Both he and Jaley were seasick the entire voyage. And nearly all the other passengers were in the same condition.

David planned to change his profession and become a farmer. He and Jaley followed the Wilderness Road into Kentucky where David had heard of Daniel Boone and Boonesville. They found the roadways into Kentucky clogged with settlers' wagons. If your team slowed you might be pushed from the highway. Expectation was high.

The Gentrys bought a small farm in the foothills of the Appalachian Mountains for $80, where their axes resounded and trees fell.

David was worried about American Indian trouble, though they had not seen a single aborigine on their trip west. He asked his nearest neighbor, "Seth, might there be trouble with the Indians?"

"Hell, no," snarled the formidable settler. "Those heathen have been destroyed. There was a time, only years ago when the Shawnee, Cherokee, Delaware, Creeks, and even the Sauk and Fox were possible trouble. But with the routing of the Sauk and Fox, and the treaty signed by commissioner of the Indian Affairs, Louis Bogy, and the Fox Chief Chekuskuk and the Sauk Chief Keokuk, the pestilence is over."

Jaley waited until she was alone with David. "I do not share Seth's opinion of the American Indian. We saw several Indian women selling merchandise along the road. They could speak English. Their skin garments, cloth, pottery and stone carvings were easily the quality of our English ones."

"True, Jaley, but they do not have iron, steel, and gunpowder!"

Eventually a son, Pleasant, was born in 1828. Pleasant was as ambitious as his father had been when he was young. He studied the farming activities of their neighbors, particularly that of the shamefully rich Virginia plantation owners.

Pleasant came to several conclusions. He could not abide slavery, the primary enabling factor for plantation owners, especially in a country dedicated to equality for all men. He soon learned that his father was not a gifted farmer and told him, "Father, our family will never prosper on this small family farm."

In 1849 when Pleasant and Mariah Park were married, he explained to Mariah, "I've made a decision. We're packing out belongings in our wagon, hitching old Bill to the shafts, and heading west."

Before they could depart, as often happens when human affairs are critical, the feared and dreadful shock of diphtheria terrified their community. "David and Jaley are dead!" reported Pleasant. "I tried to convince Dad to dig a wall, but he wouldn't hear of it. Maybe he should have stayed in England."

"No, no," corrected Mariah. "Jaley told me David was happy for the first time in his life. They owned their own farm, you know. They were never hungry. And David bragged that no man, not even the president, could tell him what to do!"

The David and Jaley Gentrys were buried on their own land, of course. And as soon as the sod was laid over them and a marker installed, the Pleasant Gentrys were on their way west.

Partly because they were both exhausted, partly because old Bill was worn out, and partially because they liked what they saw, they decided to stop. The one cabin in the valley they were passing through housed a large family who told them, "You've arrived in Bear Lick. We've just been declared the State of Kentucky."

Pleasant and Mariah spent several weeks exploring their valley. They picked a plot of forty acres of relatively flat land bordered on one side by a creek and on the other by the steep hills. "Come on, gal, we're going to Berea to get our deed." They lingered, for even this small town was exciting. "Not that we've accomplished this we can return to out land," chuckled Pleasant.

Mariah was a very headstrong woman. "I already know what kind of house I want," she told Pleasant. "It has to be a home constructed of sawed board siding." Pleasant was stunned. "There's no sawmill here, woman."

Mariah knew this. She knew she much settle for a log house. But she was bargaining. "Then I must have a large parlor, a kitchen, and four bedrooms." Pleasant was practical. He would have to fell the logs. "What is the need of four bedrooms for just us two?"

"Never mind, my husband," said Mariah, for she already had experienced Pleasant's unquenched need for sex. "Unless you spend more time sleeping at night, we'll need many bedrooms for I'm not stacking young ones in a single bedroom."

Pleasant and Mariah spent considerable time designing their new home. "I want to use the fewest number of logs possible, woman. Our home will be built with our own labor and if we're fortunate we may find help from our nearest neighbors to raise the heavy rafters."

Pleasant's property was covered with timber suitable for use in a log house. He had to work with an axe, adze, and crosscut saw to prepare them. "Mariah, you notice I'm numbering each log. Then I'm stacking them, with the aid of our newly acquired team, on our site, high above the creek, where our home is to be built."

Finally, with the help of the Turpins, the Rubles, their sons and teams, the house-raising was accomplished. When Mariah saw that Pleasant had shot a bear, a deer and a number of squirrels, she screamed, "Who do you think can eat all that food?" Pleasant just laughed, "Wait and see."

Mariah was the cook, whose backbreaking labor prepared the feasts for the hungry workers during the two days it required to raise their log house. When it was completed, John Turpin slapped his side and called out. "Folks, skidaddle over here, I've brought both sweet and sour cider."

15

One of the Ruble boys played the fiddle, "Look at these happy immigrants," whispered Mariah, "they are really celebrating their good fortune to be living in such a fruitful place!"

Pleasant Gentry declared to Mariah, "Farming, especially clearing the land, is extremely difficult, even for a man born to the land." The first few years he could scarcely feed his family, even with access to the abundant game, wild fruit and nuts close at hand. But soon he and Mariah saw the change. "We are beginning to prosper. And planting tobacco is earning us some real money."

The folks in Bear Lick knew nothing of the reasons for nor the magnitude of the great migration from Europe to the New World. But soon the Gentrys, Turpins, and Rubles realized that more neighbors were moving into their valley and onto the flatlands to the East. Mariah told the group on Sunday when the three families had gathered at the Gentrys for a Sunday meal, "We need a church and a school for our kids!"

Sarah Turpin raised her hand and everyone quieted. "There is no reason we cannot do that! I know Mariah Gentry, here, could teach our kids. Pleasant Gentry is a natural preacher." Everyone cheered. Some were thrilled that they had avoided the tasks.

All the local people were overjoyed with the thought of a schoolhouse and a church. But Pleasant, ordained by his neighbors as their preacher, wanted their church to be a beacon. He told Mariah, "These projects will be more satisfying if they have sawed lumber. We must see to it!" The very next day Pleasant left for Berea. "I'm purchasing a large saw and engine."

Everyone pitched in to help install the equipment. Two months later Mariah wrote back to her mother, "Boards are beginning to pile up at Gentry's sawmill."

Thus industry came to Bear Lick. "Men are being employed," gasped Mariah. "Purchases are being made."

Not unexpectedly, Pleasant prospered. "Buildings at Bear Lick are changing their appearance," observed Mariah. "Finally, my good man, procrastinate no longer, I demand wooden floors in my log home."

For Mariah, the wooden floors were only reasonable. "It is time for your promise to come true, Pleasant. It is time for some tangible reward for my labor, sweet man. I have produced five boys and three girls: Curtis in 1850, Albert in 1952, Cashus in 1854, Malinda in 1856, William C. in 1858, Marietta in 1862, George Washington Banal in 1864, and Dovey in 1869."

"By this time," laughed Pleasant, "I understand the need for four bedrooms in our home. Even so, it means three girls and three boys to a room and those two oldest boys in one room."

Pleasant was not only a lay minister, but a generous man. When Mariah began to notice beams and siding boards accumulating at the mill she questioned her taciturn husband. "Why aren't you selling all the lumber you're sawing, Pleasant?"

"My dear," laughed Pleasant, "didn't you guess that is your new house?" And so, first in the valley, a real, English-style home, with wonderful rooms, and wooden floors was built on Gentry property. The sometimes demanding Mariah, overcome with joy, told Pleasant, "My husband, I will ask no more, I am a teacher, you are a preacher. You have a good business. We have no debts. We have eight wonderful children. And, by the grace of God, we are free in America."

Pleasant embraced his wife, an affection he had never before shown and whispered in her ear, "Amen!"

George Washington Gentry was a conservative boy, determined to improve his status during his lifetime. He attended the school his mother had founded and learned to read and write. He attended church and studied the Bible. He worked hard on the Gentry farm. But he also worked for his father Pleasant at the sawmill and was paid generous wages for his time. He saw his savings begin to increase. Still, every family needed wild game to supplement the domestic animals available for food. So George hunted with his brothers for bear, rabbits, and squirrels, and received additional money from this source. He helped his father insure their large family was well fed and housed. He also assisted by teaching at the school and church.

Time passed. All George's brothers and sisters had married except for his youngest sister, Dovey. His mother, Mariah, cornered George one day and got his attention. George was surprised when his mother took him by his arm and looked him in the eye with an unusually serious expression and began her concerns.

"George, there are plenty of eligible girls here in this valley. You have considerable money. You're attractive. Aren't you ever planning to get married?"

George knew his mother was not only serious, but concerned. He only smiled and said, "There's still time, Mother. There's still time."

Every woman knows, whether she is from this new land, from Mexico, Europe, Asia, or Africa, that giving birth to a human child is both dangerous and in most cases unbearably painful. In the hollow, when the country side was nearly soundless and the houses were relatively close together, any sound was trapped in a traveling wave tube, and could be heard for great distances. Thus nearly every new citizen's arrival time and place were common knowledge. The piercing screams of the mother, sometimes left to her own devices, sometimes with the help of a midwife, but almost never with the aid of a doctor, announced the birthing agony. This morning in March 1878, George heard the familiar screams coming from Sidney and Sarah Ruble's home. He knew a baby was being born.

As soon as the Rubles permitted, visitors came to see the newly arrived Maggie Ruble. George was among the first visitors. When he got home his mother, Mariah, quizzed him, "George, what did you think of the Ruble's new arrival?" George laughed louder and with more enthusiasm than his mother had ever seen. He could hardly speak because he was so doubled up. "Ma'am, I've always admired Sarah Ruble. Her baby looks just like her. I'm going to marry Maggie Ruble. She's a pip!"

Mariah nearly collapsed. She could hardly breathe. Her son must be daft. "George, you're not serious. You're fourteen years old!" George just grinned. "Oh, I'm serious enough, Mom. I'm dead serious."

As time has always done, man's years moved rapidly on. Bear Lick saw many new families arrive. Mariah watched as her children grew up, married and left Bear Lick. Some went to Berea, others to Ohio and her most adventurous son, William, simply went west. No one heard from him again. His mother, as for any mother, was horrified at such a loss. But George stayed on. Mariah, seething with concern, could stand it no longer. She again cornered him. "George, you're twenty-eight years old! You're almost old enough to be a grandfather. Are you not interested in marrying and raising a family?"

"Ma'am," smiled George, "I told you my plan. The time is not far off." Close to anger, Mariah tossed her head and grimaced, turned and walked away. And so the matter seemed to lie.

But George had his own agenda. While he still lived at home he had a number of irons in the fire. His responsibilities at home had increased. He still helped Pleasant on the home farm, but he was now the chief operating officer at the sawmill and was working long hours to supply the growing local demand for lumber. Since the state had created Madison County, George had petitioned for and was awarded the job of county road superintendent. "Dad, I'm responsible for any new gravel road, the construction of small bridges, and for keeping the shoulders of the roads clear and trim. I've hired six local men to help me," he said.

Still, George knew these rather mundane chores were secondary to his real passion. He was really grooming Maggie Ruble to be his wife. The Rubles trusted George, and George never betrayed their trust.

George first began his campaign by taking Maggie, when she was just a toddler, on long rides with him astride his racing horse, Blackie. He took her fishing with him for trout in the deep pools of their creek. On hot summer days both George and Maggie took their swimming suits and rode Blackie to their favorite deep, cool pool. As Maggie raced into her teen years, she told George, "I want a fine, mill-sawed board house when I get married. I want at least four children." George just smiled for he had not had to even divulge his own plan.

When Maggie reached the age of sixteen, when many New World females felt compelled to marry, George took Maggie to the barn dance in Turpins' new barn, built of Gentry lumber. Of course, the folks of the Lick believed they knew what George and Maggie had been up to. Most of them were certain that more had transpired than was actually the case. Still this more formal date brought the affair in to the open and many a man lifted his cup of hard cider to George in complement, for Maggie Ruble was a beautiful, smart woman.

But time was passing slowly for Mariah, She pestered her recalcitrant son, "George, people are talking. Are you and Maggie never going to marry? Am I to die without seeing my grandchildren?"

George was unmoved. He told his mother his plan for the first time. "Ma'am, we surely do intend to get married. As soon as Maggie is ready. We already have plans for our house. We won't be leaving Bear Lick. And we plan to fill it with kids as soon as possible." Mariah breathed a sigh of relief.

On Maggie's twenty first birthday she and George announced in church, "George and I are engaged. We're going to marry."

The ceremony was to be held in the Bear Lick Church with a reception at Pleasant and Mariah Gentry's to follow. Everyone was invited.

Hundreds of people attended the festivities. The Rubles provided the music and singing. Couples danced on the newly mowed lawn. Venison, bear, turkey, squirrel and chicken were roasted. Vegetables were gathered from the garden. And Mariah had baked dozens of deep-dish cobblers. "There can be no doubt at long last," laughed Mariah, "that George and Maggie are married." People lingered about the bon fires until late at night, drinking sweet and hard cider and singing. George complained to Maggie, "Don't these people ever get tired? Won't they ever leave?"

One thing happened just prior to the wedding that changed the family history of the George and Maggie Gentrys forever. Their Baptist preacher came down with pneumonia a day prior to the ceremony and both George and Maggie were heartbroken. George remembered that a Seventh-day Adventist preacher, Dan Offill, had just arrived in Bear Lick to conduct a camp meeting revival. George explained their problem to Reverend Offill. Both the young people were relieved when Dan Offill smiled and replied,

"Of course I will be overjoyed to join you wonderful young folks in holy matrimony."

And so it was that this branch of the Gentry clan was unexpectedly exposed to Adventism. They both attended all of Pastor Offill's camp meetings. They asked lots of questions.

George and Maggie were both sincere Christians. Not only did they practice the laws of God but they faithfully attended church each Sunday. So it was not unreasonable when they asked Pastor Offill, "Why do the Adventists observe Saturday as the holy day instead of Sunday?"

Pastor Offill, like any practicing Adventist had his answer memorized. "The answer is known to every Adventist but it was formalized by Ellen G. White in her book *The Great Controversy* published in 1888. In the very bosom of the Decalogue in the fourth commandment: "Remember the Sabbath day, to keep it Holy. Six days shalt thou labor, and do all thy work: but the seventh day is the Sabbath of the Lord thy God: in it thou shalt not do any work (Exodus 20:8–11)."

On the night of the last meeting, when they were close together in bed, George said, "I liked Pastor Offill. What he says made good sense to me. Both you and I believe in Christian doctrine. It seems to me that the Adventists live our beliefs. I wonder if we should join them?"

Maggie was nearly asleep but she understood every word George had murmured, "Yes, George, he preaches the very things we believe. I think we would be wise to follow his way."

And so, for George and Maggie, and all of the people in the New World, a new century, the twentieth, began. It was not only a new century but an abrupt turning point for the George C. Washington Banal branch of the Gentry clan.

The Glaunsingers

The Glaunsingers had lived in Prussia since the Germanic tribes came out of Eastern Europe and settled Germany, the Scandinavians, and parts of Great Britain. They had enjoyed the regimented life of Wittenberg, but when Prussia became a part of a Confederated Germany and fell under the control of Austria they were horrified. Gottfried said, "It is time to leave Prussia! I am leaving my beloved country and going to the New World where I believe the political situation will be more stable."

But Gottfried had been deeply in love for several years with Margaret Schafer, eight years his junior, born on 22 August 1846 in Wittenberg, Germany. He could not leave her. "Margaret I am going to America. I want you to marry me and go to America, also. But the time of our departure is very critical. We can get married in a church, under God's rules when we arrive in the New World. Will you go?"

Margaret leaned over and kissed Gottfried, "Oh, yes. What an adventure!"

The young couple became a part of the great European immigration to the New World. So that by 1866 the Glaunsingers were on their way. Like most immigrants they were seasick during the twenty-nine-day voyage in their tall sailing ship.

Gottfried had done his homework and knew when he and his Margaret landed, that they were headed west where land was cheap or perhaps even free. As they crossed New York and Pennsylvania they marveled at the beauty and natural wealth of their new country and especially at its sparse population. "Mein Gott, Gotfried, it's almost like Germany!"

When they arrived in their horse-drawn wagon in Ohio. These regulated Bavarians decided to stop for a few days and rest. It so happened that they were near Mount Vernon, Ohio, and noticed the billboard announcing a camp meeting with music and good food. Because their ability to speak and understand English was poor they were surprised to find they had arrived at a Seventh-day Adventists religious get-together.

"Before we become to tangled with a certain group here in the New World, my fraulein, we should remember what we have left behind," he said.

"That seems reasonable, Gottfried."

It was a time of great controversy in Europe. The years from 1830 to 1866 had been a time of intensive middle-class liberalism. But this movement has surrendered to blatant nationalism tempered by romanticism. We have seen it reflected in Germany in the architectural embellishment of Munich. In 1859 French and Sardinia troops defeated the Austrians at Solferino, giving we Prussians the hope of slipping our Austrian keepers and so Prussia mobilized along the Rhine. Soon Otto von Bismark was planning to expel Austria from Germany. Between 1862 and 1866 the Prussian army was reorganized and reformed.

In the Seven Weeks War, Prussia and Italy arrayed against Austria and sent her scampering out of Germany

"In Pfaffingin, Wittenberg, Germany, where I was born on 17 June 1838, I became a student of history, especially that of Germany and Prussia. I told my father, 'Political tempers are hot all over Europe, Father. I believe we will soon see war between France and Prussia. I must leave. I am going to the New World!' And so, my dear, as a result of all those political factors, we find ourselves here in this friendly, stable, safe small town."

"I understand, Gottfried. These people are very nice. I like them. Perhaps we could get married here, I see a church," said Margaret.

"Yes," agreed Gottfried, "they are friendly people. And their food is good. It is *sehr gut* that so many people in the New World respect and honor God and Christ Almighty and that many can speak and understand German."

At twenty-eight years of age Gottfried was tall for a Glaunsinger and grew wavy, black hair, not typical for Germans. His mating juices were in full flow and both he and Margaret decided to marry in Mt. Vernon. However, they delayed their union until they had found a permanent home.

Gottfried and Margaret settled near Newark, Ohio, on the Licking River where they had located a good piece of land suitable for a farm. But before Gottfried and Margaret decided to look further for their permanent home they entered the Adventist Church where the preacher fondly greeted them. This kindly man turned the handsome young couple about so that they faced the large Adventist Camp Meeting congregation. "I want you all to know that these fearless young people have left their parents and friends in Germany to come and live among us. They traveled across Germany, sailed by boat across the Atlantic Ocean, and traveled by wagon from New York to live among us. They fear that soon Germany will be at war with France and they do not wish to live through such times. We Americans have just concluded a Civil War so terrible that none of us could understand it. Give them your sympathy and help."

But while the two young people admired the Adventists, Margaret was a staunch member of the Evangelical Church and remained loyal until her death.

Now, settled in Newark, Gottfried, aged twenty-nine years, and Margaret, aged twenty-one were married on 18 March 1867. Gottfried's father, a man of great generosity, had given Gottfried his share of the family savings and with that the two young lovers were able to pay for their land and begin life debt free.

But Gottfried told Margaret, "We'll need more money to live well. I've taken a job with Vogelmeyer to manufacture brick."

Gottfried and Margaret lost no time in starting their family. In yearly succession they produced Fred A., George, William, Mary, and Louise. The farm prospered, Margaret concluded she had produced sufficient babies to suit her. She told Gottfried, "Enough, yet!"

But Gottfried soon found he was suited for a more demanding trade, which paid more money. He engaged with the Baltimore and Ohio Railroad Company to work as a machinist in its shop. It was a position that was to later change the life of his son, Fred A. Glaunsinger.

Gottfried and Margaret believed they had done well at producing human beings. Years later, when Margaret was ninety-two and living in Newark with her daughter, Mrs. Jesse Rees, she was well-known as the oldest member of the St. John's Evangelical Church. Her early morning walks, *glucklich hausfrau* manner, and the rollicking, hearty chortle of her jolly German forebears made her a favorite of her neighborhood.

But now a strange thing occurred, as sometimes does, that changed Fred A. Glaunsinger's life forever. Gottfried's company sent him on railroad business to make a special repair near Grafton, West Virginia. Fred, grown and eager to explore his world, begged, "Papa, I want to go with you. I understand West Virginia is much like Germany. I would like to see it."

"Yah! I could stand some help. I might even arrange to get you on the payroll!" And so off they went, these two early men of the industrial revolution. Almost immediately Gottfried met Peter Wood. Peter invited the two men for dinner to meet his wife, Ida, and his family.

"Peter, how many children do you and Ida have?" Peter took a deep breath before answering, as well he should. Then, bowing his head he answered honestly, "Gottfried, my father and his twelve brothers immigrated together to this country. We Woods have always had large families. Ida and I were married in 1858. We have twelve children at last count. Let me see if I recollect their names. There's Delmer, Francis, Rosie, Rubie Leta, Anna Luella (born 1876), Minnie, Mertie, William, Richard F., William, Nancy, and yes, yes, there's Peter. We ran out of names and had to name him after me!"

Gottfried doffed his hat while Fred stood astonished. "In the name of Jesus Christ, Peter, you are a good man!" Gottfried noticed that his son, Fred A., seemed to disappear every evening after dinner. "Hey, Fred, are you down at the Woods' house every night. I suspect you're shinning that Anna Luella. I can't tell one of them Woods girls from another."

"Father, you have forgotten love. I saw no others. I am marrying in Grafton. Anna Luella and I are marrying."

Fred A. had enjoyed that first dinner at the Woods' more than any he had ever attended. Now he told his father, "I like Grafton. While you've been arranging your business, I've been looking around. It's on the railroad. Tygart Lake is sehr gut and nearby. And it's right on a fork of the Monongahela River, which gives it access to the whole world by water."

Gottfried, like most fathers, knew his son. "Of course there were sixteen of us at the Wood table for dinner. But I noticed that you sat next to that sweet-looking girl, Anna. Are you sure it's not her you find sehr gut rather than Grafton?"

"Father, you were young once. You even left Germany to follow Mama!"

"But son, the Woods have a total of seven daughters. They are all *schon.*

How could you pick Anna Luella?"

"Father, you have forgotten love. I saw no others. I am remaining in Grafton. Anna Luella and I are marrying.."

When Gottfried returned to Newark alone, Margaret questioned him with considerable concern. "Who are these people, the Woods?"

Gottfried told her. "They are good Christian people. Anna Luella is kind, smart, and a beauty. She seems already to have their lives all planned."

When Gottfried shook his head and wondered, "How could Fred pick one special girl from among all the Woods bunch?"

Margaret emitted the loudest, most merry laugh Gottfried ever heard from her. "*Meine Heir*, you picked me, didn't you? And Fred simply proves that few men are so fast on the trigger as a Glaunsinger."

And so for the Fred Glaunsingers, time passed on to the twentieth century. They had produced Louise, Irene, Marie, and Fred A. Jr., then Anna Kathryn in 1902 and Elizabeth. These American citizens born at the turn into the twentieth century, had no clue as to their country's future, and could not know that in the twentieth century the United States would become the dominant power on Earth.

The Kipfers

The Germanic tribes that came out of the East and settled in present-day Germany, Scandinavia and Northern Ireland, had a well-earned reputation for military action. The expansion motives of Germany were correctly blamed for World War I. Although many Germans blamed repressive measures against Germany by other nations, Hitler was without a doubt the cauldron from which would spring World War II. The Germans displayed an aptitude for war that had not been seen since France under Napoleon had conquered most of Europe.

Contrasting violently with this attitude were the vast majority of German people who showed a remarkable talent for farming, science, engineering, art and music. Many of these Germans detested warfare.

The Kuepfer (later Americanized to Kipfer) family realized that their four huge, athletic, intelligent, handsome sons would soon be forced to serve in Germany's army. To give their lives in wars, such as the Franco-Prussian one was a devastating thought for their parents.

"*Vor Gott, meine Mann, wissen nicht* you do something?" angrily asked his frau..

"Yah, yah!"

In the middle of the night, dressed as poor farmers, with a wealth of jewels concealed in the hollowed out heels of their heavy shoes, the four brothers, Andy, Will, Manly, and John, headed west to Holland. Truly, these four proud Germans were devastated. "It is the worst day of my life, to watch Berlin disappear behind us," declared John.

"Yah," agreed Andy, "but it would be worse if we were unable to see it."

They were little different from other immigrants in one respect. During their voyage to America, they were all deathly seasick on their transatlantic trip. "It is disgraceful," howled Manly, "for us strong Germans to be struck helpless by the motion of a ship!"

Still, they were better informed about America than others in one respect. One of the Glaunsingers from Wittenberg had drifted into Berlin in search of work and kept the Kuepfers informed of the Glaunsinger experience in the New World.

So when the brothers landed in New York, they headed west immediately for Ohio. Andy, Will and Manly settled in Justice, Ohio. John H. Kuepfer settled in nearby Brewster, where he used a part of his hidden jewels to purchase 640 acres of farmland on Sugar Creek. He spent nearly all of the money he had left to build a comfortable house and barn, He proudly had the family name, Kuepfer, placed in colorful tile on the barn roof of grey slate normally used for roofing in Ohio.

John eventually married into one of the largest family groups in Ohio, the Stoners. John H. and Mary produced two sons, John and Christian. Both boys were huge. Many local people referred to them as giants.

Josephine Glick, Christian's wife, told her mother, "That John Kuepfer's huge for an eighteen-year-old. Christian told me John can sweep with a cradling scythe, and take a path through the wheat field twelve feet wide. No other man can hope to do such a thing!"

John took wheat and other produce by wagon to Massillon and Canton for his father to sell. The wheat was shipped on the Ohio & Erie Canal. He always stopped at Stuhldreher's drugstore for a soda before he returned to Brewster. On one of these stops he noticed several young women eating ice cream sundaes. One in particular, tall and handsome, with wavy dark hair, caught his attention. When she smiled at him he had to walk over and talk to her. "I'm John Kuepfer. I'm up here in Massillon from Brewster. Would you mind telling me what your name is?"

Mary M. Stoner was no shrinking violet. She was raised in a very large family with four brothers and was not shy around men. She laughed and said, "I wouldn't mind at all, John. Why don't you sit down and join us, unless you're in to big a hurry."

John plopped into the one empty seat. "Mary, I just lost my interest in speed!"

John stopped by the Stoner home every time he was in Massillon and the two happy young people went to Stuhldreher's for a soda or sundae. In 1880 the two were married and John moved halfway between Brewster and Massillon onto a modest farm in Stanwood, Ohio.

Before John could harvest the first crop Charles Franklin Kuepfrer was born. In 1890 Anna Kuepfer, and then in 1895, Howard Keupfer were born. Mary Stoner was a large woman for her time and John was truly a giant. Even so no one could believe that all these babies came into the world at weights of more than twelve pounds.

Life at the Kuepfer farm was cheerful. Still there was a one problem. Mary (Mame) had been raised in the city and was accustomed to more than just food, shelter and clothing. She felt, and John concurred, that she deserved more.

John solved this problem in two ways. Charlie was more than six feet tall and weighed more than 200 pounds before he was thirteen. He had completed the sixth grade at Stanwood school and could write.

"Mame, Charlie knows everything he needs to be a farmer or a miner. I'm hiring him out as a primary hand to our in-law, Peter Hornberger, on his grand farm several miles southwest of Massillon. There he'll learn independence and everything about farming. He did not add that Charlie would also endure backbreaking work.

John himself supplemented his farm income with employment in the deep coal mines at Stanwood. He was so large and strong that he mined more coal in one day than the company would credit and pay him for. And so he took Howard, younger than Charlie to the mine so that together they could draw double John's maximum allowable wage. By day's end, Howard was so exhausted that John carried him home on his shoulders.

Then one day Mame came home sobbing, "John, some of the women are acting strangely toward me and I overheard one mention, 'John Kuepfer is a German!'"

"Mame, I knew this was sure to come. The men in Massillon and the paper, the *Evening Independent*, are fearful that the kaiser's wars in Germany are going to involve all of Europe and perhaps even us. They do not want their sons to leave them. They blame anyone German."

Mame looked at John with horror. "Nor do we, John. But your father and his brothers came to the United State to escape the German military. We are peace-loving people. What are we going to do?"

John didn't appear for work at the mine the next day. He took his horse and wagon and headed for the county seat in Canton, Ohio. He arrived home late that night. Mame met him as he pulled into the barnyard. "What have you done, meine John?"

John laughed. "Mame, I've solved our problem. Now we're truly Americans. I've changed our name to Kipfer. I've paid for the changes and now our kids have been reborn. It says so on their birth certificates."

And so the Kipfers, forming their share of America's backbone, entered the twentieth century.

Baldwin/Bell

Most Americans do not know that the Roman legions under Caesar occupied England as far north as present-day Scotland. When the battle-hardened warriors arrived at the Scottish border they ran into unbelievable resistance from blue men called Pics and Scotts, who simply refused to let Ceasar pass further north. Rather, these blue men were so fearful that they began to push the totally amazed Romans southward, To prevent this embarrassment the Romans built Hadrian's Wall. This architectual wonder ran across England from sea to sea.

On the eastern coast of England, just south of Hadrian's Wall, bustled the city of New Castle. It was famous in England for its coal mines. It was world famous for its coal and fostered the saying in use at the time universally: "That's as foolish as taking coals to New Castle!"

It was in this wealthy and warlike town in 1868 that Thomas Bell and Hanna Green were married. Thomas worked in the mines. His recreation seemed to be church, stout, and producing children. He and Hanna rapidly produced Mary, Isabel, Ruth, Edith, Cora, Elizabeth, George, and William. Hanna did not, as did many women, resent this uninterrupted flow of offspring. She took pride in feeding them, clothing them, seeing that they went to church and school.

Then one day, without any preliminaries, Thomas asked Hanna. "Please, my dear, sit. I have something to tell you." It was shocking news indeed.

"Hanna, at the mine we all know that our coal is running out. Each day we must go deeper and the veins are so thin that we must lie on our bellies to mine it. One of our men has had word from a Thomas Dayton in the New World. It seems the Americans have struck a rich vain of coal in a place called Groves Patch, near Massillon, Ohio. Thomas claims to be rich. We're going there."

Hanna began to sob. "But Thomas, we'll have to leave all our family and friends." She stopped, dried her tears on her apron. "Can I take all my pretties with me?"

Thomas knew the worst was over. "We cannot take everything, Hanna. Pick out what means the most to you and we'll do our best."

Hanna made a list. "Thomas, I've made my list. It begins with the listing of our children." After all she reasoned, they had first priority. "After that

I've listed in order, my silver tableware, my bone china, my crystal, my personal toiletry, the best of my linens, and small pieces of heirloom furniture, cherished in my family for many generations."

"Yes, girl, we can do that."

Hanna had always been an optimist. She had always been able to conquer all the Bell family problems with her positive attitude. But their voyage on the tall ship could only be described as hell! "Only the devil himself could devise such pain, Thomas. I've not eaten for the thirty days aboard this dastardly ship."

Hanna arrived in the New World thin and nearly spent. No one could bear to tell her that the whole Bell family had a wonderful time on the voyage—especially the children, whom Captain Wilson went out of his way to entertain.

Once on shore, Hanna swore on the Holy Bible, "I will never set foot on a tall ship again." And she kept that promise. But ten years later Thomas returned to New Castle for a visit. He had a wonderful time, but told Hanna on his return, "Sure, they're all much poorer than when we left. It is a sorry sight to see them in such straits."

Prearranged through correspondence, Thomas was to be foreman at one of the six mines owned by the Massillon Coal Company. In spite of his large family, because Thomas as a mine foreman had made remarkable high wages, and was as frugal as Hanna was overly generous, he had saved a considerable sum of money. Further, in spite of Hanna's freewheeling ways, the Bells had never touched Hanna's dowry.

When the Bells reached Massillon, Hanna inspected the town with the critical eye of a Pic or Scott. She turned to Thomas and gave him her unvarnished appraisal. "Sure, Thomas, Massillon is a wild place. No one could mistake it for New Castle!"

And when she saw the five acres, with a wee creek coursing through its center, that Thomas had purchased in Groves Patch, she shouted, "Sure, now Thomas, Massillon is crude enough, but did you have to bring me and my children to such a wretched country place?"

However, Thomas soon had a substantial eleven-room house built on the gently rising hill, on the northern edge of his property so that all the Bells were comfortable. He dressed the surrounding land with lawns, gardens, and trees. When Hannah believed she was alone, Thomas actually caught her standing on their front porch, viewing her domain, and saw that she was smiling.

"I've built a large barn in which to stable my black trotting horse, my dear." He told Hanna, "Love, you can go to Massillon as often as you please.

You, and Blackie, and our surrey will make a sight for everyone to admire. I've taught George to handle Blackie and everything there is to know about harnessing and maintaining the surrey."

Hanna made friends quickly with all the women in Groves Patch and also with those in Massillon's Woman's Club. They, of course, were all envious when they saw her bone china, crystal, and silverware. Thomas was happy for although he had the surrey, he could easily walk the quarter mile to his mine as a daily exercise.

Then suddenly, as bad as the sea sickness hell on the tall ship, diphtheria struck the souls of Groves Patch. Thomas, so tall and handsome and strong, was the first to die. He was soon followed by William and John. Everyone in Stark county suffered terribly. Hanna felt the loss more than anyone. She knew it was a disaster from which she would never fully recover. But she realized she was now the head of the Bell family and that there was no free handouts in Ohio. If one did not work for a day, one did not eat for a day.

When Hanna took stock of her assets she realized since three males and one female were deceased, she now had extra bedrooms. Her kitchen, dining room and living rooms were large. Her children were all nearly grown and the seven girls, and George also, were capable help. She told all the children, "We're opening Bell's Boarding House!"

Miraculously, almost a present from God, Hanna concluded, her first roomer was Alfred Baldwin. Although Hanna never knew for sure, it gave her great satisfaction to believe Alfred was related to the famous English Baldwin family of Prime Minister Standly Baldwin. Alfred was a stationary engineer for all the Massillon Company coal mines. He was well off financially, and was the same age as Thomas Bell had been.

Hanna could not have been considered the most beautiful woman in the New World. But there was no doubt that she was handsome, had a good figure and mind, and was always ready with a joke. Alfred proposed in his second month at the Bell's Boarding House; Hanna had no hope of such a thing happening especially since she still had seven children at home. "Alfred you must be daft. Look at this huge family. Look at me. I'm a human wreck. But yes, I do."

Hannah had long since closed that part of her life that had to do with producing children. But she soon realized Alfred, a bachelor all his life, was a wildly passionate man, eager to explore every hidden corner of their relationship. Alfred was so eager and inexhaustible that she felt their honeymoon would never end. And so, by working with such total enthusiasm, these two over-the-hill lovers managed to produce Charlotte Baldwin and the gorgeous, vivacious, brilliant, redhead, Laura Jane Baldwin.

Laura Jane was so beautiful people watched her in awe. And with her beauty, was a keen mind. She rushed through the Myers school in no time and her teacher knew this talented child should go on to high school and college, but in rural America there was simply no chance of that.

An unusual Bell family situation helped to shape Laura Jane's life. Because there were so many older siblings by the time Laura was born, all the household chores, such as cooking, sewing, baking, etc., had been assigned. Consequently, Laura spent a lot of time with her father and her brother, George. She worked with both of them in the gardens. George considered her his personal slave. As he brought fish, birds, and four-legged game home, he forced Laura to clean them. Laura hated this job and often buried some of the fish in the cornfield behind their home. But Laura was an exceptional gardener and was reputed to be one of the most knowledgeable in Stark County. Male relatives and friends consulted with her on this subject the rest of her life.

Thus the Bell/Baldwin family eagerly entered the twentieth century.

2

1900–1944: Maturing:
We're All A-Building

Newark, Ohio

George and Maggie Gentry eagerly prepared for their move to Academia, Ohio, near Mount Vernon, Ohio. George chuckled and told Maggie, "I like the sound of Mount Vernon. And Pastor Offill says Academia is bonny. We're all set. We have the offer of a house there."

Maggie smiled in her determined way. "George, the most important consideration to me is that the boys can all go to an Adventist school and live in an Adventist atmosphere. By the Grace of God, they will all be saved."

And so the George Gentry's moved to Scyker Road, Academia, Ohio. George worked on the county roads and Maggie kept busy raising her boys and attending church and social meetings.

George was more regimented in his treatment of his sons, though he was unaware of it, than an Army drill sergeant. They were ordered to be in at night by 11:00 P.M. If they were late there was no forgiveness. The house was locked. When they reached sixteen years of age, he sent them from what had always been their home to make a life of their own. Dorsey, the oldest, was first to leave, He found employment with a machine shop in Mount Vernon. As the other boys left Scyker Road, having nowhere else to sleep they went back to Dorsey's. Then as soon as possible they went on to whatever employment they could find.

The young women, and some older ones, in Mount Vernon, saw the Gentry boys as handsome, and knew they were especially talented. Only their God knew, of course, that given a chance they could all have been chief executive officers.

The first part of the twentieth century was acted out against the debilitating specter of World War I. Great Britain, France and Russia on one side; Germany, Austria-Hungary, and Italy on the other, as they would attempt to tear out each others vitals. On 3 August 1914 Germany advanced through poor little, defenseless Belgium and attacked France. World War I had begun.

There were many reasons, some correct, some purely lies, that formed American opinion. The sinking of the passenger ship *Lusitania* by a German submarine certainly tilted public opinion. President Wilson, provided a reason hard to refute, declared, "The world must be made safe for democracy." And so, condemning thousands of United States sons to death, on 6 April 1917, the United States declared war on Germany.

By 1918 it was clear that the United States' allies would loose World War I unless the United States poured huge amounts of war material and troops into the battle. So the United States responded and by 18 July 1918 even the prime minister of Germany knew the war was lost. It was official on 11 November 1918. The astronomical cost in lives and materiel to the United States should have been a lesson never to have been forgotten, However, the lag time for a nation to lose its memory concerning such a despicable event seems to be about three months. Shame be on all humans for such an unforgivable characteristic!

Of George and Maggie's sons, Tracy was the most religiously inclined.

He had the intelligence required to be an influential preacher. He had a voice comparable to any of the popular vocalists of his time and was a popular professional vocalist at local weddings and funerals. Tracy had met the love of his life at a camp meeting in Academia. Her name was Anna Kathyrn Glaunsinger. She was beautiful, talented, in nurse's training and reciprocated Tracy's love. For humans who have truly experienced the power of its attraction, love is irresistible. Tracy rode his bicycle twenty-three miles from Mount Vernon to Newark, Ohio, just to see his Anna.

Anna Glaunsinger's family was well off. Her father, Fred A., owned a farm near Marne, Ohio, and a tailor shop in Newark. His customers were businessmen from throughout Liking County and as far away as Columbus. He had resettled his family from the Grafton, West Virginia, coal mine country to Newark to rejoin the Glaunsinger clan.

Fred A. needed a means of getting his dairy milk from his farm at Marne to Newark. He bought a truck, but he could not spare the time from his tailor shop to make those daily runs. So he went to Newark and told the chief of police that twelve-year-old Anna would make the runs if that was okay. "Sure," said the chief. "Fred, we don't even have any guidance for auto driver's license, as yet. No one has even considered truck drivers. You're the only truck owner in the area!"

So, it was not surprising, though Tracy was embarrassed by it, that when

Tracy came to visit Anna, she taught him to drive the family auto, the first in Newark. Tracy immediately fell in love with the automobile. "Gosh," he told his mother, Maggie, "Mom, it's better than riding a bicycle." On his second visit to Newark he went directly to the local Ferris Tire Building Company, got a job, and moved to Newark.

Tracy worked hard and took all the overtime he could get. Anna signed on at the Newark Sanatarium where her brother-in-law, Eber Opdyke, was the superintendent and where she was awarded a registered nurses diploma and license.

But George B. had not shot his last wad! For him, four sons was not enough. In 1912 Glenna Maud Gentry and in 1914 Vada Mae Gentry arrived unexpectedly. Maggie loved her daughters but never forgave George W. B. for jerking her from her well-deserved retirement from production management.

World War I was a disaster for the people on Earth. The Seventh-day Adventists are unequivocally opposed to killing and thus to war. Philosophers know that national leaders have their own agendas. The people, able to exercise their own minds freely, would never opt for war. Too often the leader's agenda calls for expansion of the state or increased personal power. When that happens, two or more countries come to collision and a war, fought not by eyeball-to-eyeball engagements by the countries top leaders, but primarily by objecting citizens.

Germans had not only peopled Germany, but much of Scandinavia and Northern Ireland. Offshoots had conquered England and as Russ, had settled Russia. But none of this activity added land to the German homeland. German Prussians watched as England, Spain, and Portugal became empires. This was more than the imperialistic Prussians could stomach. So they began to steal real estate in Africa and rattle their sabres in Europe.

Prime Minister Stanley Baldwin quivered and hesitated in cautioning Germany to behave. Too late, this timid man reacted. Germany had already tasted blood and begun the first world war. It was a war that touched every human being on Earth.

Finally, realizing that Great Britain needed help to prevent its defeat and annihilation, Prime Minister Baldwin appealed to President Wilson for help. In his defense, it must be said that President Wilson abhorred the thought of war. But faced with no alternative to the loss of many United States citizens country of origin, he agreed with Prime Minister Baldwin's frantic plan. To gain popular support, he sold the American public on the idea the World War I was a war "to make the world safe for democracy." This decision saved the Anglo-American civilization. However, the United States lost a large percentage of its best young men, mountains of war material, and uncounted tons of food. But, because of that effort, the Allies prevailed. Fortunately for the George B. Gentrys, all their sons were to young to serve.

Tracy and Anna could wait no longer, The personal pressures were to great to resist. They were married at the Glausinger farm on 28 October 1923. The reception was one of the largest held in Ohio that year. All the Gentrys, Glausingers, Rubles, Woods, local neighbors, church members, and businessmen attended. Roasted beef, mutton, chicken, all varieties of vegetable, and coffee, and pumpkin pie and walnut cake were served. The happy couple moved to a modest home at 56 Jefferson Street.

On 10 August 1924 a blessed event occurred at the Jefferson Street address that not only changed the lives of the Tracy Gentrys but was to nudge the lives of many of Earth's citizens to more moral, more productive lives. Edna Mae Gentry was born.

Every profession has it competents and incompetents. Anna's doctor was no genius. Her daughter's birth, at home, was a breached one. While everyone heard the screams during births in Bear Lick, no one heard Anna's. Fortunately Anna was an R.N. and so fortuitously was Mamma Glausinger who assisted Anna's doctor.

"Please, doctor," begged Mamma. "The baby is breached, but I believe I can turn it. Please don't use forceps. Bad things can happen." But this shyster could not be dissuaded.

Mama worked therapy for the next month to straighten Edna Mae's leg, which had been injured by the doctor's forceps. Finally she pronounced to Anna, "She will be okay. She can now use her leg normally."

"Anna," smiled Mama, "this baby is one to be proud of. Her body is perfect. She already has coal black hair. Even her first cries sound sweet and strong. There is something very striking about this child that I do not understand!"

"Mama," whispered Anna, who had been through an unusually brutal experience, "I only care that she is healthy! But both women had been touched by the birth of this baby. They somehow sensed that she would be someone very special.

Akron, Ohio

Business had been unbelievable for everyone in the United States. The stock market was at an all time high. Tracy was optimistic and so when he was offered a promotion in Akron to supervise building tires, he accepted immediately.

Edna Mae questioned her mother, "Mother, why do we have to leave all our neighbors and relatives?"

"Angel, your father would like to be able to give you and I and Margarette more good things."

Edna Mae sensed her mother was no more pleased with the move than she was. But as compensation for her losses, she was given a large new doll and off the Gentrys went in their new Ford auto to Akron.

"Mother," exclaimed Edna Mae. "I do not like this small, hot apartment where we're going to live. Why is Dad working nights and I hardly ever see him? I miss my father." In partial replacement for their losses, Anna took the girls for walks during the day so Tracy could sleep. These walks were very interesting for children from a small-town atmosphere.

The preachers, the business tycoons, the media all suspected that a great depression was approaching. No one suspected that many wealthy men would commit suicide because they had lost their fortunes. But Tracy sensed something. He confided to Anna, "Work at the tire company is slowing down. I am concerned for my job." But then almost providential, by letter, came an offer that was certainly unexpected. Papa Glaunsinger wrote: "Tracy, I cannot handle both the farm and the tailor shop. If you will come live on the farm and run it, when Anna Luella and I die, the farm will go to you and Anna. Let me know. Signed, Fred."

Tracy and Anna discussed Fred A.'s offer. "Anna, we both long for land of our own. This may be our only chance."

Anna agreed, "Let's accept." And so they packed their things and returned to Newark. When Edna Mae saw that their car was packed to overflowing, she was very concerned because her playthings, especially her special doll was not aboard the auto.

When Edna Mae questioned Tracy about this oversight, he explained. "I'm sorry, Mae Mae, but there just isn't room for everything. We'll come back later and get your things."

Edna Mae was old enough to see through such subterfuge. She suspected that her father's promise would never come true. But she did not want to add further to what she sensed were grown-up problems. The return to Akron was never made. She told her husband many years later, "I've never gotten over that loss and betrayal. It may be that I never will get over it for the rest of my life"

Newark, Ohio

Life on the farm was a great change in Edna Mae's life. She was assigned one cow, a small jersey, to take care of, and she had to milk her each day before she left for school. This cow had strange, curved horns and Edna Mae named her Crinkle Bar.

Now, in 1930, she rode a bus to school at Madison Township. In order to get to the bus she had to walk several hundred yards through a pasture ruled by a huge, fearsome bull. She told a classmate, "When I safely make that passage past that ferocious beast, it seems to me to be a near thing!"

But then the Great Depression, more damaging than a tornado, jolted the Glaunsingers and Tracy Gentrys. Tracy, just getting the farm into a really productive posture, moaned to Anna, "No one has any money. Our crops cannot be sold." And at night Fred would rave, "No one can afford tailored clothing."

Everyone, including both the Glaunsingers and Gentry families were nearly penniless. But the government's servants, those people who were elected to represent and protect the citizens, seemed unable to understand this. Often, for no more than a few hundred dollars a family's home or farm was sold by the authorities and resold to unscrupulous carpetbaggers for a small faction of what it was really worth.

Without compassion, the government demanded their taxes. It was no different for Fred A. When he could not pay, nor borrow from any source to pay the taxes on his farm, it was sold by the county to satisfy this debt.

Edna Mae watched this damnable drama unfold with the terror of a young, angry child. She vowed to herself to devote her life to helping the less fortunate and to strive for a kinder society.

Tracy's good job was lost and he and Anna's inheritance had vanished. It was a betrayal from which Tracy really never recovered.

The Tracy Gentrys had to move to Central City, Ohio. Tracy worked in Granville at the "Sugar Loaf" with Mama Glaunsinger house for a year. He rented brother-in-law Opdyke's house on Mount Vernon Road and sublet the apartment upstairs to renters with a vicious, police dog.

The Depression was unbearable for Americans at all economic levels in many ways. But the challenge also drew families together in strange social ways. Edna Mae picked strawberries, beans and peas in her Uncle Tom's farm for sale in his roadside stand. She walked back and forth to Cherry Valley Elementary School where she did well in academics but was one of Newark's outstanding female athletes. She helped many depressed kids find something worthwhile in life by encouraging them to participate in sports. She, as a twelve-year-old, helped her family survive by running the Gentry household while her mother was absent doing private nursing. Certainly twelve years old was a tender age to learn the effort, pain, and skill needed to tend a young family. But in undertaking this responsibility, she learned lessons that many women never learned.

Edna Mae was fortunate in having three uncles nearby. Uncle Tom Powell, who owned and operated Powell Electric, also owned a sprawling summer camp near Black Hand Gorge at White City on the Licking River where all the relatives gathered on weekends. The kids swam and canoed from morning to night. Everything was free and wonderful. Uncle Alvy West and Fred Glaunsinger Jr., took the kids to the local gravel pit, a clear, bottomless artificial lake. They would have the kids climb onto their shoulders and then would jump from the high bank into the water. Naturally these human cannon balls sank to frightening depths. The kids would hold their breath, but their lungs would seem to burst before they came popping to the surface.

Uncle Fred ran an auto repair garage. Based upon these skills and his creative ability, he built skis onto a bicycle frame; he fashioned skis and in wintertime all the cousins performed at downhill races on one of the steep hills on his farm. None of these kids knew they were poor.

Mae knew everyone was having the times of their lives. She knew that this phenomenon was independent of their desperate economic situation. She could only reason that a determined, close-knit, supportive group, such as her family, could survive anything. She knew that this same attitude must also apply to larger state and national groups.

Still Mae was determined to escape this pattern. Then, out of nowhere, she got one of life's first breaks. She had been taking care of her three younger sisters and brother while her mother Anna was being paid to do domestic work. Helen Moyer Southard also lived on Twenty-first Street in a creative home designed by her father and featured in a national fashion magazine. She and her lawyer husband, Franklin, lived in a different economic world. Knowing Edna Mae's experience and her personality, she invited her to act as governess for her baby son, Jack.

Not only was Helen's husband, Franklin, a lawyer, but his father had also been a lawyer and had lived in one of the most lavish homes in Newark on an estate high on the hill bordering 21st Street. Mae's work for Helen was so successful that instead of an hourly wage, Edna Mae was soon paid a small weekly salary. She not only looked after Jack, but also prepared meals and relieved Helen of many household duties.

This was another step up for Mae. And it was also an opportunity for her to learn from a special group skills that would help her throughout her lifetime. Edna Mae had well-defined duties at the Southard's. Involving herself in the Southard's social affairs was not one of them. So, it meant little to her when Helen announced to her, "Mae, two Sundays from now my mother and father, my favorite aunt, Laura Kipfer and her husband, Charlie, and their two children are coming to visit and will be here for dinner. I hope you can be here to help me and to serve dinner."

Edna Mae was pleased to be helpful and had answered, "Yes, I can be here. I'll do whatever I can to help you."

Don Kipfer

Helen had laughed. She knew she was overstepping the line of intimacy between her and this lively young girl but she took her chances. "Aunt Laura will have her son, Don, with her. He's a very good student, a hard worker, and besides that he's tall and good looking. He's just your age, Mae. Maybe you'll like him."

Of course, Mae had all the curiosity about boys that most girls her age harbored. But she had never had a special boyfriend. Her agenda did not include one. She looked at Helen in surprise, and also with a question, but she did not answer.

Edna Mae's aunt, Marie Powell, who lived across the street from Tracy's, was in charge of the Red Cross swimming courses at the YMCA for all of Licking County. She knew Edna Mae was a wonderful athlete. She also knew that her niece, Mae, took no back seat in any sport when competing against her three rambunctious Powell sons, all of whom were older than Mae. Marie was being flooded with kids who wanted to learn to swim. She needed help. She called to Edna Mae when she saw her in her yard, "Edna Mae, I have a job for you if you want it. I need an assistant to help in the swimming classes at the Y. You would be perfect. I will check you out and qualify you as a Red Cross swimming instructor!"

Edna Mae had beamed. She passed her tests with ease. And so at fourteen years of age, enrolled at Woodrow Wilson Junior High School, she not through necessity, but with pride, began her contribution to public service. She taught hundreds of children the professional way of swimming and the lifesaving technique of rescue.

Mae simply adored Helen Southard. Helen was a lady. Helen was super intelligent. But beyond those grand qualities, Helen dressed in beautiful athletic clothes and went off to golf at Mound Builders Golf Club in Newark with supreme class, several times a week. Edna Mae knew the first time she saw Helen leave home in her auto for the golf club that she wanted to be a golfer. She also knew that Helen might be her opportunity to realize this ambition. So when Helen asked her and Margarette to go to the Moyer family reunion at Long Lake, halfway between Newark and Massillon to care for Jack, she could not refuse even though she expected it to be a boring day.

The Moyers' reunion gathered more than fifty people. As soon as families arrived and placed their baskets of food on the tables, the young people went swimming from a flawless beach into clear, cool water. All went swimming, of course, except for Edna Mae and Margarette. They were to look after Jack But suddenly there was Don Kipfer, outfitted in swimming trunks, coming toward her. Don was on a different frequency. He knew he would never forget the girl he had met in Newark. She was almost a mirage in his mind. He remembered her as a beautiful angel. Now here she was, only feet away. He found himself with a difficult time talking.

"Hi, Edna Mae! Helen told me you would be here." For some unknown reason, Mae's knees felt a little weak. "That's the only reason I came. Why aren't you swimming?"

Mae had regained her full composure and was determined to avoid anything personal with this boy she considered a stranger. "Hi, Don. This is my sister, Margarette. We're not here to swim. We're here to watch after Jack." Mae had not noticed Helen approaching and before she knew what was happening, Helen interrupted their conversation, "Edna Mae, you and Margarette go swimming. I can take care of Jack for awhile."

Margarette had never seen Don before. But even at twelve years old she considered herself an expert on boys. "Edna Mae, why didn't you tell me Don Kipfer was so good looking? He looks like Flash Gordon, He's got blond hair and blue eyes."

Edna Mae Gentry simply pretended she didn't hear her sister. "Long Lake," Mae told Margarette, "is beautiful. Look at the grand picnic grounds. And it has plenty of apparatus in the water." In the water, Margarette imitated Mae's swimming strokes that were so professional. She could see that Don was a powerful swimmer, but his strokes could certainly stand improvement.

For lack of anything else to say, Don explained to Mae, "I learned to swim when one of the older boys threw me into a deep swimming hole in Pigeon Run Creek. You might call that instant instruction. But of course it's not professional as your swimming is." And now, more relaxed, he laughed along with Edna Mae.

Edna Mae, followed by Margarette, called from the top of Long Lake's fifteen-foot tower. "Come on up, Don. We're going to do some diving." She could see that Don was not keen on accepting her invitation! Don knew he was terrified. But those two young Venuses kept badgering him. Finally, he could resist no longer. He slowly climbed the ladder. The girls had gone over into spectacular water entrances twice before. Don knew he could muster the nerve to try. Over he went. Later he told his dad, "Dad, it seemed I was in the air for hours and when I hit water I thought my head would snap off!"

Don believed Edna Mae was one of the most striking women he would ever meet. She is a natural beauty with such grace, and he could see that was not lost on the men of all ages assembled at the reunion. Don Moyer, older, and able to drive his own car propositioned Mae almost as soon as she left the table. "Say, Edna Mae, how about going for a ride with me?" teased this Rubin's Romeo.

Edna Mae had no interest in such ribald activity. She knew all about the dangers of the jungle. "No, thank you," she answered in as rude a tone of voice as she felt wise, and so that method of encounter to her was terminated forever.

When Don Kipfer asked her, "Would you like to go for a rowboat ride?" something about his invitation seemed different. Mae didn't hesitate, "Yes, I would, thank you."

Margarette had never known Edna Mae to show the slightest romantic interest in any boy. When her sister and Don were out rowing for nearly two hours, she knew this was a total new chapter in her sister's life.

Don was ecstatic to have such an opportunity to talk to Edna Mae in private. "Edna Mae, tell me all about yourself."

Edna Mae explained as much as she understood about her life so far. For Don her most important statement was, "I want to accomplish something important."

"Now, what about you? Helen has told me that you have won all kinds of academic awards. She says you are a first chair clarinetist and in Massillon's Swing Band. She says you are serious and already have your own business."

Don cringed. "My cousin Helen is too kind. She is also my mother's favorite niece, so she is certainly partial. But she is right about one thing. I am determined to do something, just like you, that is important in our world. For someone like me, I know that education is the only way to do that."

Edna Mae sat very still and quiet trying to apprise and understand this unusual boy who sat in the same rowboat with her. But he was certainly not as bashful as she had at first thought. He looked directly at her and smiled. He reached and held her hand. "I want you to think about something important, Edna Mae How about us two taking on the world together? I need a sympatico partner. I don't have to look any further. You are the one I want to walk the walk with."

Edna Mae was not certain she was really hearing what she believed she was hearing. She knew she did not totally understand the message. She didn't know what to do or what to say. She knew she was blushing. After a few minutes silence and careful though she answered, "I believe we better go ashore, captain."

The summer before Don turned seventeen and began his senior year at Washington High School, he talked his business partner, LeeRoy Flounders, who owned an auto, into taking him to Newark to see Edna Mae. For all intent and purposes, WWII had begun for the United States. President

Roosevelt had initiated, Lend/Lease. And for anyone who read the newspapers' small print, the United States entry into the melee was just a matter of time. Rationing was under way and LeeRoy had only four tires with no spare for his car. When they reached Mansfield, Ohio, only halfway to Newark, one tire went flat. Don and Lee managed to make repairs but Lee said, "We can't risk going on. It's back to Massillon for us."

Academia

Don was devastated. It was bad enough to miss seeing Edna Mae again. But this mishap may very well cost him the life he had visualized that would have surely formed a partnership that could have accomplished some high purpose.

Edna Mae received the letter from Don telling her of his attempt to come and see her in Newark. The letter had been delayed because Mae's mother had to forward it to her in Academia, Ohio. Mae paid Don's offer of further liaison little notice. She wrote a short impersonal letter back to him: "Dear Don, I am no longer in Newark, Ohio. I have moved to Academia, near Mt. Vernon, to attend the Adventist Academy here. I have burned all my bridges and left my old life behind! Edna Mae."

Don was horrified. That sweet Edna Mae may believe she has left him behind. But this one time, she is wrong.

Attending school her junior and senior years at the private Adventist Academy with zero economic resources had been her most optimistic dream. There were tuition and room and board charges that her parents had no possible way of paying. Edna Mae knew that God himself had intervened on her behalf for a third time.

Edna Mae had a restless, inquisitive mind. She was interested in understanding life and everything around her. She had totalled both the pros and cons of her situation. She had many friends in Newark High School. Her grades were all top echelon, and she was active in sports and school activities. Still, she yearned to hold some position of responsibility, either elected or appointed in her school. She soon noticed that such positions went to the sons and daughters of politicians, business men, doctors and lawyers or wealthy farmers. She mentioned this to her aunt Glenna. "Aunt Glenna, I was taught to believe that if you were moral and worked hard that appointments or election to positions of responsibility would come naturally. I am heartbroken to believe such a thing, but the whole process seems to be rigged. It seems to be purely political!"

Glenna was a wise woman. She drew in a deep breath and said, "Edna Mae, my dear, sweet girl, you have just learned one of the important rules in life that you must face as an adult. Of course the process is rigged. You must get on the inside. We must do something about that!" Glenna knew her niece, Edna Mae, so eager to conquer the world, was indeed a special person. Mae deserved a chance that she felt she, herself, had been denied and would never be given. "I'll tell you what, Edna Mae. If you are to get the break you want and deserve, you must leave Newark High School. I still need help with Jacquelyn. You could handle that for me. Then, my dear niece, we will see if your prospects for gaining responsibility don't change!"

Edna Mae's mouth dropped open. This of course, must be a dream. But she quickly gained control and realized that her problem was not yet solved. "But, Aunt Glenna, where would I get the money for tuition?"

Glenna, too, was besides herself. She liked her plan more and more. "Maybe, for once, I can change what, the devil seems to have sealed as a certain fate!

"You may not know that Lee is manager of the academy's print shop. He needs good, reliable help. He will give you a job that pays enough to cover your tuition!"

"Glory be," Mae exclaimed to herself. "Here I am, enrolled in a private school and on salary." Thus began Edna Mae Gentry's advanced education as an assistant printer.

Lee was delighted to have Mae in the press room. When she arrived, the office seemed to brighten. She was always upbeat and cheerful while performing her duties.

Fraternization among students was not only frowned on at the academy; it was grounds for dismissal. However, several times a week the school had marches. The boys marched one train and the girls marched in another. These trains would march around the large hall. They served several purposes. The marching helped to dampen the sexual drive of tormented students, and of course gave the boys and girls ample opportunity to inspect each other as possible future mates.

But despite all these precautions, sex among humans is a fearful force to quell. The older boys were constantly measuring the older girls. Mae knew this. She had a serious agenda on which there was no room for such diversion. Still, one day after classes, the senior boys and girls had gone to the parking lot to inspect Emerson's new car. Mae noticed Emerson moving slowly toward her. He grinned and whispered in her ear, "How'd you like to go for a ride with me in my new auto, sweetie?"

Edna Mae had read the book, *Call of the Wild*. She moved away toward the girls' group. Emerson grabbed her by her arm and attempted to push her into the front seat of his car. Emerson was correct concerning Edna Mae, about several things but he did not know her well enough. Edna Mae said nothing, but simply rotated instantaneously, and setting her right foot solidly, kicked the astonished male in his crotch. Emerson hit the deck with a look of sickening horror on his face. The girls and boys were shaking with disbelief. As they recovered, they began to laugh.

Edna Mae's cousin, Irene Glaunsinger, clapped and yelled, "That Edna Mae is dynamite." And so Edna Mae Gentry became Dyna to a whole generation of her classmates. None of them ever forgot the incident and for the rest of her life they referred to her in no other way.

Edna Mae and Glenna had been correct about the achievement of position and power. The Gentrys were not wealthy people. But in the Adventist faith they were top echelon. They attended Sabbath and Wednesday night meetings. They tithed and Tracy directed the church choir. And so Edna Mae encouraged and led her school's girls in athletics, coached and refereed, and was elected vice president of her senior class. She told Aunt Glenna, "I have not arrived, Auntie, but you've helped me get under way."

Edna Mae laughed when she recalled some of the experiences at Newark High for her Aunt Vada. "You know most of the kids thought I was Jewish because my hair is so black and I go to church on Saturday. And Adventism got me into trouble in other ways. I wanted to go to the graduation prom at Woodrow Wilson Junior the beginning of high school in the worst way. But it was on Saturday, the Adventist holy day. I knew my father would never approve, so I quietly pleaded with my mother."

"All right, Edna Mae," agreed Mae's mother, Anna, "but you know the restrictions on Adventists on Saturday and especially at dance parties!" Edna Mae understood all of her restrictions. No dancing, no alcohol, no smoking, and no improper games. However, when she was coaxed, she agreed to play a game of Ping-Pong. Horrors! Still, no one could blame the photographer for his mistake. By now Dyna had matured into the figure Don Kipfer had anticipated, a figure enjoyed by few women. Her blue-black hair, and large brown eyes contrasted unbelievably with her flawless white skin. In a word, she was irresistible from a male's viewpoint.

The party's newspaper photographer did not hesitate about who was to be featured in his local newspaper. Of all the young women present he had of course taken Dyna's picture playing Ping-Pong on Friday night after sundown, of course. Her picture was featured in Newark's *Saturday Advocate*. To her Aunt Vada, she explained. "I couldn't think of facing my mother and all my Adventist friends for breaking so many Adventist rules!"

"What happened?" quizzed Vada.

Mae smiled. "I really don't know that it was so terrible. If it was, perhaps no one that I knew could bear mentioning it to me."

"Good," laughed Vada. But then, just as life seemed to be to good to be true, LeeRoy Applegate was promoted to be head of the college press for the Washington Missionary College in Takoma Park, Maryland. Dynamite seemed to wilt. That meant no free room and board at Aunt Glenna Applegates and perhaps even loss of her job. She was inconsolable. But the next day she got word from her grandmother Gentry: "Come to my house for an important visit!"

Prior to Grandma Maggie's decision and message to Mae she had discussed her plan with husband George. He was mystified. "But Maggie, all our kids are gone! Have you forgotten all the complications teenagers carry with them? And teenage girls are likely to be short on work and long on boys—even our remarkable Edna Mae."

Maggie smiled in pleasant contemplation. "Anna says Edna Mae is an angel. I believe her. She had never caused Tracy any trouble. She is a serious girl and a hard worker. You know she nearly ran Tracy's house for him while Anna was occupied helping to make a living. Besides, she's a happy, bright girl and I think she's just what this old house needs!"

"You mean," chortled George, "I'm becoming a mean old man? No doubt, Edna Mae would sweeten me up!"

When Maggie asked Edna Mae if she would come and stay with her grandparents until she graduated, Dyna knew that God had helped her once again. Maggie was an experienced and cagy person. She made her offer to Edna Mae sound like it was of considerable benefit to her and George. Mae ran to her grandmother and gave her a warm, lingering, hug and kiss. "Yes, Grandma, you and God have answered my prayers."

Tracy, having been raised by Maggie and George, with strict discipline, was not sure Mae would appreciate their rules. He offered to have Edna Mae back home if Grandmother mistreated her.

Edna Mae certainly impressed the staff at the academy. Of course they respected her competence at her printing job and her excellence in academics and sports but from the academic viewpoint her compassion and help for her fellow students simply thrilled them. They knew the United States would have many more Christian citizens because of her.

The staff had concluded: "We believe this student is intended to do great things in her lifetime."

Consequently, they awarded her their most prestigious scholarship, a $50 stipend, to attend Washington Missionary in Takoma Park, Maryland, physically a part of Washington, D.C. When Edna Mae heard the news she was thrilled to vibration but then at once sobered. When she spoke to her grandmother about the opportunity she was very solemn. "Grandmother, I don't even have the money for a bus or train ticket to Washington, D.C. And the $50 the academy has awarded me won't pay for much of my tuition. Where would I stay? What would I eat? And even a poor soul like me must have clothes."

Grandma Maggie pulled Edna Mae to her and hugged this remarkable girl. Edna Mae had never presented her or George with a problem. Instead, her vitality and good humor had relighted their lives. "Edna Mae, you are a God-fearing person. People like you should be trained to be our country's leaders. God will provide a solution."

Surely enough, within the week, Glenna had sent a letter to Mae at her grandmother's address: "Dearest Mae, LeeRoy and I have just heard the good news that you have received a scholarship to attend Washington Missionary College. Jacquelyn no longer needs a nurse! But it would be nice for her to have company when LeeRoy and I are away from home for such long hours. Also, since I work full time, it would be nice to have help with meal preparation and the household work. So, we would be delighted to offer you the same arrangements we had at Academia. You would share a room with Jacquelyn. We would be so glad to have you. Love, Your Aunt Glenna."

Washington, D.C.

In July, Lee, Glenna, and Jacquelyn visited Mount Vernon and Edna Mae rode back to Takoma Park with them. Her close relatives had a small good-bye party for Edna Mae, Aside from the others, Tracy handed Edna Mae a $10 bill. "This is all your mother and I can afford. I want you to know that it would be pointless to send any bills to me. We will give you all the support we can but I'm afraid that will not include financial aid. Your mother and I know how hard you have worked. We know how you have prepared. We wish you luck."

Immediately upon arrival in Takoma Park, LeeRoy drove Mae straight downtown to the night-lighted monuments of the nation's capitol. What an unbelievable sight. Lee turned to his niece and remarked, "Some day, Edna Mae, you may live here." Edna Mae's fortunes seemed to be rising, Her arrangement with her aunt Glenna was perfect. And her job at the college press paid enough to cover her tuition and enough left over to cover inexpensive personal items.

Unexpectedly, Mae received a letter from Helen Southard. It certainly contained exciting and perplexing information: "Dear Edna Mae. Franklin and I are overjoyed that you will have a chance to attend college. We know you will do your normally good job.

"I thought you might be interested in hearing some news concerning Don Kipfer. Since his graduation from Washington High, he has played his clarinet professionally in the Dalton, Ohio, um-pa-pa band. He has also worked as a machinist at Republic Steel and was able to buy a new car. His plan for attending case School of Applied Science in Cleveland was nearly a reality. But you know how this World War II has affected all of us. When I asked Don at Luna Lake what he planned to do about the war he told me. 'I'm uncertain. I thought I might volunteer as a tail gunner.'

"I was aghast. My God, Don, their combat life is only eight minutes!

"Of course, I know Don very well, I knew the wonderful record he has accumulated. I suggested that he join the Aviation Cadets. Having Silver Wings is as glamorous and not quite so dangerous as being a tail gunner! Don took my suggestion seriously and before I knew it he was gone to Miami Beach to begin his training. Then again, like lightning strikes, his mother told me that he has taken a Civil Service exam and was going to enter West Point this coming summer. West Point has a romantic history, Edna Mae. It is as near to royalty as anything we have in our country. Perhaps he will invite you to West Point for a weekend. If he does, I pray you will accept! Love, Helen"

Edna Mae read Helen's letter numerous times. She knew she had made a lot of progress since she knew Don Kipfer at Long Lake. But my goodness, so has he! West Point . . . for him she knew it must be a dream come true. But that means he will be a professional soldier, trained to fight wars, to kill people. Everything he is doing is opposed to everything I've been taught. Still, Helen knows all of this!

Edna Mae knew that World War II was the greatest undertaking her country had ever attempted. Everyone was involved in some way. She was in her country's capitol and she intended to learn everything first hand about effective leadership.

Almost all the men were gone from their normal pursuits. If one saw a male on the streets of Washington between the ages of eighteen and sixty you could be sure that in some way he was an official part of the war effort. Groups of girls from college went downtown together and toured Washington stores and ate at their restaurants. LeeRoy took Glenna , Jacquelyn, Vada, and Edna Mae to see the Capitol, the White House, the Mall and reflecting pool, the national museums and the art museums. They ate at Oleney Inn, Mrs. Kay's Toll House, Water Gate Inn and many others. These things alone constituted an education. But when Edna Mae read the local papers she could directly connect the actions with the responsible people in Washington.

None interested in making an impact on the course of world events; no one aware of what the stakes were in World Was II; No one capable of insuring a positive outcome to the war could conscientiously set it out.

Edna Mae and her roommate, Mary Lou Leng, had been struggling with this problem. "Dyna, what can we do? What are we qualified to do?"

Of course, Mae knew. "We could enlist in a proud profession and become a cadet in the U.S. Nurse Corps. And when we get out we can get a lifetime education free. There are tens of thousands of women signing up."

"And," smiled Mary Lou, examining her image in her full-length mirror, "their uniforms are simply stunning." And so off to downtown Washington went these potential World War II recruits. Happy, smiling, girls bound to help win the war. Into the recruiter's office they marched. Mae looked at Mary Lou. Mary Lou frowned back.

Mae whispered, "Are we sure we want to do this?"

Mary Lou whispered in Mae's ear, "No, there must be another way." And back out they marched.

Mae had totally forgotten the letter and information Helen had sent her concerning Don Kipfer. So it was a total surprise when Glenna handed her a letter postmarked West Point. She had no idea what it might contain. She opened it with some apprehension: "Dear Edna Mae, I suppose you are shocked to hear from me. But I certainly haven't forgotten you. It seems we have both gotten a good start on our plan that we discussed!

"Plebe year is very difficult, but I'm determined to do well. One of our most difficult problems is that we never see a female, hear one, or are able to talk to one. All plebes must remain at West Point over the Christmas holidays. We have a week of social activities all planned for us, but the best part is that dates may attend.

"Although it would be presumptuous for me to call you my date, I can tell you honestly that I have never forgotten our good time at Long Lake. I am inviting you for Christmas week at West Point. I will make reservations at the Hotel Thayer for you where you will stay with other dates and be perfectly safe.

"Edna Mae, please let me know if you will accept my invitation and are able to attend. Hopefully, Don Kipfer. Cadet, Fourth Class, USMA"

What to do, pondered Mae. Supporting a military organization and getting involved with a professional soldier is contrary to everything I've ever been taught. Still, what an experience it would be and Helen is a very wise person . . . however!

Edna Mae wrote to Don. "Dear Don: I received your wonderful invitation to visit West Point. Yes, I remember Long Lake and I am pleased to learn that I made a good enough impression that you would want to see me again. However, I cannot, at this time, accept your flattering invitation. Sincerely, Edna Mae"

And so the academic year progressed at College Park. Edna Mae felt that Don Kipfer was a person of history. Still she was not completely certain she had done the correct thing. And then a second invitation came from West Point: "Dear Edna Mae, Here I am again. June Week is the biggest even of the year here. First classmen receive a baccalaureate in military science and are commissioned as second lieutenants. We plebes are recognized and so are relieved of the humiliating requirements for fourth classmen. The week is filled with sports activities, parades, walks, dances and dining. Frankly, I don't believe I'll really enjoy it unless you come here and enjoy it with me. I will make all the arrangements at the Thayer Hotel. You can meet me at Grant Hall. Please come."

Edna Mae's Aunt Glenna knew this time what was in the letter from West Point. She asked, "Well, Edna Mae, are you going? I wish it were me!"

Edna Mae wouldn't believe her Adventist aunt would make such a comment. But then she remembered her aunt's complaint that she was married right out of high school and never had a chance to experience other avenues. Mae finally conceded, "Well, not everyone gets a chance to go to West Point. I'll take my pistol with me," and both women laughed and shed several tears.

3

1944–1978: World Travelers, Searching for Earth's Secrets

West Point

Edna Mae went from Washington, D.C., to West Point by train. At the West Point train station there were buses that took the "drags" or dates, from the station to the reception point at Grant Hall. Edna Mae had done her homework. She knew that West Point had been founded by Slyvanus Thayer on order of the U.S. Congress in 1802 so that any deserving man could become a U.S. military officer. This was intended to help form a competent officer corps rather than one based upon an officers political acceptability.

She also knew that West Point had been the fortification that prevented the British from separating New England from the remaining colonies during the Revolutionary War. But she was unprepared for the solid stone buildings that gave The Point its air of military strength.

Almost instantly, when the receptionist paged Don Kipfer, a tall man in a grey uniform, with broad shoulders and blond clipped hair tapped her lightly on her shoulder. "I'm Don Kipfer. Remember me? I cannot tell you how happy I am to see you again Edna Mae! Did you have a good trip?"

Edna Mae was so shocked by the fantastic environment she was instantly exposed to, and by the complete change in her recollection of the Long Lake Don Kipfer, that for an instant she was speechless. "Yes, Don, the trip was fine and I'm looking forward to my weekend here at West Point."

Don was as surprised as Edna Mae. She was no longer a teenaged girl but a mature woman, more beautiful in his eyes than any other he had ever seen. "I'll have your luggage sent to your room at the Hotel Thayer. The weekend will be filled with athletic games, parades and dances. Our Saturday night ball is really pretty formal. There is a reception line, with the superintendent and his wife, and the commandant and his wife as the principal greeters. Then, of course, there is the dancing. I already have your 'hop' card all filled out so that you can meet some of my friends."

Edna Mae felt her legs go weak and her knees begin to shake. "All of that sounds wonderful, Don. But you know I am an Adventist. I've never learned to dance!"

Edna Mae was to learn right there that Don would never be deterred from his objectives by seemingly impossible barriers. Don took Edna Mae's hand, held it up and bowing, lightly kissed it. "Never to worry, my beautiful miss. We will go a bit early and I'll show you exactly how to dance. I know you are a quick read. You won't have any problem. Besides, when my friends look into your bewitching brown eyes, they'll forget about dancing!"

Now Don looked at Edna Mae with an expression she had no trouble understanding. She immediately knew that West Point was not totally safe. "I'd like to show you as much of the academy as I can, Edna Mae. But first, on their initial visit, every first time 'drag' must take a walk down Flirtation Walk, where you can get a bird's-eye view of the remarkable Hudson River."

There was no need for her to see another river. Edna Mae was still skeptical. But with so many cadets and other people moving around she felt it would be okay. So off they went, beginning the conversations that would update each other on the years since they had last met. Flirtation Walk was of packed earth but was very close to the Hudson River and the view was absolutely beautiful. Without her noticing it, they had approached an outcropping of rocks. Don gently took her hand and turned her to face him. "Flirtation Walk is where a cadet takes his 'one and only' girlfriend. When they get to this point tradition has it if they do not embrace and kiss, something terrible will happen!" he said.

Things had been progressing too fast during the past hour for Edna Mae, and now this transgression. She prepared to resist, but felt it was too late. Without intending to, she had reciprocated. Don's kiss was the only ardent one she had ever experienced.

Mae had intended to avoid such personal entanglements. She knew any such show of affection would be abhorrent. She knew any hint of cooperation would be obscene. And yet, for some reason, it had not been in any way hurtful.

Then Don released her and smiling, had taken her arm and continued their walk. Edna Mae had still not decided how she felt about such exploitation. She looked up at Don and asked him seriously, "Where did you learn to do that?"

"What?" Don smiled.

The military is noted for its scheduling. West Point was especially conscious of that. Don escorted Edna Mae back to Grant Hall where she caught a taxi to the Hotel Thayer. It turned out her roommate was Arnold Tucker's drag, Pat Small. The two girls liked each other immediately. Pat was emotionally very high. She laughed as she asked Edna Mae. "Is this your first trip to West Point, Edna Mae?"

Edna Mae didn't want to seem uninformed about the academy and its procedures, but she knew she had to tell the truth. "Yes. What about you, Pat?"

"I've been here to see Arnold a number of times. I love West Point and so will you!"

Mae had not brought a suitable evening gown for dancing with her so she went to Highland Falls and purchased one from her carefully budgeted money. Skipping dinner made up a part of the expense. Then several of the drags shared a taxi and were off to the hop. Don met Edna Mae at the entrance way. "First, we have to go through the reception line."

Edna Mae was thrilled by what she saw inside the ballroom. It was huge. The Army Band was tuning up. The general officers in the reception line wore their splendid, formal uniforms, with dozens of medals displayed on their left chest. And packed almost shoulder to shoulder and back to back were that handsome cadets with their drags. West Point, Mae realized, is certainly a long, long, way from Academia, Ohio!

Mae was scheduled to dance with Don the first dance according to her grey leather-bound hop card. Don smiled at Edna Mae and asked her for her permission. "Edna Mae, you call me Don, but Edna Mae seems a little long for me to handle. Could I perhaps call you Edna?"

Edna Mae's eyes snapped. "To tell you the truth, Don, I hate the name Edna. But 'Mae' would suit me fine." And so, for the rest of Edna Mae's life she was identified by Don with his favorite name, Mae.

When the two girls returned to their room in the Thayer Hotel, they were tired but excited. Pat asked, "Mae, didn't you think the hop was wonderful?"

Mae answered truthfully, "Pat, I'm from a small town. And although I know Washington very well, I live in Takoma Park. I have never dreamed of being part of such a royal affair. But I think my chest will be sore for days from the dress grey uniforms huge gold buttons crushing me!"

Pat snickered. "Those healthy boys do like to dance close!"

The following morning after breakfast, Mae and Pat went to the chapel for church services. Again Mae could hardly keep her lower jaw from dropping. "My heavens, Pat, I've been in oodles of chapels but this one is in a class by itself. I can barely see the preacher's podium nor the organ." And as the cadets marched in and later sang along with the organ music, Mae understood she had become a part, perhaps temporarily, of something larger than life as most people knew it. Was it true their organ is the largest east of the Mississippi?

Don and Arnold met Mae and Pat at the Hotel Thayer for lunch. The girls necessarily paid for lunch; cadets were not permitted to have money. But Don knew Mae was on a very restricted budget and would not permit her to pay. He had the bill put on to his cadet account.

"Don, you don't have to do that," pleaded Mae.

Don laughed out loud. "Mae, I wouldn't have it any other way. You will never again pay for anything so long as you are with me. I want to take care of you. Besides, I haven't done anything yet to be paid for!"

Mae pretended to cuff Don. She had relaxed. She was fearful she might really care for him.

Arnold suggested, "Let's go back to the gym and I'll show you some movies of last year's Army football games."

When they entered the gym, Mae was really astounded. She had been in a number of gyms she considered very good, but none were like this one. There were basketball courts, workout rooms, wrestling rooms, swimming pools, handball and squash courts. But Arnold took them right to the head office and Mae could see a name tag through an open doorway on an inner desk she recognized: Coach Earl Blaik!

Mae, Pat and Don were seated in the athletic office in comfortable chairs. Arnold had the movie projector out but was having trouble threading the film in properly. Now Mae showed these miracle men her leadership qualifications and they were never to forget it. She sprang up and hurried to the table where the cantankerous projector was being manhandled by Arnold. "Let me do that, Arnold," suggested Mae as she displaced him. Almost within seconds, the movie projector was doing its thing. No one present would have had the nerve to embarrass Arnold. Everyone was awed but no one said a word.

The total audience was conspicuously quiet. Don and Pat could not really believe Mae had moved the formidable Arnold Tucker aside to take over. Hardly. Not really. But Don Kipfer knew then, and never forgot it, that he had met a young woman like himself, who would let no barrier deter her. After all, Arnold was the backup quarterback for the number one college football team in the nation.

No time can be wasted by a cadet at West Point. It was now already well past noon. Don had to be in quarters in a few hours. Still the two couples parted and Don took Mae for a leisurely walk to Fort Putnam, one of the highest points near the academy. Mae had been at the academy for just two days, but her viewpoint of life had changed. The view of West Point and the

Hudson River from this height not only was special for a military commander but was intended to and usually did steal the affection of anyone viewing it.

"Don," suggested Mae, her active mind at work every second, "if I had the grey material I could make a West Point suit from it for myself."

"My sweet girl," replied the cadet from Ohio, "My roommate, Tom Rogers, is the Company D-2 clerk. It's custom for graduating first class cadets to leave all their belongings they no longer want with their favorite plebe when they depart these cold grey walls. We've got four or five overcoats lying in a box in our room now. I'll box them and put them in the mail. You should be quite a show. Imagine, the first female cadet at West Point!"

Mae couldn't help but laugh. "Right, but you wouldn't let me play on any of the athletic teams. By the way, general, what's all this going to cost me?"

Don took Mae by both hands. "What I want most from you, Mae, isn't money." And with this, Don stole a kiss that dwarfed the one at Flirtation Walk.

Mae could not believe this man's audacity, nor her own pleasant reaction. She was shocked. "I believe we better go back to the Plain, Napoleon, before things here get out of hand."

And so the drag and the cadet went reluctantly back to the heart of West Point, she to return to Washington, D.C., and he to West Point's relentless routine.

Don kissed Mae impersonally as he put her into a taxi. "Mae," he said, "I am so glad you came. These have been the best days of my life!"

Mae didn't show any of the deep emotion she felt when she departed. She had much soul searching to do. Committing oneself to a military career would be the largest decision of her life. "Don, I really enjoyed myself, too."

Mae returned to Takoma Park and went immediately to Garland Avenue to report on her West Point visit. Glenna, Jacquelyn, Vada and Lee were sitting waiting for her in the living room. Glenna saw the transformation in Mae . . . the transformation she had believed all her life she had missed. She could hardly wait to ask Mae, "What did you think of West Point, Edna Mae?"

"Aunt Glenna, it's beyond anything I could have imagined. You gave me good advice. Everyone should see it!"

Jacquelyn was squirming in her seat, her teenage curiosity nearly killing her. "But Mae, how did you like the cadets. What kind of person was Don Kipfer?"

Mae hesitated, more womanly than Glenna would have ever guessed, then bubbled over. "Jacquelyn, the cadets are really special. They are just like toy soldiers except that they're so tall and handsome. For sure, you'd love them. Don Kipfer? He's bonny. I've asked him to come to Washington for spring break."

Everyone clapped.

Mae really did understand. And yet she couldn't understand. Don's father had died rather suddenly just after "Beast Barracks," beginning Don's third class year. Don idolized his father. The academy had permitted him to go home for the funeral. It was an awful load to carry through his time at West Point. He had told Mae, "What I'm trying to do is as much for Dad as it is for me. Now, he's gone. He'll never share the wonderful things I'm experiencing."

And so when Christmas came, Don went back to Massillon. He had told Mae that he owed that much and more to his mother. Thus it had been a less than joyful Christmas for both young people.

Spring break is really a very short period. Mae intended that Don meet some of her relations. So all activities were directed toward that end. Don arrived Saturday at noon time and after hugging Mae in a brotherly fashion, met Glenna, Vada, Jacquelyn and Lee. Then they were off to Iron Gate Inn. Since Don had to be back at the academy by taps on Sunday, his visit was limited. Still, they ate out that night at Olney Inn and at Mrs. Kay's Toll House for lunch Sunday. Mae realized it was becoming more difficult to just have Don leave.

During summer even the West Point Cadets had a short vacation. Mae wrote to Don and invited him to come to Washington. Don promised he would after visiting his mother in Massillon. However, he planned to stay with a classmate which was disappointing for Mae. His classmate's father had been the head of the Republican Party and his mother was the executive secretary for a Republican congressman. Mae understood the importance of politics for a career officer.

Mae received Don's call on Wednesday night. "Hi, sweetheart. I'm here in Washington. Can you meet me here at the Museum of Natural History at 10 a.m. tomorrow and we'll spend the day together?"

Mae was thrilled. "I'll be there, soldier boy!"

Mae had no trouble finding Don. The tall, handsome man in a cadet grey uniform standing in front of the Museum of Natural History was very difficult to miss. The visitors, thousands of them, inspected Don as though he were one of the exhibits.

Mae was radiant. She had been to the museums many times, but somehow they seemed more gigantic now as she dazzled Don with her amusing commentary. Still Don had difficulty concentrating on history with Mae so near. Mae turned her beautiful face up at Don and suggested, "Sir, we must see the Hope diamond."

Don looked back at Mae, then laughed. "No, madame. I certainly remember my promise but I will not buy you the Hope diamond. I am not so rich as Richard Burton."

Both laughed. Mae went on, "Isn't our capital city wonderful, Don? There is no place like it I'm sure. Can you come back tomorrow? There's much more to see."

"No, I'm sorry to say. I've been invited to spend the day in Jack's mother's congressman's office to see how government works. I couldn't refuse. But we're invited to a party at a congressman's apartment tomorrow night. His daughter is a friend of my classmate's."

Mae was a little overwhelmed by the way events were moving so fast. "Of course, I'll come. Will you pick me up at Glenna's?"

"Yes, my dear!"

Mae was of course expecting a special home as a congressman's residence. She was unprepared for the lavish décor she entered. The building was sturdy, and beautiful, of stone. Carriage lamps lit the entrance where a doorman waited. The apartment itself was large, and beautifully decorated with antiques and original oil paintings wherever one looked. Don began introducing Mae to the some ten couples at the party. The men were dressed in uniforms and the women in beautiful evening gowns. *What handsome couples*, Mae thought.

The other couples had arrived early and were beginning their second round of drinks and sampling the copious variety of hors d'oeuvres. By now their voices were really loud and some of their jokes Mae considered obscene. Don fixed Mae and himself drinks and no one noticed that these two were drinking straight ginger ales. Mae whispered to Don. "Are these the kind of social affairs you would be throwing in the military?"

Don had known what he was facing when he took Mae to this party, but it was only fair for her to understand what some parts of the military life exposed one to. "Mae, I'm sorry to let you see this small part of military social life, but these are the rich, privileged young set. Believe me, there are plenty of teetotalers in the military. Most dinner parties are little different from the ones you are used to."

But almost before Don had finished his explanation, Mae looked around and was aghast. She could not believe it. These rich, privileged, educated young men and women, dressed so splendidly that mortal Americans would never even see such finery, were sitting on the floor, playing catch with large sized ice cubes. Mae looked at Don with a look he recognized as restrained disgust. *"Mon general,* I believe it's time for us to depart."

Mae had nothing to say on her way home. Don departed the next morning for West Point. He thought he had probably lost Mae. How could he expect a girl, who had nearly been banished for playing Ping-Pong, to accept the conduct she had just witnessed first hand, up close?

Don wrote a letter, he believed, of explanation to Mae as soon as he returned to the academy. He also acted on Lee's suggestion. "Don, Mae's birthday is the tenth of August. I'm betting a dozen roses from you would be genuinely appreciated."

Don soon received a letter from Mae postmarked Newark, Ohio. He was concerned that it might not contain good news. 'Dear Don, I received your beautiful red roses for my birthday in Takoma Park before I left!" Here, Don's heart skipped a beat. "Mr. Hoover, principal at Madison Township School has offered me a teaching position that I cannot refuse. I had only to pass a Licking County teacher's exam to be hired. So you see, I have a new address!

"Don, I'm a big girl. I have rationalized in my mind the activities at the party we attended. I hope you will invite me to the academy again. As always, Mae."

Don was ecstatic. He began planning for the Army/Navy game.

Mae lived with her father and mother, one sister and a brother on Swan's Road, south of Newark, in a country atmosphere. It was an environment a world away from Washington, D.C., and especially the cadets and décor at West Point. Still, returning to the Adventist church, the Grange meetings and sports events she reexperienced the strength of the communities of the Midwest.

Mae loved teaching the second grade. She introduced many innovations such as having the best students help the weaker ones and giving the mischievous students many classroom chores.

The parents of her students appreciated what Mae was doing for their children and gave her their support. They all agreed their children would benefit from her guidance the rest of their lives. One woman remarked, "My little girl now calls me Mother and says 'yes, ma'am, and no ma'am.'" Mae was especially proud of the "Quiz Kids" radio program and Miles Laboratories Certificate of Honor awarded her as a part of the best teacher in the United States program.

Mae's father, Tracy, had always been a talented vocalist. Music was a large part of the Gentry's lives. Mae had sung duets when she was seven years old with her four-year-old sister, Margarette, all over the local area and as far away as the cathedral in Columbus. So it was not surprising that Mary

Dennis at the piano with Mae and Margarette adding two voices, formed a trio and sang at local affairs and on the radio.

And so the routine of life seemed to take over. Tracy kept introducing Mae to young preachers. Now Mae had always been a strict Adventist, but being a preacher's wife was not in her plan. She simply ignored the offers.

Finally, finally, a letter arrived from West Point. "Dear Mae, Sorry to be so tardy, but it has been a hectic time here. Nevertheless, I think of you no matter what I'm doing.

"I have tickets for you to attend the Army/Navy game. It will be held in Philadelphia at their football stadium. Wannamakers always give the corp a splendid dinner in the evening after the game and then a dance in their grand ballroom. I will make reservations for you to stay that night at a nearby hotel.

"I'm wondering if I will get to see your new cadet uniform at the game?

"I know I am presuming you will accept my invitation. I would be devastated if you do not! As ever, Don"

Unless a person has attended an Army/Navy football game, such a stupendous affair could never be described. The corp and the midshipmen in massed and perfect formation enter the stadium. The crowds are wild with enthusiasm. Mae had many advantages on the other attendees. She knew Arnold Tucker, the Army quarterback, and had met "Doc" Blanchard and Glenn Davis. And she was very proud, but also a little embarrassed that everyone she passed inspected her female West Point uniform, the first ever to exist!

It is not difficult for two people who are in love to find each other, even in the midst of mayhem. And sure enough Don was there to meet Mae. "My, you look splendid in your West Point uniform, Mae. How did you like the game?"

Mae took Don's arm. "Thanks for the compliment, Don. It seems I have created my own attention. The game was just marvelous. And Arnold really is the best college quarterback in the country!"

"Mae, you know women are gaining more freedom every year. Perhaps, someday they'll really be wearing a uniform like yours and attending West Point."

Mae had considered West Point was splendid beyond anything she would ever experience but she told Don, "Wannamaker's dining room is awesome. Look at the height of the ceiling and all the expensive crystal chandeliers. I can't imagine feeding 2,400 cadets and their drags."

But Mae hadn't seen anything yet. The ballroom was decorated with Army posters, flowers and comfortable tables and chairs to use when you weren't dancing.

Mae and Don danced every dance. Mae looked up at Don with stars in her eyes. "You were right, Staff Sergeant Cadet. Not all Army parties are like the one in Washington. This one must be as near heaven as it ever gets!"

Don didn't answer, but he did agree. After they had checked into their hotel, neither young person could face the separation as they entered separate rooms.

Don discussed at great length with Mae how he felt about her. "I told you at Long Lake that I wanted to go through life with you. I'm deeply in love with you. If you agree, I'm going to invite your parents to my mother's house at Christmas. I want to get Tracy's okay before I ask you formally to marry me!"

Mae was very quiet. Her beautiful face was more serious than Don had ever remembered. "Don, I hoped you would ask me. Of course, I'm in love with you. I want to marry you. I will do my best to make you a good wife."

Tracy and Anna arrived at Laura Kipfer's home in Groves Patch on Sabbath afternoon. Laura, knowing the Adventists held the Sabbath determinedly holy, served a light dinner. Talk revolved around past family matters and current family activities.

Don's mother had told him when he announced that he intended to marry Edna Mae. "Mae is a beautiful girl, very intelligent, determined, serious and a very hard worker. I know she's in love with you. Certainly you have known each other long enough to understand whether you are compatible or not. I sincerely hope you can deal with the strict beliefs that the Adventists hold so tenaciously!"

Don had seriously considered his beautiful, auburn-haired mother's advice. He knew she had attended church and Sunday school all her life. She had participated in, not just attending, all the Chautaugua program, and was a true Christian. She had made sure that he and his sister were indoctrinated in the Christian faith. Of course, she also knew he had been a deacon in the church, had taught the men's Sunday school class when he was sixteen and had served as the Sunday school superintendent when he was the same age. She knew one the reasons he intended to serve his country in the military service was to make sure all people had their choice of religion.

So he told his anxious mother, "Mother, I know you love Mae and she loves you. What you have said about her is true. There can be no doubt that our different religious beliefs will cause a need for compromise, but we have discussed them and I believe, since we are both Christians, we can deal with them."

Don's mother hugged her son. She looked directly into his inner self.

"Then bless you, my son, for I know you will be happy."

After breakfast on Sunday morning, the women were busy in the kitchen preparing Christmas dinner. Don was often to remember but never to divulge that his task that morning was the most difficult of his life. He was not sure his fortitude nor his voice were up to the challenge but he knew for him there was no alternative. Both men, apprehensive, knew what was about to happen. Don looked seriously at Tracy. "Tracy, I suspect you know why I invited you to Massillon. You must remember that I have known Edna Mae for nearly a decade. I have loved her throughout that time. Anna told me that Edna Mae is an angel. I totally agree. She has the kindest disposition of anyone I have ever known. But far beyond that, she is beautiful, intelligent, and industrious. I intend to provide her with a happy and challenging life. I would like your blessing on our marriage."

Tracy was pleased at Don's analysis of his oldest daughter. He himself had never believed in warfare and knew little of military life. But he felt he knew Don and trusted what he told him. "Anna and I have raised Edna Mae in the best way we know how. She is our crowned jewel. I believe you will support her, as we have done and will make her happy. If she is willing, you have our blessing."

Proposing to Mae was much easier since they had already discussed and planned their joined lives. Mae questioned her messenger, "Well, my lover, how did it go?"

"You know your father, Tracy, is a very stern person." But curling his right hand and making an upward victory motion, the happy groom-to-be yipped, "He said 'yes.' But you know I can't give you a miniature before we have our West Point Ring Hop where all the perspective graduates will get the ring that for most of the world makes them 'ring knockers.'"

Both Mae and Don were always emotionally stricken when it was necessary for them to part, either Mae back to Ohio, or Don east to West Point. Planning ahead, last summer, Don had suggested a solution. "Mae, you are a teacher. You can get a job near the Point and we can see each other every weekend."

Mae had written to a private school on Long Island suggested by a friend. She went to be interviewed and was accepted. It was apparent that no one could reject this determined young lady. But Mae was so analytical she soon had annoying second thoughts. For once she had been so concerned with her independent decision that she could not face Don directly. She solved the problem by putting the matter in a letter.

"Dear Don, I have decided that it is best for us if I remain in Newark and teach while you finish your final year at the academy. First of all I do not want to be a disruption for you during your important training. Second, we have waited these many years to explore love for each other and I hope to marry you in a white wedding gown. I know you will understand. My Love, Mae"

However, Mae continued to attend football games and reveled in the Ring Hop and her gorgeous miniature ring. Immediately, having donned this engagement miniature, she became the envy of the many drags present. Now she had to prepare for the 8 June 1948 wedding.

The West Point graduation ceremony was really impressive and was carried on all the television networks. The presentation of the diplomas and the flinging of caps were impressive.

On the other hand, a wedding at West Point is not only spectacular but unique in many ways. Mae was well aware of the preparations required. She had to select her own bridal gown with all its accessories (something old, something new, something borrowed, something blue). She had to purchase five different size gowns for her bridesmaids; her sister Margarette, Don's sister Mary Helen, Mae's college roommate Mary Lou, her cousin Lola and Jacquelyn.

Mae's guest list was staggering, especially since lodgings had to be arranged in the local area in private homes at a time when three hundred other cadets were making similar arrangements. Since most of the academy's former graduates could also be expected for the formalities of June Week at West Point, and they enjoyed priority, rooms at the Thayer Hotel for cadets guests were nonexistent. Mae's parents, Don's mother, her bridesmaids and husbands, if any, aunts and uncles, cousins and friends were all invited.

All the cadets' guests were invited to attend a luncheon in the huge dinning room called Washington Hall. All of Mae's and Don's guests attended. It was a meal none of them would ever forget. Don's relatives all hoped he would take each of them on tours of the academy. Mae knew Don would manage somehow, but he also had to make last minute arrangements to pack and send the accumulations of belongings from four years at The Point to either his home or to their first station.

Mae was terrified by the necessity of such tight timing at the cadet chapel. She knew her wedding party had little leeway in arriving for the wedding ceremony. Unbelievably, marriages took place every twenty minutes. She knew Don would be punctual. She was assured that her bridesmaids had already departed in private cars. I'm the only one remaining she suddenly realized. *My good God*, she thought, *I don't have transportation.* Suddenly she saw the faithful Bill Blosser standing by so that she and her father could ride with him to the chapel.

The aisle at the cadet chapel is two hundred feet long, but to excited young women about to say "I do" it seems much longer. This magnificent work of art is simply an indescribable religious cathedral.

Outside of his responsibilities for official activities Don liked to generate a little humor or human excitement. He had told the organist, the musician at the keyboard of the largest pipe organ east of the Mississippi, to play Tracy's favorite song, "Because," during his march with Mae and the bridesmaids down the aisle. When the organist began this song and the pipes belted out their perfect notes, the audience seemed to quiver.

Mae told Don later, "I felt my strong father's legs go weak when they played 'Because.' Rather than him supporting me, it was I who was supporting him. I was not sure he could make it."

The actual wedding ceremony, one of dozens, was militarily correct. Don had arranged for twelve of his former proud plebes, with swords drawn and crossed, to form the arch for their wedding departure. Mae sneaked a kiss from Don as they entered the auto to go to the reception. She whispered, "Lieutenant, you and I have come a long, long way!"

Don gave Mae his graduation-day smile. "Yes, my dear, that is true. But our journey has just begun."

The reception at the Officers Club was an affair fit as repayment for all the relatives and friends who had assembled to see this wedding at West Point. The wedding itself was an event they were not likely to attend again. Mae cut the cake with Don's saber as she reveled in the applause of all present. Mae had arranged plenty of tasty food for everyone. A three-piece string combo played parlor music.

Unfortunately, the whole imaginary pageantry was soon over and the guests had departed. Mae and Don standing there side by side strangely felt lonesome. Vada told Mae later, "Most of the relatives assembled in Highland Falls at a restaurant for dinner. We had all toasted you two happy people, and since we knew Don was going back into his Army Air Corps to train as a pilot, we applauded and wished you both 'happy landings.'"

Mae laughed as she told Vada of her and Don's circumventing the clamoring crowd. It was his surprise. "You may not know, but cadets are not allowed to stay at the Thayer Hotel. On the other hand, lieutenants are. Everyone from the wedding thought we had left to go north for our honeymoon. But Don had made reservations for us to stay at the Thayer. A special way for a newly commissioned officer to start his married military life, wasn't it?"

Vada and Mae had lived with and confided in each other like sisters for many years. Vada was older but unmarried. She had never been known for being bashful, "Well? Speak to me, Mae. The last time we spoke you were single. Now you're married. How does the change feel?"

Mae was not shocked by Vada's obvious attempt to learn some intimate information. She laughed. "Vada, you know you're not going to get any inside information. You're only going to get what you see. However, if it will help you, when we left West Point, Don left his new, expensive shoes under our bed in the Thayer! This from my militarily correct groom."

And with Mae's admission, both these sensitive women enjoyed a hearty laugh. They both understood the sweet ritual of love. They both knew that all was well in Mudville!

Roommates at West Point are closer than brothers. It is a relationship other officers attribute to snobbishness. Not so. It is the result of sharing so many damnable experiences. Both Mae and Don had met Don's roommate Phil's parents, Colonel and Bonnie Whitney when they visited Phil at West Point. Mae and Bonnie hit it off immediately, perhaps because Bonnie did not have a daughter, and perhaps because any woman would love to have a daughter like Edna Mae. Whatever the reason, the Whitneys, when they learned that the Kipfers were to honeymoon at Rangely Lakes in Maine, invited them to stop by in New Canaan, New Hampshire, and stay with them as long as they wished. Mae looked at Don and when he nodded yes, she told the Whitneys, "We'd love to do that. We'll let you know which night we'll be in New Canaan."

Now the newlyweds were truly on their wedding trip, headed north in their new, (red, at Mae's request) Chevie Aerosedan. New Canaan was still much like an American Revolutionary town. The Whitneys' home was large, beautiful in the English style and surrounded by breathtaking gardens. As Colonel Whitney and Don took their suitcases to a second-floor bedroom, Mae went with Bonnie Whitney to the kitchen where Mae was totally fascinated by the fireplace with its iron cranes and hanging kettles.

Here, Mrs. Whitney formalized the informality Mae had already assumed. "Please call me Bonnie, Mae, and I'll call you Mae. I hope you like our colonial home. It's been in the Whitney family for three centuries. Phil has spent a great deal of time restoring it to its original condition. Of course we have added electricity, plumbing, sewerage, bathroom and kitchen conveniences. But we have tried to make these updates as inconspicuous as possible. What do you think?"

Mae was too astonished at first to speak. Then her thoughts came flowing out, "Bonnie, I'm speechless. We have nothing in the Midwest to compare with your home. The idea that our first immigrants lived in homes so splendid as yours changes my whole concept of revolutionary American life."

Dinner was a real treat. Bonnie used bone china plates, cups and saucers, crystal goblets, sterling silver dinnerware and linen accessories. These Ohioans were served crab cakes, cod fish fillets, rice and lightly brazen vegetables. Wine was served for the three who cared for it. Glazed, lightly seared peach halves were served for desert with their coffee.

Colonel Whitney told many stories about World War II. Then in a serious moment, he provided them council they never forgot for the rest of their lives. "You two young people will be the front lines of defense for our wonderful country. Make no mistake, our free, democratic government is the best man has ever had to offer. I am thankful that young people such as you are willing to take on such a burden. God bless and guide you."

Colonel Whitney's comments were certainly serious. They charged Mae and Don with a mission they had never really seriously considered. His comments were too pertinent for anyone to expect comment. Everyone simply said, "Amen."

While Mae and Bonnie cleared the table, Don and the colonel sipped cognac in front of the crackling fireplace. Colonel Whitney told Don some of the highlights of his long army career which included serving as the commanding general's executive before the invasion of Italy, as well as some of his frustrations.

When Mae returned to the living room, she said in a slightly embarrassed voice, "Don, we must be off early in the morning. I think you need a little time to rest."

Mae was astounded by her bedroom. A large trundle bed with hand-quilted bedclothes. Antiques everywhere. And on the walls were original oil paintings by American artists.

Mae was in bed first. "Don, if this is the way military families live, count me in!" Don came diving in soon afterwards. "Don, can you believe we are staying with a senior retired federal officer and his wife in their seventeenth-century home? Can there be more beyond this?" Mae laughed and whispered, "*Meine Lieutenant*, I told the Whitneys you were tired!"

"Never that tired, you lovely, sweet thing."

Early next morning the Lieutenant Kipfers were off to Rangely Lake. Mae could hardly believe the beautiful wooded countryside they were passing through. The forests she had known were not solid pines. She again asked Don, "I know you have arranged with the retired police captain in Portland to rent us a cabin, but you said he is a new owner and this is his first summer as manager. Do you think he'll be there to meet us?"

"Don't worry, sweetie. I'm sure he's dependable. But he did say that we're about two weeks early for the season and there won't be any other visitors at the lake."

The captain from Portland waved them down as they approached his small campground. "I'm Captain Roland." Then he pointed, saying, "There's our one small store run by Sam Little, an Abenaki Indian. His wife, Ruth and her kids are there by themselves now because Sam is off trapping. But follow me and I'll take you to your cabin."

It turned out the cabin had two bedrooms, a great room and a small kitchen. The captain tipped his hat. "Here's your key. There's plenty of split firewood in back of the cabin. The canoe is down at the dock. You can get basic supplies at the Little's store. And above all, have fun."

And with that the captain was gone. Don and Mae were truly alone in the deep bush. The next morning they slept late. Don hugged Mae and kissed her. "How about a canoe ride around the lake, Mrs. Kipfer?"

"Sounds wonderful to me if you'll do the paddling. I'm plain tuckered," joked Mae.

So off they went, carefree, in the canoe with two paddles and no life jackets. They had not bothered to check the weather, inexperienced in such country, Don started directly across one of the deepest freshwater lakes in North America. Mae was resting, seating on the floor of the canoe with her back supported by a restful seat. They had reached the opposite side of the lake when they noticed the first thunderheads coming over the mountain and saw lightning, followed by ear-shattering thunder. Almost immediately the waves around them mounted to dangerous heights. With their frail canoe on the top of a wave, Don could not reach the water with his paddle. "Mae, you'll have to use the other paddle to help me keep us straight. We can't go back. It's too far and too dangerous, and on this side are sheer stone cliffs. We'll have to find a ledge where we can land."

Don did not tell Mae of their danger because the situation was already serious enough. But Mae knew they were in trouble with such treacherous water in a frail canoe. She did not panic. She kept scanning the shore. Finally she yelled, "Don, I believe we can get ashore just ahead to our right."

Don shook his head thankfully and nodded yes. With considerable difficulty they edged themselves to the relatively protected shore and dragged the canoe to safety away from the huge waves. They both huddled, silent, thankful to be shore and safe. Two hours later the sun was out and the lake was smooth.

Mae was doubtful. "Don, do you believe it's safe to go on this lake in a canoe?"

Don did not smile. "Mae, it's really the only way to get home. There is not a cloud in the sky and the wind is almost calm. I'm sure it'll be okay."

While the honeymoon couple was resting and recuperating in their cabin with a blazing fire in the stone fireplace, Mae picked up an old newspaper to look at and fill some free time. Shaking in her shoes, she called to Don, "Look at these headlines!"

Don could hardly believe his eyes: HONEYMOON COUPLE DROWNS IN RANGELY LAKE. The paper went on to explain: "Apparently while the young couple were canoeing on the deep water lake, they were swamped by a sudden thunderstorm and were unable to swim to shore."

"My Lord," whispered Mae. "We were lucky."

The rest of their time at Rangely Lake went very smoothly. They saw no one except Mrs. Little and her three kids. Mae remarked, "These are the first real American Indians I have really ever had a chance to speak with. They are no different than we are. How could anyone refer to them as savages?"

They trolled for and caught enough landlocked salmon to feed themselves each day. And in addition to enjoying such fine food, Don was grateful for the fishing experience. "My first salmon, my love!"

Finally, reluctantly leaving their secret hideaway, the Lieutenant Kipfers' Aerosedan headed north. "What can be more wonderful than the past two weeks, commander?" purred Mae.

Not having been to Canada before, Don could not really answer. "We'll see, sweetie. We'll see!"

Mae had studied her history. She knew about the battles between the French and English over Canada. She knew who generals Montcalm and Wolfe were. She suspected Don would want to inspect all the fortifications. She was unprepared for the city of Montreal, itself. She and Don checked in at the Hotel Carleton not because the mind-boggling Frontenac was too grand for the lieutenant and his wife, but because it was too expensive for their budget.

But Mae and Don again circumvented such an annoying problem by pretending they were guests at the Frontenac and savoring dinner each evening in the Frontenac's grand dinning hall.

Mae, dressed in her finest gown, looked up from her beautiful plate of lamb chops, mashed potatoes and vegetables. She looked around at all the splendidly dressed people enjoying their dinners. "Don, I really didn't know there were people who lived like this."

Don had been scanning the dinners just as seriously as Mae. "Neither did I, patootie. But we are just beginning our journey. We cannot expect such rewards so soon. Hopefully, we will earn and come to accept such a lifestyle."

But as soon as the Kipfers left Quebec City and began their trip west toward Ottawa, they realized that the average citizens were not in the class of the people they had dined with in the Frontenac Hotel. "These people" guessed Mae, "are very poor. Very poor indeed!"

"Yes, you are correct, ma petite. But have you noticed the size and grandeur of their religious cathedrals? How can such extravagance exist in the midst of such poverty? We're going to stop and look at one for ourselves."

When their inspection was complete Mae summed up their findings. "By the robe of St. Peter, that sanctuary can only be described as a huge crown covered with jewels. Yes, I have been in huge buildings. I have seen ridiculous wealth, but I have never seen a building so obviously rich in finery, even the finest museums in Washington, D.C."

Don seemed too chagrined for any negative comment. "Well, anyway these poor, hopeless people have an inspirational place to visit and in which to pray on Sunday."

An so the auto moved on, slowly, because of the many potholes on this national highway. Mae laughed. "The Canadians have gotten ahead of us. They have surely found a way to slow down their road traffic, haven't they?"

Don became a little more serious than usual. "Well, sweetie, the Canucks have a unique problem. Canada is much larger than the United States. The distance their roads cover is staggering. And, my sweet wife, their population is very small so that the cost per person of building roads is huge. Then consider the climate. The temperature is very pleasant this time of year but contrast that with thirty-five of forty degrees below zero Fahrenheit in the winter and you can easily see their problem."

Although they had been smartly jarred several more times during Don's explanation, Mae had dismissed the road situation and was thinking ahead. She said almost apologetically, in such an excited state she almost forgot who she really was, "Don, I've never been to a foreign capital before. I don't know what to expect. Do you know anything about Ottawa?"

Don kept his eyes on the road. "One thing patootie, is in our favor. The Canadians speak English. We'll learn together my frau. I've heard and read that Ottawa is a beautiful capital. We'll be staying at the Elgin Hotel just across the street from the Hotel Laurier, for obvious financial reasons. But we'll eat our dinners at the Laurier. The literature says it is the equal of the Hotel Frontenac in Quebec City. We'll see."

They found Ottawa to be an especially clean city with attractive buildings. The centuries-old stone capital buildings were superior in aesthetic perspective to any they had ever seen. Their Elgin hotel was spacious and beautiful but the hotel Laurier where they dined, although very expensive, afforded them sensual and gastronomy experiences they would never forget.

Mae coaxed, "Can you believe that hotel? Can you believe the food? But I want to see the famous botanical gardens and shake hands with a Northwest Mounted Policeman."

Don agreed, "The botanical gardens are okay but I understand the Northwest Mounted Policemen are very handsome. Be careful, my darling wife."

But since Don could manufacture no reason to say no, before the sightseeing was complete and they turned southward Mae had visited the gardens and had her picture taken with a Northwest Mounted Policeman, with his arm around her shoulder. Don knew Mae had made the horse soldier's day. "Now," concluded Don's princess from Ohio, "my Yankee husband, I'm ready to leave. Ottawa is certainly a bonny place."

Don knew Mae was not eager for her honeymoon to end. And as they departed Ottawa headed south he laughed and told her, "Not so fast, my pretty little maid. I have one more surprise for you. Close your eyes and count to ten."

Mae did, then screamed. "You devil! What is it?"

"There is a spot that both Canadians and Yanks revere above all others for their honeymoon. We're stopping there," promised Don.

"Yehasafat!" yelled Mae. 'Niagara Falls!"

They stopped for the night at a hotel right on the rim of the Niagara River from whose front porch one could see and hear the magic rush of crashing water. "We're staying on the Canadian side because we'll soon be back home and we'll be staying in the United States for quite a spell."

Mae walked with Don and viewed the falls from every angle. They boarded the headboat named the *Maid of the Mist* and ventured beneath the falls thundering water. "Now that," exclaimed a somewhat shaken maiden, "was scary."

That night after dinner, again they wandered about, capturing as much of the falls' ambiance as possible. "Now I know why the spot is so memorable for honeymooners," exclaimed Mae. "I will never forget it!"

Motoring again, the excitement of their travels subsiding somewhat these two neophyte world travelers had time to consider many less exciting but perhaps more important matters. Mae began to philosophize first: "My father was a rather stern man but he treasured his family and not only was good to me, but supported me in everything I did. He stressed morality and religious belief. And, of course, he was a superlative vocalist and music was a large part of his life.

"My mother was what in political circles would be called a liberal progressive. As you know she was the first female motor vehicle driver in Licking County. She's ready to experiment with anything. Also as you know she's a top-notch chef. Her dishes are always different than anyone else's and always better. I suspect she might have traded the rest of her life for the trip I've just taken."

"I sincerely doubt that, Mae. My mother was always good to me and like your father, supported me in anything I tried. Her big issue was education and she made sure I understood what a powerful tool it was. My father was different. He was too honest for his own good. He stressed honesty and hard work. He was one of the most competent sportsmen I ever knew. He loved to travel. He would have luxuriated in discussing our travels. But he is gone. I will never enjoy the luxury of discussing them with him."

The philosophers say that travel broadens one's mind. Now both Mae and Don had been to Washington, D.C., West Point, Quebec City, Ottawa and Niagara Falls. Massillon, Don's beloved city, the home of the first semi-professional football team, the National Champion Tigers of Washington High School, and the origin of professional football, seemed to have shrunk since he had left. He had to admit it was not as clean as he remembered.

Don explained some of his family's and Massillon's background. "My uncle Howard Kipfer played semiprofessional baseball and football with Knute Rockne, Gus Doraie, and Jim Thorpe. My father also played both. A young man named Ben Fairless was my father's team manager.

"Ben lived near my mother's home in Groves Patch and he and my father were close personal friends. Ben was more sensitive to the value of education than the others, perhaps more ambitious, and got a college education in Wooster, Ohio. He kept rising in the steel business. While his other boyhood friends were still doing hod carrying work in the mill, he left Massillon to take over the huge steel operation in Cleveland. He wanted my father to go with him in the worst way, but my mother, her tight-knit family close by, was not leaving Massillon," said Don.

"By the time World War II began, Ben was president of United States Steel. There could be little doubt that he had more to do with winning World War II than any other single man. Ben plotted alongside our president."

Mae, suspecting that her husband might be exaggerating was not convinced. "How could that possibly be, exalted leader?"

"Well, sweet patootie, war is won not just by strategy and with brave men. The World War II effort required ships, tanks, trucks, autos, guns, cannon, munitions, airplanes, submarines and all sorts of other material. Nearly all of those require huge amounts of steel. Ben Fairless and U.S. Steel provided most of that for the United States, Great Britain and their allies."

Mae backed off. "Okay, okay, but what has that to do with your job at Republic Steel this summer?"

Don smiled. "You know, fraulein, I am not rich. I've never misled you about that. It will be necessary for us to work together to solve that dilemma. Yes, we have a new car, but I don't have money enough to buy gasoline to get us to San Antonio. This high-paying job is not only a part of our plan, it is vital to us."

Mae suddenly became more interested. "So, it is not a vacation, but a job in the steel mill you have for the summer. How did you arrange that?"

"My father and Jack Price played football together, hunted together, fished together, socialized together and tossed a few beers together. Mr. Price didn't have a son and I was sort of a surrogate. He happens to be the employment agent for Republic Steel in Massillon. I wrote and told him what I needed and he took care of it. You learned about politics in Newark. Remember? Here it is at work all over again!"

Mae sat contemplating. "Yup. Oh, that will keep you busy, but what about me?"

"You're going to help me, sweet lips. Up early, drive me to work so you can have the auto. Pick me up when I'm finished at three o'clock and the rest of the day is ours. That's better than we have ever had it, even at The Point. Madam, we're free!"

On that first afternoon when Mae picked Don up he laughed as he glanced at the young woman sitting beside him who was bravely attempting to smile. "Being stuck in Groves Patch also has its up side, my dear. You can learn a lesson here that will help temper your outlook on mankind the rest of your life. You were raised among men and women who were doctors, nurses, singers, pastors and teachers. They basically saw the 'up' side of life. The people here have spent their lives in coal mines or in the steel mill. They begin life depressed and then life never changes.

"When I reported in the morning, everyone greeted me almost like I had never left. The place was as dirty as when I escaped. The machines sat just as I remembered them. The faces of these good men were already drawn and tired from a workday that had not yet begun. They were men who would stop after work and drink far too much before they staggered home.

"For me, sawing, rolling, shaping, drilling and polishing steel, iron, stainless steel, brass, copper, and lead is just a small diversion. I feel like I'm on a vacation. The eight hours of relatively easy work has no comparison to the driving, competitive sixteen-hour days I've endured at the academy. Yet I am high and these men are cowed. They are necessary links in our fruitful industrial revolution, but what a price they and their families pay. Remember this lesson. Perhaps you can help to correct this inequity someday."

Mae went with Don to family dinners and reunions. They visited old friends of Don's. They visited Newark for a weekend. Mae helped Don's mother and before either one realized it, Don had his wallet bulging with money and they were headed southward.

The Lieutenant Kipfers had not realized it. America's roads were in terrible shape and its trucks were a menace to all other traffic. Uphill, the trucks, traveling at five miles an hour, blocked the two lane roads and downhill they rocketed full speed and seemed to want to crush you. Mae seldom complained throughout this punishing trip but she did remark. "The roads in Arkansas are abominable. A mile on single lane pavement, a mile of filthy dirt. You can count on it. But Don, I never dreamed our country was so large. Traveling across it simply wears out one's butt!"

The second day out the heat in the non-air-conditioned Aerosedan was simply brutal. Healthy as they were, fainting was always a distinct possibility. They kept seeing large commercial type tanks in which soft drinks might be cooled at a large salon.

Signs announced: COLD WATERMELON!

Mae could tolerate her pain no longer. "Macho, what say we stop and get some cold melon?"

Don, she was sure, was no more comfortable than she. He didn't argue but swung into the next station. He motioned for Mae to come. "We'll split this melon and sit on that bench under the trees and eat it. It may be messy because I've only got my Swiss Army knife to cut it."

With the first bite, Mae giggled. "I'll live. I've never had a melon so sweet, juicy and cold. Even the cold juice running down my chin is a good thing!"

"Amen," agreed Don, and from then on about every hundred miles it was melon time. Don laughed, and said, "After all, these big melons only cost a dollar apiece."

San Antonio

Finally they both simultaneously saw the big sign announcing TEXAS.

"My," responded Mae, "Texas is certainly flat!"

"Yes, my dear and big."

Mae knew Don would be working at Lackland AFB training new Air Force recruits for part of July, August and a part of September. After that he would be in flight training at Randolph AFB. So they had agreed that they should find housing near Randolph AFB so they could not have to move twice.

When they went into the base housing office, the sergeant who was to help them find housing was not optimistic. "Frankly, Lieutenant, there is no housing available on the base. It is nearly as bad off base. The nearest and only thing I have are some apartments in Seguin, not far up the road. See a Mrs. Horn."

Mrs. Horn was a congenial Texan. She and her husband had bought a large, old, wooden home and cut it up into one-room apartments. The one she showed Mae and Don had a bathroom and efficiency kitchen in one corner of the large room. Don and Mae both noticed that there was no window for cross ventilation and the temperature at the time of their visit was more than 100 degrees F.

Mae cringed. "Mrs. Horn, is there no way we can have a room with cross ventilation? We're Northerners and not used to such high temperatures."

Mrs. Horn's splendid disposition turned sour. "I'm afraid this apartment is all I have. But I'll give you a break on the rent since you're from Randolph."

So the two famished, fatigued, bedraggled, protectors of their country's freedom moved in. That night they discovered the black Baptist church across the street. It might be more correct to say the black Baptist church discovered them. "Don, those black folks have wonderful voices but they certainly are loud. You'll have to get up at 0500 to make it to Lackland. You'll never get a night's sleep."

And so it proved that first night. Don suggested that they eat lunch out to try to avoid the heat but since the small restaurant was not air conditioned, that was no help. When they returned to their apartment, Don's even-tempered bride was near revolt. "Don, we have to do something. I cannot, I will not endure living in this oven!"

"Okay, sweetie, I'll fix it."

How? Mae wondered.

Don was gone about a half hour, then returned with a hundred-pound block of ice, which he put in the bathtub and covered it with water. "Mae, that's a temporary solution, but I'm going to do something more permanent."

Mae managed to survive. She lived in the ice cold water of the tub. But she knew Don was on the parade ground and rifle ranges most of the day and when he got home at night after a fifty mile drive in a hot car he was simply limp. "Lieutenant, it's a good thing you are in top-notch condition. How's your love-making energy holding out?"

Don managed a weak smile. "Fine my dear, I never lose that!"

Sometimes God smiles on Christians in their hour of need. Mae knew it was time He smiled on her. Lieutenant Arnett was a classmate of Don's. His older brother was a retired lieutenant colonel who sold life insurance in San Antonio. He always had an afternoon party for each West Point pilot class that arrived for flight training at Randolph. He was a knight in shining armor. Of course, he hoped to sell the young officers insurance, but he sincerely wanted to help each couple in any way he could. When Don explained their dilemma to him he nodded understandingly. "I understand, I believe I have just the solution for you. I'll call you tomorrow night."

The Arnetts' quarters were air conditioned. There were about twenty couples at the party in their large living room. The Cokes were iced and spiked with lime juice. The hors d'oeuvres were fresh and good. Mae recovered her native energy almost instantaneously. Having regained normalcy, Mae gathered several of the young wives around her in the corner of the room. "Girls, if you feel like I do, you feel isolated. What say I get your names, addresses and telephone numbers and we can remedy that problem." There was a very quiet but determined clapping of hands and Mae soon had all the young wives' identification data.

Colonel Arnett was true to his word and called Monday evening. "Don, I've got something for you just outside the gate at Fort Sam Houston. It's a small house and within the budget you mentioned. It's at 1207 Tilden Avenue.

"Colonel, I can't possibly commute from Seguin to Lackland and work in the sun all day. I don't want to be absent without leave. Mae and I'll be packed here in an hour and meet you at the Tilden address by 2030 hours."

"Sorry, Don, I won't be there, but the small house is in the side yard of an old-time grand ranch house. Knock on the door. Kate Findley is the owner and she'll get you settled."

Mae was a little wary. No one could blame her what with the tribulations they had been through so far in their military life. "Don, your Colonel Arnett must be a miracle worker; a house? Impossible. I hope this improves our situation. House-hunting has not been our best talent so far."

"How could it be worse, Madam Mae? I'm sure Colonel Arnett has alerted the Findleys that we are on our way."

Kate and Frances met them at the front door. It was love at first sight. Kate laughed, "Aren't you two wonderful! Frances and I are so excited. Come, I'll show you the house."

The petite house had a small combined living room, bedroom, a nice kitchen and a wonderful bathroom with a shower. It was furnished ready to live in and spotlessly clean. Mae was bubbling. Kate told them. "This building has a fabulous history. It was once a church, once a bar, and once a studio. Now it's to be a home!"

After Kate left, Mae danced around for joy! "Don, it has three windows on each side of the living room that stretch from floor to ceiling. And we are here on Fort Sam's mountain. Feel that freezing, arctic circle breeze?"

Don knew then that things would be better for the Kipfers from that day on. "Fort Sam is hardly on a mountain, my sweetie. But there is no denying the cool breeze. Hallaluja!"

Mae called Ann Butler the next day and invited the Butlers for dinner the next Friday night. The Butlers arrived precisely on time. Mae was a talented chef. It was no surprise when Ann commented, "Mae, your dinner was wonderful!"

Don was amused when Blaine added, "You are lucky to have such a nice, cool place to live."

Mae knew the Butlers played bridge. When Don asked Mae, "Mae, are you a bridge player?" she had replied, "Yes, of course."

Actually Mae had played bridge only a few times and it had been auction bridge and not contract. Still things didn't go badly, until halfway through the evening. Don had a bust hand, but Mae kept bidding to game at four spades. Finally Don gave up and let the chips fly.

It turned out Mae made the game without any difficulty. Blaine was incredulous when he saw Mae's hand unfold. "By the saints of St. Mark, Mae, you had thirteen spades! You should have bid a grand slam!"

Mae was unperturbed. "Really, should I have?"

Mae and Don continued to play bridge the remainder of their lives and never again would they have such a hand. Tuesday morning, after Don had departed for Lackland, Mae noticed a strange-looking book on her end table. She picked it up, puzzled. *Contract Bridge for Beginners* by Ely Culbertson. Enough said. At that moment, a new competitor was born. Mae determined to be a good bridge player.

Mae, assuming the reins of leadership, had arranged for a luncheon meeting of all the West Point wives, some twenty of them. Since Jamie Della Chiesa had the largest apartment, the get together was to be held at her place. When Mae arrived, first as usual, at Jamie's front door, she found the young, beautiful girl in tears. "What on earth is wrong, Jamie? Are you ill?"

Jamie could hardly answer for she could not compose herself. Mae immediately jumped to the conclusion that either Jamie or Wally had been injured or were having marital problems.

Jamie blurted out, embarrassed as though she had been caught with her hand in the cookie jar. "My God, Mae, I'm pregnant!"

Mae burst out laughing. She put her arm around this gorgeous, distraught girl, years her junior and whispered, as though in confidence, back to her. "Jamie, calm down. Don't you know we're all pregnant?"

"Really?" purred the pregnant one, looking at Mae hopefully. And as the young wives dropped in Jamie slyly examining each, realized that almost every one seemed to have a much fuller figure.

Mae discussed children with Don many times. Both agreed that they wanted children to complete their lives. Mae had broached the subject again during the trip to San Antonio. "Don I think we should wait a year or so to begin a family. We should make sure we're compatible as we now believe. What do you think?"

Don wondered. Is Mae getting cold feet? Is she apprehensive about military life? No matter. "Mae, I believe that our country, probably most countries, especially men of all stripes, under rate the extreme importance of the mother and household executive. You will not find me in that group. I know and understand that you will be the one who has the titanic burden of bearing a child. You will have a great responsibility—perhaps the major one—in their raising.

"It is a blot on our modern civilization, one almost as great as our treatment of the American Indian, that it seems to value the piddling clerk-level jobs held by women in the business world as more important than the household executive. You ladies' responsibilities are simply the lifeblood of our future and not even a president or four-star general can replace you. Whenever you feel the urge, we can start our family . . . "

But the production of children was still dependent upon vitality and love. The Lieutenant Kipfers had both in abundance. In spite of her careful and meticulous planning, Mae must surely have set a record, she never endured a period in her married life.

Mae never complained about morning sickness, but Don realized his young wife was really uncomfortable. "Mae, I've heard about the new drug Thalidomide, which seems to eliminate morning sickness. Why don't you try that?"

Mae almost got nauseated on the spot. "Don, you really don't understand. Thalidomide is an untested drug. No one except God knows what effect it will have on this generation's crop of babies. I'm not using it. I'll go through my pregnancy in God's natural way. I'm even campaigning against its use among all our young wives."

During the next three years Mae gave birth to three healthy sons. Then the Thalidomide babies began to appear—minus one limb, two hands, three limbs, even four limbs, delivered to heartbroken couples.

Even one couple among her friends were brokenhearted. The government finally reacted to the use of Thalidomide.

Don was an avid fisherman. In Mae's ninth month he went with her to a lake that required travel over a bumpy road. To his credit, he was concerned. "Mae, in your condition, this road is no place to be. I'm going to turn back.

We do not want nor need a tragedy!"

Mae knew how much Don loved fishing and how strenuous his groundschool and flight school training were. She even listened and checked his accuracy as he read and memorized his checklists. So she just tensed up and lied to him. "It isn't too bad. I'm all right."

Before Don and Mae were born, Don's mother, Laura, had frequently had the four Moyer girls, Helen, Mary Alice, Letha, and Isabel, as guests at her home because of her large lawn and gardens where the girls could play. Long before much of the world had heard of international aid, Laura's sister Mary Bell, the first nurse to graduate from Akron's City Hospital, went to Lebanon. There she saw an orphan girl she fell in love with. Even as a single woman, she adopted this unfortunate child.

Suddenly this Arab girl's present changed and her future was enviable. Sally spent many happy days with the Moyer girls at Laura Kipfer's home. Now came a letter to Mae from Helen Moyer Southard. "Dear Edna Mae, Hope you and Don are well, Mae, Aunt Laura has told me that you are pregnant. It is a small world. Sally Graham's husband (an Army full colonel) is the chief surgeon at Fort Sam Houston. She has informed me they live in quarters just inside the gate at Fort Sam Houston, so you must be near each other. I'm sending their address and telephone number. You must call them. Sally and I were such close friends. Love, Helen."

Mae called Sally at once and Sally invited the Lieutenant Kipfers for dinner. Mae knew from this gracious lady's attitude that she would love her just as Helen did.

Mae had told Don, "Goodness, Lieutenant, I'm thankful we stayed with the Colonel Whitneys. I won't be scared out of my wits dining with the Colonel Grahams."

Sally Graham met Don and Mae at the door. "I'm so glad to see you, Mae and Don. Don, your mother was always so good to me. I can never repay her. Come in and meet my husband."

Sally led the way into their palatial quarters. Mae immediately realized the truth. The Graham's broom closet was as large as their house! "George, these are the two wonderful kids I've told you about, Mae and Don Kipfer."

George got up from his easy chair and smiled at the two visitors, making a quick evaluation. "Sally has told me so much about you two. I know we are fortunate to have you in the United State's military."

Don shook hands and answered, "Thank you, Colonel. You can be sure, certain, Mae and I will do our best."

George held Mae's hand longer than necessary but Don knew that it was because George already had a soft spot in his heart for this beautiful woman form Ohio, even in this instantaneous interval. "Please, both of you, don't call me colonel, George will do."

Don flushed. "Sir, that is good of you to suggest, but I believe that would be a bad habit for me to fall into."

Dinner was splendid, Midwestern-style, prepared by Mexican help. Conversation drifted back to Massillon, but never to Lebanon. Colonel Graham told his best stories about World War II. In the course of the conversation, Colonel Graham looked at Mae and spoke like a father, "Young lady, I can't help notice that you are pregnant. I suspect you are checked in at Brook General Hospital?"

Mae scutted a little uneasily on her chair. "Yes sir. If necessary, I can walk from my home to Brook General."

The colonel took a deep breath, rolled his eyes and said, "I believe being the head surgeon at Fort Sam's Brook General Hospital should be good for something. Major Picard is our best obstetrician. I'll assign him as your doctor. He'll call you tomorrow. Feel free to call him day or night."

Mae could hardly believe her ears. She had always known that rank had its privileges, but even at the academy she had never so obviously been the beneficiary of it. Still, she was not at a loss for the appropriate words. She replied, "Colonel, that is wonderful of you. We know you need not to do this for us. We are certainly thankful. We can never repay you. But be sure, wherever we are, we'll always fondly remember the kindness you and Sally have shown us."

Mae and Don's social calendar was full. They ate seafood captain's platters at Christie's, Chinese delicacies at Tai Shans, two-pound T-bone steaks at the Teepee Restaurant, and Mexican food at the historic restaurants along the San Antonio River.

Mae asked, "Don, what in the world is the Free State of Bandera? I thought Texas was Texas.

"You'll never understand it nor believe it unless you see it. It's within easy driving distance of San Antonio. The folks there have their own flag and claim they are an independent city-state. We'll have to go up there Saturday for lunch."

Mae could hardly wait to broaden her experience. Bandera was all that Mae had heard and that Don had promised.

She joyfully narrated for Don as he drove. "Look at all the old western false-front stores and salons," she reported knowing that Don had never been in Bandera before himself. "Look at all the folks here dressed in authentic western outfits. There are even horses tethered at the hitching posts. But most important, where shall we eat?"

"Come on in to this restaurant with me. You should see the inside. We'll ask the barman here at the Silver Dollar."

Don expected the barman to recommend a restaurant in Bandera. Not! "There's only one good place to eat if you really want good food. It's Slats Rogers." And the barman drew a map for the Kipfers.

Mae was apprehensive by the time they had driven several miles through the cottonwood and mesquite trees. She was even more insecure when an old barn materialized, stating in crude, difficult, scrawled script, "Slats Rogers."

The inside of the barn wasn't any more encouraging. The tables were rickety wooden squares with unsteady looking chairs. Mae whispered, "I see a rotating grindstone with a manual handle, attached to that old counter. What do you expect that's for, pathfinder?"

Don wasn't really sure. It couldn't be possible. Still he had no better idea. "Maybe it's to sharpen your dinner knife if the steaks are too tough?"

Mae shuddered. "Ugh!"

By that time one of the tallest, skinniest men either one had ever seen, dressed in western clothes with a twenty-gallon hat perched on the back of his head, appeared at the bar. "What would you two city slickers like to eat?"

Mae slunk down. She wasn't certain whether she was scared or embarrassed. Don finally caught his breath and answered, "Well, we are from San Antonio, but originally from Ohio. We'd like to westernize. We stopped at the Silver Dollar for directions and they sent us out to see you."

Slats clapped his huge hips with his huge hands. He fairly howled. "They did, did they. Well, relax and we'll get started. How do you like your T-bones?"

The spell was broken. Mae began to laugh. She began to think she might enjoy this saga. Don answered, "One medium rare and one well done."

Both the Kipfers asked for coffee. It certainly woke them up! The salad was the best they had ever been served even if they didn't recognize some of the ingredients. The roast potato and brazed pinion nuts were perfect. But the steaks were so good, Mae declared, "I name thee truly, the Free State of Bandera. Nowhere else in our country, I'm sure, can brag of such wonderful beef. Slats, we'll never have another the likes of this one!"

The social affairs between the wives and the West Pointers went on continuously with picnics, affairs at the Gunter Hotel and at Randoph's Officers Club. The girls and their husbands cemented friendships that would last throughout their lifetimes.

Mae knew Don was a patriot. He believed so strongly in the value of personal freedom that West Point's credo—duty, honor and country—came in his life before any other consideration. So when Mae was confined to Brooks General Hospital for the last week of her pregnancy, she naturally expected Don to go on with his flight training. He spent all his off-duty time with her and she knew he blamed himself and the rough ride to the fishing lake for her predicament that kept her in bed for her last week. Then on the 8th of April, 1949, when Don arrived from making a solo cross-country flight out of Randolph AFB, at Brooks General, he was greeted by shattering news. The nurse smiled and told him, "Lieutenant, you have a fine, healthy son. And your wife is fine."

Don went immediately to the hospital's canteen and bought a dozen red roses. Then he virtually ran to Mae's room. Before she could speak he ran over and soundly kissed her. "Congratulations, sweetie. I know you've given the Don Kipfer family a male heir and immortality!"

Mae herself was bubbling over with happiness. "Chief, I can assure you, it wasn't all that easy. And the name we picked, April Dawn, won't work. He looks just like you. I've named him Donald Charles Kipfer Jr."

She knew Don would be pleased, but she had made this decision all by herself. She demanded, "Go see him!"

Because Don believed that all men should be their own personality, Don knew that such a name would be a great burden for his son to bear. But he knew Mae would never agree to a change. In the nursery room, the nurse pointed out the Kipfer baby. Don was ecstatic. He even believed Don Jr. looked up and winked at him.

Only one thing bothered him and when he returned to Mae's room he enthused, "Mae, he's just beautiful, and perfect, and smart. He even winked at me. But his complexion, it's not red like the other babies. It's pure white. Even his hair and eyebrows are white. Are you sure he's not an albino?"

Mae almost hurt herself laughing. Only the pain of her delivery stopped her hilarity. "Don, don't be foolish. He's blond and blue-eyed just like you." Then shaking her finger at her dubious husband, she declared, "Believe me, he's perfect!"

Mae knew Don would be a good father. But she was not prepared for his diligence. He questioned her about every detail of Don Jr.'s care. Immediately he began giving the baby gentle exercises. He located a small, deep metal tank and furiously sanitized it. Within his first month, Don Jr. could dog paddle and stay afloat.

Most of the West Point wives gathered every morning at Fort Sam's swimming pool. In keeping with military fastidiousness, there was a large sign up.

No children in diapers permitted. No one had ever, nor Don eventually found out, would ever, question an action taken by Mae. First, all her actions were carefully considered and were undertaken only with consideration for others. Aside from that, when this beautiful young woman dressed in a spiffy bathing suit, her blue-black hair tousled, her beautiful, chiseled face smiling, but determined, there were few who wanted to displease her. Would anyone risk crossing such a woman? And so, at three months, a tailored swimming suit in place, Don Jr. was swimming in Fort Sam Houston's Officer's Club pool. Naturally no one could believe what their eyes told them was true. Even some of the officers came by to see this special treat.

Mae had met Don's flying instructor, Tony Greget. She was later to learn this exasperatingly rambunctious, confident, curly haired pilot was the archetype of the fighter pilot. Before Don left Randoph for Barksdale AFB, Don approached Mae saying. "Tony has guided me successfully through basic flying training. I feel obligated to say thank you. Let's stop by and see him and his new bride."

Mae was still very much an Adventist in her heart. She wondered. *Can I handle this?*

Most of the Kipfers' visit was spent watching Tony chase his sensuous bride around the Greget quarters. Tony was having the time of his life and she was squealing happily every time he was about to catch her. Actually, Mae and Don both enjoyed this ad libbed entertainment. Before they departed, Tony betrayed his true inner self by speaking seriously to Mae, "Don's a darned good officer. Also he's a good contact pilot. But when it comes to instrument flying, he's a zinger! I wish I were as good."

As they walked to their car Mae whispered, "It seems Tony's still attempting to catch her. And it seems she's still escaping. But there's no doubt they're having a great time."

"Believe it, wise one. Before I turn over the old Aerosedan's engine, she'll slip and Tony will catch her!"

Everyone had been apprehensive, their assignment to an advanced school would determine their military career. Then orders had been published. A majority of the students wanted to be fighter pilots and go to Williams AFB. That was the glamorous and macho road. However, Don had a different agenda. He had requested multi-engines in the hope that he might get to fly the multi-engine B-52. Don had no trouble getting this unpopular request. But first he had to complete the multi-engine course at Barksdale AFB, Louisiana.

Things were better organized in Louisiana. Don came out of the housing office and told Mae, "Good news, mamacita. We've got quarters off base if we like and can afford them. But negotiations are our own. There's a living room, bedroom and kitchen."

When Mae saw both the inside and outside of these quarters she was completely relieved. "Well, general, things are looking up. These are the best digs we've had so far."

There was only one thing that bothered the Kipfers in Bossier City. The heat and humidity were simply unbelievable. It was so hot on the flight line that Don had to wear leather gloves during preflight to keep his hand from being burned on the metal fuselage of the B-25.

Mae summed up conditions within their quarters: "The evaporative cooler the landlord installed to con us doesn't work in 100 percent humidity. But I've negated that part of the problem. I filled the drip pan with ice cubes. That helps. I'll tell you a secret, bomber man. If you sit real still it isn't too bad. If you get up and move, the perspiration and condensation rolls down your body and drips onto the floor."

Don laughed. "I guess Tony's bride couldn't be hip-hopping helter-skelter around these quarters."

Mae tried to keep the social activities of the brides swinging. But now it was different. These young wives, now with babies, would be here only a short time and then all separate, perhaps forever. Nearly all of these heat-hassled women had their hands full. Neither mother nor baby could handled the heat. Still they did get together several times at the base pool.

Almost immediately the Kipfers discovered the Mirror Restaurant in Bossier City. Mae was beside herself and almost cried for joy. "Mon male, this place is just beautiful. And beyond any doubt, its best feature, thanks to its enlightened management, is its air conditioning. Let's eat here every night. Please no hurry. I believe I might be able to survive."

Don discovered almost at once that his first lieutenant instructor and his wife were bridge players. "Mae, let's invite my flight instructor and his wife over for bridge." Mae made a snort but nodded okay.

Don's instructor and his wife were indeed good bridge players and won each time they visited. Don had told Mae he was sure his lieutenant liked him because he often complimented him, even in the presence of his other students. Tony had never once complimented him, about anything he did. So it wasn't a surprise to Mae when Don went to fix drinks, that Lieutenant Ford told her, "Don is a natural multi-engine pilot. He's the best student I've ever had. I've even sent him up on missions to help others." Mae knew how serious and mission-oriented her husband was. She could only beam.

From what little Lieutenant Ford had told him, Don believed his assignment from advanced flight training would be to multi-engines. When orders were published for assignment, Don was not only rocked to his toes but was very disappointed. He told Mae, "No multi-engines! Of all things, its back to Randolph AFB for instructor training and then to Goodfellow AFB in San Angelo, Texas, as an instructor pilot in T-6s!"

Mae cared only that Don was happy. "Your instructor told me you were a natural multi-engine pilot. Did he tell you why he recommended you to be a single-engine instructor?"

"Yup. He claims I'll learn more as an instructor pilot in a year about flying than in five years sitting as a copilot in a multi-engine aircraft."

The training at Randolph was thorough but really a piece of cake. "Face it, my copilot, let's enjoy San Antonio."

San Angelo, West Texas, deserts!

"Neither you or my mother, who was along to help with Don Jr. and who had just learned that Mae was pregnant again, have ever experienced the desert. Believe me, it'll be a shock. They haven't had a substantial rain here in seven years! They're tanking the drinking water in!"

But the visit to the housing office was encouraging. "Mae, let's you and I go see these quarters. You're our ship's captain. See what you think."

It turned out their prospective landlady was Mrs. Albro, a philanthropist. Her husband had died recently and she planned to live with her son. "I'm going to keep the back bedroom and bath with its separate outside door. They're not included in the rental deal, just in case. If things don't work out to well living with my son, I may come back occasionally."

Mae could hardly wait to see the inside of this beautiful home, nestled in its upbeat neighborhood. She was really astonished. "Don, it has a giant living room and large, separate dining room, two large bedrooms and a huge kitchen. The tile counter in the kitchen is more than twenty feet long! We can have a ball in this place. None of our relatives have ever lived in a house like this. But can we afford it?"

Don discussed this with Mrs. Albro. "Lieutenant, God has been good to me. My husband made sure that I don't have money problems. I want to give something back. You young military couples deserve that." Then she mentioned a ridiculously low rent. Don quickly shook her hand.

Mae loved to entertain, especially in such a spacious, modern home. At various times she had Don's flight commander, Captain McDonald, and the other flight instructors and their wives for dinners and bridge. These affairs were not just social events. At dinner at Mae's house was like going back again to these men's own roots. They reinforced every officer's resolve.

The first time Mae took Don Jr. to the base nursery she returned home full of ideas. Mae had practically raised her younger siblings. She had coached all manner of sports. She was a Red Cross swimming instructor and had completed pre-nursing at Washington Missionary College. When she volunteered to supervise the base nursery, she was appointed immediately. It was not only the infants at the nursery who benefited from Mae's tender, loving care, but their mothers from watching and talking with Mae.

Don loved flight instructing. He was already completing his second class of eager students. He told Mae, "Sweetie, I believe almost anyone can fly if they truly want to. I had to fail only one student, named Ramos. I'd put him in a straight and level attitude, tell him to put the nose and wingtips on the natural horizon and then let him take over. Off we'd go in a gut-wrenching spin. I really liked Ramos, but if he were by himself he would simply self-destruct."

Mae knew all the flight instructors and their wives. The women were all beautiful, smart and athletic. To her, the instructors she had met were pretty much all carefree souls. So when Don mentioned discipline, she was a little surprised. "Mae, I know those easy going friends of mine seem pretty undisciplined. But Captain McDonald has been hinting his reservations concerning the new cadets. He told me, "These kids don't even know what a uniform is or how to wear it. They don't know their left foot from their right. They never heard of the *Manual of Military Law*. Not one of them has ever heard of discipline. I'm counting on you to change that."

Mae was more sober than Don had ever remembered. "But Don, you love instructing, and the half days at work are bonny for us. You've had your share of the harshest kind of discipline."

Don didn't panic. "Sweet patootie, I suspect that's the reason they chose me. Besides it will be my first independent command. I'll have a lieutenant, and four top-grade NCOs working for me and you'll be a commander's wife."

"Now what in this cookie world does that mean? Undoubtedly there are other factors at work in this reorganization."

Of course no one at Don's level was aware of it. However, the base wing commander, Colonel Wheatly, and the training commander, Captain Howell, may have been briefed on the total issue. Korea was upon the agenda for the United States. The United States had offered to give the allies flight training. "Can you believe this, Mae. All these allied flight students are to pass through our Goodfellow Preflight School, the only one in the world, now commanded by your friendly First Lieutenant Kipfer."

Before Don could finish his grade slips for his final graduating flight students, nor move to his first command, Mae broke into the base hospital housed in a former World War II barracks.

The duty nurse laughed and asked Mae, "Mrs. Kipfer, are you back in here again?"

The obstetrician had told Don that morning, "Lieutenant, you don't need to hang around if you have something to do. Your wife will be busy for a few more hours."

Don went across the street to the flight shack and finished his instructor's paperwork. He was back in a little over an hour. He could not believe his eyes. Walking down the corridor toward him, unconcerned, was the insensitive medical officer, holding something that appeared to be a newly skinned rabbit, head down, his feet between the doctor's thumb and forefinger.

The doctor grinned, recognizing Don. "A fine, healthy boy, Lieutenant!"

Don told himself, "If you weren't holding my son, you'd be decked." Then recovering, Don gasped. "Another boy?"

The doctor kept smiling. "Yes, Lieutenant. If you don't want him, I'll take him back."

Don didn't answer. He just hurried to Mae's room. He kneeled beside her and kissed her. "How are you, my love?"

Mae was not at all distressed. She was radiant. "They don't get any easier, penetrator! I'm a little tired but otherwise just fine, absent one. Did you see your new son?"

"Yes, my dear, we just had a formal introduction in the hallway."

Just at this crucial time, but before Mae had gone to the hospital, Mrs. Albro had told Don. "My living arrangement with my son is working just fine. I'm going to sell the old Albro home. I'm sorry to bring such bad news."

Back to the housing office went Don. Staff Sergeant Stauffer told him about the very rich rancher, Mr. Volkman and the very nice house he had for rent at 130 Morris Avenue. Don took the house key and looked at the two bedrooms, living room, and large kitchened house. He took it. Mae visited and approved. But both shared a problem. The house was unfurnished.

Mae was ready to deliver momentarily so Don inherited the repugnant chores of the move. Since that was the first home Mae and Don had furnished, he had added problems. "Truly, we don't have much furniture," he admitted. "But I'll get all the necessities we need from base housing."

Now Mae returned not to the elite home she had departed, but to the much more modest home at 130 Morris Avenue right under the landing flight path for Goodfellow AFB.

Mae had always known that Don loved to hunt and fish. "Mr. Volkman, their landlord, an immensely rich rancher with his own, officially acknowledged airport, had become a close friend for whom Don collected payments from reluctant renters. This Royal Texan had called while Don was at work and told Mae, "Tell Don I've reserved a section for him for the fifteenth. I want him to come on down. It will be a party of three. There will be a restaurateur who has a truck, guns and a large tent and the housing sergeant from the base, who Don knows. The sergeant will contact Don about details."

Sergeant Stauffer, Don later told Mae in strict confidence, did call. "We met Mrs. Volkman about dusk the day before the hunting season opened. She took us to an old adobe building, once used by vacaros and I helped the other two men set up camp. By now it was dark. Immediately those two jumped into their truck insisting I go with them. Along the road we went, their powerful light searching for, and lighting, the glowing eyes in the darkness. 'Shoot them, Lieutenant, shoot them,' they shouted over and over. "Hey, men, those are not deer, they're cattle. Mr. Volkman wouldn't like that.'

"I wondered, *after all, Pedro* (the only name Don ever heard) *owned a restaurant.* Finally, realizing the roads were nearly lined with the cars of other hunters, and several police cars, the two seeming sportsmen gave up. But long before sun up they were remounted and determined to go summon Mrs. Volkman. 'Hey, don't get excited, men, the lady said daybreak. I'm sure she wants to sleep."

"Mrs. Volkman was dressed in western clothes and took we three men to the section Bill Volkman had assigned them and opened the gate. 'Now remember boys, no does!' she cautioned, and motioned them in.

"Mae," moaned Don, "almost before Mrs. Volkman's truck departed down the road, "these two meat hunters were out of their truck shooting into a herd of some twenty deer about a hundred yards away. I didn't see a buck in the bunch! I left. I couldn't afford to make headlines in the local paper for illegal hunting. I wanted no part of something so asinine."

Mae was astonished. "But Don, I noticed you brought a nice buck home."

"True, faithful observer. Two does and a buck approached a water tank I was watching just before sundown. They were beautiful. I dropped their proud buck with one shot. It was revolting. I'll never hunt again."

Mae wasn't finished. "Didn't the other two shoot anything?"

"I don't know. They already had been to the early deer season down by the Rio Grande to get venison for the entrepreneur's restaurants. What they had under their canvas on their truck I don't want to know!"

But Don's fishing career was more pleasant. He fished with Loyd Capps in all three Concho rivers that joined in San Angelo.

They used motor boats from the Air Force Recreation Center. Occasionally Mae went with Don. "Don, the wind is really getting strong. I'm worried about tornadoes."

"Take it easy, girl. We're down low between the banks. It's safe as it can be. Maybe the change in pressure will change our luck."

It did. Mae caught the first largemouth bass. "Reckon it'll do more than four pounds, lucky."

In all, they caught two more bass just as large. Don took care to keep the bass alive. When he got home he put the large fish in their bathtub. Don Jr. precocious, could walk and he stood for hours watching these strange toys move about.

Mae and Don had always believed that one makes his own luck. Now Mae wasn't so sure. "Don, you know how wonderful Major Richard was to me. My doctor here in San Angelo is just as nice. He told me there is to be an area-wide contest in San Angelo to determine the area's most healthy baby. He wants Don Jr. and me to be his entry. What do you think?"

Don had roared, "Your doctor is a virtual Einstein. He knows no judges could resist you two. A coal-black-haired beauty with a blond, curly haired, blue-eyed son, able to play many sports while other babies are just learning to walk. Go for it, girl!"

Home comes the hunters from the wild! Don simply put his hands on his hips. "So, you two came home with the first place loving cup! It's wonderful to be among such celebrities. Congratulations!"

Among her many talents, Mae had written, cast and directed a full-length minstrel for showing at Madison School for folks throughout Madison County. So when Don complained to her, "You know I now have fifty French flight cadets, directly off the streets of France who don't speak a work of English. I have Danish Flying Cadets who are superb. There are also Norwegian, Turkish, and Thai officers. Their court-marshal, athletic, military and disciplinary training is going okay. But the enlisted cadets, in particular, have very low morale. I would say they're depressed.

"They've been restricted to base so that they haven't seen, heard, or talked to females. For a Frenchman, that's the pits. One has already sneaked down to Mexico. I've heard several have vowed that they would rather clobber in than face the music in France, having failed. Depression is no baggage to take with you into flight training; either for the student or the instructor!"

Mae curled her brow in deep concentration. She knew Don had not told her this woeful tale just for jawbone exercise. "Don, I'm sure they have the same problem you female-starved cadets suffered from at West Point. If you agree, I could prepare baked goods, provide iced lime-spiked Coke, and host a couple hour party every Saturday afternoon. It may help."

Don smiled, and said, "Sweetheart, I thought you would never ask!"

Mae was no ordinary person. Her sweet, gracious disposition almost immediately made a difference in the attitudes of the young Frenchmen who had been rudely shanghaied from their country's streets and sent to a foreign land.

"Thank you, copilot," complimented Don. And now, by the grace of her God, Mae had entered into the field of international relations. And of course, the cadets were also more interested in learning to speak English.

Preflight classes graduated every month. This event was always accompanied by social celebrations with many plaques, as this was one of the milestones in every pilot's career. Colonel and Mrs. Morgan, their wing commander, their military training squadron commander, Major Heston Daniels, and preflight commander, 1st Lieutenant and Mrs. Kipfer sat at the head table. Such a position gave Mae instant recognition on Goodfellow AFB.

But soon it was time to move again. Now the Lieutenant Kipfers faced their final challenge at Goodfellow. Don kept abreast of all the news concerning the Air Force. It was clear that everyone on the general staff at the Pentagon was pushing formal advanced academic degrees. They even claimed they were tying promotion to them. Don, still a bit naïve, applied for advanced academic training.

"Mae, I've been accepted for graduate training at the United States Air Force Institute of Technology at Wright Patterson AFB in Dayton, Ohio. I have a mandatory report date of 30 August 1951! We'll have to leave here by 18 August!"

Mae turned pale. "Miene Gott, Mister Hyde, you know I'm carrying our third baby. All three will have been born within three years. This one isn't even scheduled to emerge until past your latest departure date. I'll just have to make the doctor start my labor early. You can believe me, I'm not staying here by myself!"

"Mae, I apologize. You know I would not intentionally cause this problem. I'm calling my mother at once and asking her to come and help with the chores during packing and more importantly, to help you with the other children."

Don had told Mae many times, "Sweetie, no matter how disastrous a situation seems, even World War II, while some people suffered, others profited."

Thus it had been the previous summer. Don had arranged to sell their Chevy and had negotiated for and made a down payment on a Pontiac sold by one of the Steiners, his friends, in Navarre, Ohio. Don, Mae and two sons had traveled by plane to Massillon, Ohio, from where Don could call Navarre and make arrangements for picking up their car. His friend had told him, "Your Pontiac wasn't delivered. The Korean War, you know. I can't help you!"

Neither Mae nor Don had suspected the fallout from the Korean War would spook the American people so deeply about capital items. Don had never believed that loyalty between friends could be discarded so easily.

Mae had almost cried. "Don, you know he got the car. Someone offered him more money. Our Chevy is gone! Sold! How can we operate without an auto?"

"There's no other solution. I'll have to spend my vacation finding something."

Mae knew Don went to Canton, Akron, Cleveland, Toledo, Columbus, Dayton and Cincinnati. No luck. Finally on the fifth evening Don came home smiling. "Mae, I hit pay dirt in Urichesville, Ohio. A brand-new Olds 98 sporting General Motor's first rocket engine. It was owned by a multiple amputee of the Korean War. Under the United States government's free auto support program he gets a new one every year. All the controls are hand-operated now from the dashboard. I explained our situation to the owner. Thanks again to our God. He's a patriot. The controls will be changed and the car will be ready tomorrow. It's just perfect for us. It's huge and only has four thousand miles on it."

Mae beamed. "Must I say it again, Moses?" Mae demanded. "God has again smiled on us."

Now, after enjoying what was left of their leave, back in San Angelo with three adults and three wee children, the Olds 98 was a blessing. "Mae, I am really concerned about you traveling so far so soon after you're giving birth."

"Don't worry, commander, I feel fine. I'll let you know when I'm tired."

Getting housing, especially since the Korean War had commenced, had been a heartrending problem so far during their military career for the Kipfers. But Don had confidently and foolishly told Mae, "My dear, we are going back to Ohio. We are Ohioans. Ohioan are patriots. We won't have any trouble getting housing!"

Mae was skeptical. "Not!" she replied.

First they sent Don's mother by bus to Massillon. Then they went out to Swan's Road for a joyous reunion with Mae's parents.

Dayton, Ohio

Next day a trip to Dayton and Wright Patterson AFB to the housing office and a civilian female, with no apparent sympathy nor concern for her military constituents. Don later told Mae. "That woman said, instead of helping, 'We haven't had any rental property for ages. Do you have children?'"

Don had replied proudly, perhaps believing this motherly female might have some sympathy. "Yes, three infant sons. From two weeks to two and one-half years old. Why?"

"Ugh" groaned this long-fanged Ohio woman. "You'll never get a rental.

Try the downtown Dayton housing office. Here's their address."

Downtown Dayton was the pits! With three small kids along to help! If the base was so calloused, what could they expect from the civilian world? The woman at the desk inquired, Don told Mae later, "Any children?"

"Yes, three very small ones."

The unperturbed antagonistic public servant almost chocked with glee as she smiled. "No chance!"

After Don reported to Mae she was deflated for the first time in her life. "Have these people any concept of what you're doing for them? Do they want us to drown these three beautiful Americans? They'll be the men who will someday protect these people's right to be nasty?" What are we going to do?"

First, I'm taking you and the boys back to Newark where you'll be safe and comfortable. Then I'm going to put a plea for help in the local paper. Somewhere here there must be a Christian person, I'll call you every day and come for you as soon as I locate something."

When Don came back to Dayton he went directly to the Dayton newspapers. He placed this ad: AIR FORCE LIEUTENANT, WIFE AND THREE SMALL SONS UNDER THREE YEARS OLD DESPERATE FOR RENTAL HOUSING. ALL FIVE US ARE AMERICAN PATRIOTS. WE HOPE THAT SOMEWHERE IN DAYTON THERE IS ANOTHER PATRIOT WHO WILL HELP US.

Unbelievably, Don only received one call in response to his ad. Two days later his phone rang. "This is Mr. Wukmer, I have just completed building a new house at 1646 Darst Avenue from which you can see Wright Field. My wife and I would be happy to rent to you, Lieutenant. Come on over and take a look. I'm calling right now from the house."

Don arrived ten minutes later from the room he was renting in a nearby house. He could hardly believe the Kipfers' good luck. Once more God had taken a hand. Mr. Wukmer was waiting. The house was beautiful, sparkling. It consisted of a living room, kitchen, two bedrooms and a full basement and the rent was far below Dayton's inflated standard. "God will surely bless you, Mr. Wukmer. We'll take it!"

By the next evening, Don had been to Newark and back. Mae almost exploded after she had inspected their new home. "Don, God has again heard us and answered." When she met Mr. Wukmer she told him. "No one will ever hold you and your wife in such high regard as we Kipfers. Ask anything of us. You will be in our prayers so long as we live!"

Mae knew Don would be very busy because he was determined to do very well at anything he attempted. She knew his course, "automatic control," was not only a first for the Institute of Technology, but beyond the capability of most engineering students. Don told Mae. "Sweetie, the next year and a half will be tough. You won't see much of me because I'll be holed up in our bedroom studying. I'm buying you and the boys a twenty-four-inch television, the largest made, to help all four of you have a more pleasant time. Don produced what he promised. The huge box was called a TRAD and was the only one of its kind ever produced.

Mae knew that with flying, school, home study and being a father and husband, Don would be stretched. She didn't line up any "honey-dos," however, she did help supervise the base nursery and held a minor position in the Officer Wives Club.

Almost immediately, Mae knew she had taken another step in her ascendancy. Wright Patterson could very well have been the hub of the United States Air Force. It housed the Air Material Command, The Aerospace Division, the Air Force Institute of Technology, the Armament Laboratory and many other units. When one toured Patterson AFB from stem to stern one saw dozens of what to her were mansions, all occupied by generals and generals' wives. Some homes went slumming and accepted full colonels as occupants.

Don kept Mae up to date on his progress. "Squeezing flying in and concentrating on both it and academics try all our abilities. One of our professors gives lectures that none of the students, or perhaps none of other instructors understand. In the midterm exam I got a twenty-one—the highest grade in the class. We students finally convinced another lieutenant colonel professor to explain what they should know about 'The Response of Higher Order Physical Systems.' He did and subsequently everyone managed to pass that course. It was obvious how happy the professor was with himself."

One really good thing happened to Don at the Air Force Institute of Technology, Mae thought. His advisor was Colonel Harold Teubner. Colonel Tuebner is a gentleman. He was in the first class at MIT in the United States that offered graduate work in automatic control. He had assigned Don and Charlie Johnson as coauthors of a paper on 'The Dummy Gun System.' Still only a concept, it will to improve the effectiveness of our fighters many fold, if it is valid. I believe he likes me. He's invited we Kipfers, from among all his students, to his home to meet his wife."

Don didn't flatter himself. He knew Mae played a role in Colonel Teubner's invitation. Mae had already been to Officers Wives Club meetings. Few could pass up the opportunity to know Mae. Later, Don felt that Mae looked enough like Colonel Tuebner's wife to be her sister. And by the time the Lieutenant Kipfers left the Tuebners' home' Mae had already become assistant to Mrs. Tuebner in the Officer Wives Club.

Mae never blamed God for setbacks; however, she did give God credit for all their pluses. When Don had been checking into personnel that first day at Wright Patterson AFB with all his hand-carried personnel records, a West Point classmate, who was just leaving personnel, had hailed him. Don reported what he had said. "Hey, Kip. The list for promotion to captain is going out from personnel tomorrow. They just put me on it. Talk to the master sergeant."

"Mae, you wouldn't believe it. I showed the sergeant my records and he said, 'Lieutenant, you're eligible and now you're on the list.'"

When the promotion list was announced at USAFIT, Don could hardly wait to let Mae know. "Kiss your former lieutenant husband, mon ami. You hubby is now a captain. You, my dear, are a captain's wife."

Mae could hardly stand steady. "My, my," she kept repeating. "Now our family finally has a captain to steer its ship. I remember what a powerful man Captain Howell was at Goodfellow AFB."

Don, Mae knew, had been creating unique solutions to difficult problems all his life. Now, he confided to her. "Mae, I'm learning things I would never have conceived of. Charlie Johnson and I are doing our master's theses on a Reeves Analog computer. It may be the first time such a task has been done at college level. The computer takes up much of the area in a room. It must be totally air conditioned. Its program is hand-hardwired in a multi-contact board. Whatever, we'll be making electronic and computational history!"

Mae was always attentive when Don talked so seriously to her. "It sounds terribly complicated, Sir Einstein. But what is its value?"

Don was not disturbed. He knew that Mae's question probably reflected the reaction of the majority of laymen. Most general officers would ask the same question.

"Sweetie, speed and accuracy in computation are important in all complex problems. Napoleon said he beat the Austrians at Austerlitz because they didn't understand the value of a minute. What he meant was that as the time for the Austrians to fire elapsed, his cannons had made the Austrians only memories. I dare say someday such fantastic speed and accuracy will be vital to the very existence of the United States. Compared to the capability of the system we're testing, the solution of a gun control problem melts."

When Don and Charlie had completed their theses, Colonel Tuebner called his computer friends at the Massachusetts Institute of Technology. "Hey, professor, the peons down here at the USAFIT have scooped you! We've resolved the validity of The Dummy Gun System!"

For Don and Charlie, Colonel Tuebner bubbled, for the first time either young officer could remember. "You've both maintained a grade average high enough to go for a doctor's degree. "You can apply any time!"

When Mae heard the news she wondered aloud, "Well, wonderbar? And?"

Don laughed as Mae had never heard him do for more than a year. "Need you ask, my overworked frau? This past year and a half has been hell for me—a mind and back breaker. I'd like to get back to earning my pay the easy way."

The Air Force had notified all of its officers that if they expected to be promoted they should get advanced degrees. Like most government edicts, this bombastically political correct propaganda did not disclose the whole story. "Mae, I joined the Air Force to fly. Now, the system has tagged me and many others. I did too well at USAFIT. And now I'm seen as a technical officer. Example: Joe Gorell, my classmate got a doctor's degree at Ohio State but now no one knows what to do with him. Certainly, the government is devious. They tell you to get more education so you can get promoted, but hell's bells, promotions go to operational officers, not to scientific ones!"

So, as he expected, Don was assigned to the Weapons Laboratory at Wright Field as a division chief. Mae had always realized Don was intended to do special things. "Don, Major William Fort, Al Zemeskel and Frank Roe take you with them to Eglin AFB and to Washington. They have invited us to their homes. Don't you realize why?"

"I like Bill Fort, Frank Roe and Al Zemeskel. I believe they like me. They have years of experience that I must benefit form. They have made me responsible for the Low Altitude Bombing System (LABS), the Tactical In-frared Bombing System (TIRBS), the Airborne Moving Target System (AMTI), a Self-Destructing Anti-Rail System, a pencil beamed radar, and the latest, a Tactical Bombing System at International Telephone & Tele-graph. I'll have four outstanding engineering officers, several senior enlisted senior sergeants, and a secretary to help me."

Captain John Camera is working on the rail system (it was later the key to McNamara's Line in Vietnam/Laos). Lieutenant Woolen had just married. Mae had arranged for him to rent an upstairs apartment at the Wukmer's home. Mary laughed, "Those kids keep us up all night long with their love making. Stanley just lies there snickering. Apparently Lieutenant Wollen had learned a great deal from the pencil-beamed radar he is administering. Jules Appleman, like Woolen, was a product of New York University. The Airborne Moving Target Identification (AMTI) later made it easy to locate targets in places like Vietnam and Laos where high value targets were scarce. "He claims," Don confided to Mae, "that Ohio girls have drained all his energy."

"He's bragging, of course," retorted Mae.

There were many perks to Don's appointment. "Mae, can you believe," he reported after a trip to Norden, Inc., in New York and Raytheon in California, "Mr. Norden had tickets, my own I paid for, of course, on the first nonstop flight from New York City to California. Danny Kay and many other celebrities were aboard. I received this certificate."

After International Telephone and Telegraph (IT&T) had submitted the winning proposal for the Tactical Bombing System, Don went to New Jersey to help with contract negotiations. There was a sticking point concerning funding that had to be favorably resolved for the Air Force. IT&T senior officers were balking.

"For heavens sake, miene Captain, what did you do?" queried Mae.

Don almost choked. "I stooped pretty low, my dear. I told them. "I know you are IT&T. But much of your company's welfare depends upon the welfare of the United States. Whatever your origin, I know everyone here is American. I hope we are all patriotic Americans. I was raised to believe our country is the only hope of universal freedom for all men. Is there anyone here who doubts that? You, better than anyone, understand what the Tactical Bombing System is, what is represents to the security of the country. I believe, and I hope that both sides should bend a bit."

Mae was enthralled. "What did they do!"

"They signed."

Mae had especially liked the one Canadian Officer Squadron Leader Doug McKellar and his wife when both he and Don were at the USAFIT. Perhaps it was because Doug, in many ways, reminded Mae of her father. Neither Mae or Don ever expected to see Doug McKellar again after he departed Dayton. Further, although they had spent their long honeymoon mostly in Canada, Mae really never even hoped to return. Now, out of nowhere came earth-shaking news. Don came home from work almost trembling, with orders.

"Mae, please give the boys something, perhaps ice cream, to occupy them. I have some really, really big news."

Mae did not appreciate unexpected, upsetting news. It was not always good. "Now what?"

"I believe S/L Doug McKellar may be behind this. Maybe even his wife."

Now Mae was really perturbed. "What on earth do you mean?"

"A request from the Canadian Government filtered down through headquarters USAF to Wright Air Development Center. It was a request for an exchange engineering officer with knowledge of the Dummy Gun System. He is to be assigned to the U.S. Embassy in Ottawa with duty station at

National Defense Headquarters."

This time, by Saint Peter's holy robe, Mae, too, was speechless. She sat mum and immobile. She knew God was at work. After all, in such a very short time she had advanced from a student at Washington Missionary College, to teacher at Madison School, to West Pointer's wife, to hostess for the Allied students in Goodfellow preflight, to wife of a division chief at a major scientific laboratory. Now of all things, to be a member of the U.S. Embassy in Ottawa and to be stationed as an RCAF officer in National Defense Headquarters was just too much to comprehend.

"And are you accepting, exalted leader?" secretly prayed a hopeful spouse.

"*Meine schon frau*, what I hold in my hand is not an invitation. It is an order. Start planning your strategy."

As part of the outprocessing for Canada, all members of the family had to obtain various shots, depending upon their destination. There were many other wives on the move for distant overseas stations. Several of them asked Mae. "And Mae, what distant place are you going to?"

All of those expected Mae to reply, Germany, France or perhaps Afghanistan. Mae really groaned and showed a slight blush. "Can you believe, Canada?"

The response was uniform. "Oh, no!" It was not that people didn't love Canada. They could not believe that Mae's God was giving her husband credit for an overseas tour not more that two hundred miles from her home.

Ottawa

When the Kipfers arrived at the American Embassy, in Ottawa, Mae could not believe it was housed in a beautiful stone building directly across the street from the mind-boggling Parliament buildings. "Don," she gasped, "here we are back where we spent our honeymoon and this time we're to be residents."

Five-year-old Don Jr. was standing, looking out the auto window toward the Parliament buildings. "Mom, I want to see a Northwest Mounted Policeman."

Mark, aged four, echoed. "Me, too, Mom!"

David, aged three asked, "Mom, is this where we see the man in the red coat riding on a horse?"

Mae really laughed. Then she looked toward the entrance to the main government buildings and sure enough the boys' idol stood there. "Don, you go check on housing. We're going to have our picture taken with a real Northwest Mounted Policeman."

The boys could hardly move fast enough once they spotted the red coat.

It was jut as thrilling for the policeman when he spotted Mae, her blue black hair swaying in the breeze, accompanied by three very small boys with long, curly white hair and blue eyes.

He stopped what he was doing and arranged to have their photographs taken with him. Of course, he didn't miss the chance to put his arm around Mae's shoulders.

The boys could talk of nothing else as they returned to the car, just as their father also returned.

Mae was still flushed but not too much that she forgot their primary objective. "Well, pathfinder, what did they tell you?"

Don pretended to be grim but then smiled and said, "By gad, the embassy actually knew we were coming. They have an efficiency apartment for us to rent just west of Ottawa. They also have a house that sounds good if you like it. It will be available in less than one week."

Yes, the apartment was nice. But the house, stuccoed but with large red white and blue, raised stucco circles on a buff background, was unusual to say the least. Don Jr. really laughed. "Mom, it looks like a giraffe."

"Yes, it's a giraffe," agreed Mark.

"Let's call it the giraffe," chimed in David. And so that's what this French, blue-doored home became.

Just a week later their furniture arrived and they moved in.

Almost before the moving truck had left there was a knock on the door and a handsome, reserved gentleman introduced himself. "I'm Art Hewitt. Our backyards abut each other. I'm a commander in the Navy and work in National Defense Headquarters."

Don was no stranger to such introductions. "I'm Don Kipfer, I'm a captain in the United States Air Force. I'll be working in NDHQ. This is my wife Mae, Don Jr., Mark, and David."

Don knew immediately that Art could barely keep his eyes off Mae. Still he was a gentleman and proposed to Don. "Perhaps we can carpool. We'll get together before Monday."

On Sunday evening, the Kipfers were invited to the Hewitts for cocktails and of course to meet the remainder of Art's family. Eunice was a handsome woman who would have been at home in the Royal British Court. All five Kipfers liked her immediately. Karen was older than the Kipfer boys. They were suspicious of her possible attempt at domination. But Richard was perfect and just their age. These two families were to remain close friends until their deaths.

Across the street from the front of the Kipfers house lived twin girls, just David's age but too young to be of interest to Mark and Don Jr. David loved these jolly girls and he also wanted to be friends with their gentle, huge yellow tiger cat named Napoleon. One day soon after they had moved into the Giraffe, David came running to the back door. "Mom, 'Poleon scratched me!"

Mae was terrified because the injury could be to one of David's eyes. Also, back in the states an attack by an unprovoked animal could mean rabies. "What happened, David?"

"Well, I tried to pick him up so I could hug him, but he began swishing his tail. So I grabbed a hold of his tail and held it. Then I bit 'Poleon's tail!"

It was all Mae could do to keep from laughing. She stopped the bleeding and applied antiseptic. When she told Don about the encounter she thought he would explode with merriment.

Don again met Doug McKellar his first duty day at headquarters, as well as all the other officers, including the very able wing commander Frank Phripp. The wing commander told Don, "You will be called upon to solve a variety of problems but you will be primarily the RCAF's project officer for all aspects of avionics and armament on the CF-105. We know you understand systems engineering. So your responsibilities will include such auxiliary things as the adequacies of the proposed readiness hangers and the CF-105 interface with the Distant Early Warning Line. From time to time you will be expected to brief Air Commodore Easton."

Don began his tour with a task totally independent of the CF-105. He suspected it was a trial run. He was to evaluate the validity of a proposal to shortcut the design complexity for the interior ballistics of a gun barrel. Next he was supposed to develop a method for determining the envelope an interceptor had to enter to make a successful intercept on a high-speed bomber.

Don requested orders so that he could tour the dew line and evaluate the state of its technology. On his return he reported his findings to Wind Commander Fripp who took him to see Air Commodore Easton. "What I'm going to do, Commodore Easton, is in no way intended to detract from the method the RCAF is using to track boggies and friendly interceptors. The USAF must solve this same problem."

The air commodore, Don noticed, turned a bit pale. "Don, what are you trying to tell me?"

"Sir, I did my master's thesis just two years ago on an analog computer. Unless you've watched a computer at work it is impossible to conceive of its speed. Since then, progress in computer technology has been astonishing. Now we have the beginnings of digital computation, making the computer's speed and accuracy simply unbelievable. Your controllers are doing their boggie and intercept tracks by hand. In our business, as you know, Sir, speed and accuracy are what determine success. They determine life and death."

The air commodore raised his hand for Don to stop. Obviously this officer was razor sharp. He understood the message. "Thank you, Don. I totally agree. I will take this up with the air vice marshal immediately."

On the homefront, Mae was soon involved with the ladies of the embassy and the RCAF. As winter approached and the snow and ice became a permanent fixture, Mae was the only U.S. female with nerve enough to drive the streets of Ottawa and so became the ipso facto heroine of all the U.S. women. Without her help these attractive, educated women would have been housebound, helpless cripples.

Most people of the world live in temperate climates. Not the Canadians. When Mae moved in to the Giraffe, she noticed a platform near her kitchen door, six feet above ground level, with steps leading to it. "What, pray tell, Don, is that?"

"Frankly, my dear, I hesitate to tell you. It's to get you elevated in winter time above the snow level so you can hang your clothes out."

"Surely you must be kidding. How nice of you men!" But she came to realize the platform was necessary and that the extremely cold weather also dried her clothes.

Mae sent Don Jr. and Mark just one block distance to DeRoy Kennedy School. During the coldest weather she totally covered their heads and faces. She watched them from her living room window until they disappeared into the school. When she went out to get her quart bottles of milk in the morning she complained to Don, "Look at these milk bottles. There's a column of frozen milk three inches above the top of the bottle with the cardboard lid straddled crazily on top!"

Their neighbors convinced Mae and Don to host the community skate rink in their backyard because the Kipfers were renting and damage to their grass would not be a loss for them. Mae and the three boys watched the process of building from their living room window. "Boys, the temperature is now 30 degrees Fahrenheit below zero. The water the men are spraying from the hose seems to freeze before it hits the ground." She noticed that the rink building crew consisted of six men when just two were required. She knew what that meant and put the boys to bed.

In came the half-frozen workers, their hands stinging and their faces rosy. Don, of course, was officially a part of the NATO force. He obtained alcohol almost free. These genial Canadian men smiled when Mae helped them off with their coats. They beamed when Mae coaxed, "Would anyone like a tea royale?"

Someone answered back, "Amen, amen!"

A drink, half tea, half scotch whiskey, warmed the hearts of these men. And surprisingly, when Mae raised her hand and asked, "Anyone for seconds," she heard their bass and baritone voices respond like a choir.

One huge man reckoned, "Mae, I was so stiff from the chilly temperature during the first round I could barely taste it. Of course I'll need a second."

These men were top drawer in Canada. Whenever they got together in future years they always lifted their cup to the Yankee lady who knew the way to a frozen man's heart.

When spring came, there were more problems. Art was a veteran of Ottawa's weather. He had left his auto out on the edge of the main road and convinced Don to do the same. Winnington Avenue bordering the Giraffe, had completely collapsed. Mae knew she had to go for provisions. She did. When Don got home Mae was alternately fuming and laughing hysterically. "Bruno, you know it's so cold here in winter that the car tires really do stay flat on one side, despite the heaters in the garage. But that's nothing compared with Ottawa's spring."

Don stopped in his tracks. He had never seen his unflappable wife in such an exasperated state. "What now, honey?"

"Well, I had to go for supplies. I put on my knee-length leather boots and started down our muddy Winnington macadam road. I soon got stuck in mud halfway to my knees and couldn't move!"

"I can see you now, Mrs. Beaver, swinging your arms. What did you do?"

"Only one thing possible, senior. I unlaced my boots, stepped out of them and walked the rest of the way in my stocking feet! You'll have to retrieve the boots!"

But for every hardship suffered because of the cold, there were bonuses. The Kipfers skated, rode sleds, tobogganed, and build snow forts. The younger generation was ecstatic.

Don had always believed that the female in the United States had never been given the credit they deserved for their part in building this country. To anyone who would listen, he beat his drum roll. Our women bear our children. It's a task no man would be willing to stand for. They do the messy work of raising the children. They are the ones ultimately responsible for keeping the family focused and happy. Generally they are the ones responsible for training and educating the next generation. And yet, mind you, we calloused men accept this as our due. Then the man leaves these responsibilities each day, perhaps doing no more than rotating a stop and go sign for a road construction gang and he is macho hero. "Men, attention! If you do not correct this wrong, you will live to regret it. Our women will shirk these gargantuan responsibilities, go to a business office, sip coffee, answer a phone occasionally, flirt with wealthy businessmen and come home just as bushed as the male sign toter! Hear me before it is too late!"

Actually, compared with other nations, Don suspected the United States was reasonably liberal. So when Mae noticed when she first arrived in Canada, while driving past a building where alcoholic beverages were sold, in one of the cities they had passed through on their way to Ottawa, signs on either side of the building that proclaimed MEN ONLY and WOMEN ONLY she blew a fuse. "These Canadian men have never been blitzed, macaroon! But they are about to be!"

When Mae learned that women had never and still were not allowed in the RCAF Officer Clubs she raged, "We women in the United States spend more time on various beneficial projects through our Wives Clubs and Officer Clubs than the men do. Canada is not Muslim. It's Christian. You can believe that things must—are—going to change!"

Mae's ability to safely drive the snowy, icy streets of Ottawa when many men would not try became known. Her ability to ice skate, snow ski, play tennis, and fish were clearly second to none, especially the men. She was such a competent, supportive hostess at the all night parties thrown for twenty of more officers and their wives in her full, decorated basement that her reputation spread for her organization and sensitivity. Of course, the nearly free alcohol from NATO helped. Mae kept track of the men present at her affairs. If one disappeared she sent search parties for him as the snow and temperature outside forgave no one. She always offered breakfast before the parties broke up and nearly everyone remained.

Mae's surveillance of her guests paid off. One early morning she missed a young flight lieutenant. After searching the basement and the upper part of her house, she sent out searching parties into the bitter cold. They found the contented lieutenant lying face down in four feet of snow! Had Mae not been completely sober this humorous incident might have resulted in the RCAF losing one of their most-qualified technical officers.

"What the hell are you going out here, Ted?" the searchers screamed.

Ted seemed happy enough, unharmed and grinning. All they ever got from him was, "Mush, mush, mush!"

When the neighbors learned of Mae's background as an educator they came calling and begged for help. "Mae, we know you have attended college and that you've been an elementary school teacher. We know you have supervised the operation of a school and a Parent Teacher Association. Our DeRoy Kennedy school is brand new. This is our first year. We want a Parent

Teacher Organization, but no one here really knows what to do nor how to get started. We would appreciate it if you would give us a hand. What do you say?"

"My good friends and neighbors, I can only make one answer to such a flattering tribute. Yes, of course, I will help."

After the first couple of meetings, Don asked Mae, "How are things going at the PTS, sweetheart?"

"Don, you know the people here are brilliant. You work with them. The work they are doing is for their country and their children. They are enthusiastic and good workers. They need only be shown the way!"

"I had only one problem and you could never guess what that turned out to be."

"I give up, babe. Clue me in."

"I knew it was mandatory that I serve lots of hot tea. But you know they cannot drink tea unless its cozied. In principle, I couldn't do that. So, I made concentrated tea at home and diluted it with boiling hot water secretly at the meeting."

Don showed surprise. "My Lord, did you think you could get away with that, Delilah?"

"Not to worry, Sampson, they all agreed. It's the best tea we've ever drank!"

Still, even the cleverest, even the strongest people have moments when their strength is tried to its breaking point. Mae's trauma occurred during the second winter when Air Commodore Easton's famous winter excursion was in California having fun at Hughes Aircraft Company, dining nights at the Hawaiian Tiki, with baked Alaska in the form of a CF-100 for desert, hosted by Alan Pucket, HAC's chief operating officer.

She fantasized that perhaps Earl Hughes himself, even Gail Russel, might be helping her husband have fun. Here, on the other hand, it was 35 degrees below zero. The car wouldn't start. They were about out of food. The boys couldn't go to school.

When Don arrived home Friday afternoon, Mae was in bed, the boys playing around her. "What on earth has happened here, sweet thing?"

"I'm really glad you're home, macho. I feel really bad and had a very itchy rash. I had the embassy's civilian Canadian doctor come out to see what my problem was."

"My gosh, lover, what did he say?"

"I refuse to admit what he said, even to you. His brilliant diagnosis: 'Mrs. Kipfer, you miss your hubby.' That was just yesterday. Then he got serious and told me, without so much as a second's hesitation. 'Mae, you've got to get away from your family for a couple of weeks. You are suffering from acute nervous and stress syndrome.'"

Don sat down on the edge of Mae's bed. "I suppose civilians will never understand what we military have suffered to protect them. I'm home now. The boys and I will take care of the house and any necessary business. We'll prepare all the meals. I want you to rest and sleep, secure in your own bed for forty-eight hours. Then we'll see what needs to be done."

Mae grimaced. She knew that Don was serious about the boys helping. They were now five, six, and seven. But because they were kept inside so much by the weather Mae had taught them to do some unusual tasks. Everyone could set a formal dinner table; they could clear the table, wash and dry the dishes, and store them. She had taught them to cook and bake and there were few American housewives who could do any better. So that wasn't what bothered the sick one. "Don, we have hardly any food in the house. I just haven't been able to shop."

Don saw that Mae was already beginning to smile and function almost like she was waking from a bad dream. "That's my surprise, wounded one. Our last stop before returning to Ottawa was Rome Air Development Center, I picked up a truckload of food. How does onion soup for hors d'oeuvres, green salad, brazed lamb chops with rice, and ice cream with fresh strawberries sound for your first convalescent dinner?"

"Unbelievable, my wonderful man! And before Don could close the bedroom door, he realized Mae had dropped off to sleep and the pained expression he found when he entered her bedroom had been replaced with a beautiful smile.

By Sunday evening Mae seemed normal. "I'm ready to take over, captain. You go off to work in the morning."

Mae and Don had always been so healthy and vigorous that neither one had ever considered that there were tasks that only God could do. Now Don realized he had expected too much. How can one compensate for lack of consideration? That night he wrote to his mother and asked her to come visit for a month as soon as the ice went out on the Canadian lakes. Almost as soon as Laura arrived, the whole family was packed and on their way to a vacation spot that was a secret. But when they crossed the Ottawa River and headed Northeast, Mae told the boys. "Hey, guys, we're in Quebec!"

Their cottage was large, clean, beautiful and not more than twenty feet from a lake filled with fish. For the duration of their stay, they saw only one other human being. Mae watched the every other day rowboat ride Don made, accompanied with one boy, to ferry the ice from a French farm across the lake where it had been cut from the lake and stored for summer use.

Mae rested and watched as one by one each boy returned from the bush with several small brook trout. "And, Mom," each explorer shouted as they returned, "we saw huge moose tracks, and chased flocks of grouse from where they were roosting in the trees."

Mae was certainly rested. "Truly, Don, I've enjoyed a wonderful vacation."

But when they arrived home at noontime. Don announced. "Mae, mother, with any help necessary from the Hewitts, and our sons, are going to run this place for the next ten days. Pack your suitcase. Put in some tennis and hiking clothes and at least one nice outfit. You and I are departing in the morning."

"I can't do that, number one" Then realizing everything had been arranged she burst out laughing and teased. "Where to, Genie?"

"To fairyland, my dear. To fairyland."

Mae knew they were headed east. When they crossed the Ottawa River and headed north she knew they were in Quebec and headed up the Gatineau. What beautiful country! It was almost two hours later when Don left the main highway and stopped at the most rustic Inn she had ever seen. "Don, look," Mae shouted and pointed. "Our inn has a sod roof and I see several goats up there mowing the grass."

By this time Mae had moved up the mountainside of life from being a student at Academia to her station as a part of the international circle. She was deeply involved in the activities of the United States Embassy and Canadian National Defense Headquarters. She was a part of the city of Ottawa's public school system. But now Mae was entering another stage of her already unbelievable life. Their room was perfect, decorated by a French designer, with a gorgeous view of Quebec's vast forest and the inn's tennis courts. After a day Mae told Don, "These people are French Catholics— quite different from Adventists. They wear French clothes. And their food is simply divine. I have always heard that French food was the best in the world. I never believed that. Now I do!"

Mae finally realized this was a rest and recuperation camp, just designed for her. She and Don played tennis, took long walks on trails through the beautiful forests and discussed any subject that came to mind. They arose when they could sleep no longer, and ate three fairyland meals. She rolled over, hugged her husband and whispered in his ear. "Yes my dear, you were right. This is a fairyland."

Mae and Don's relatives were curious about their military lives. It was natural that they should want to visit.

First Mae's parents, Tracy and Anna, her sister, her brother and his fiancée came for a week. They all explored Ottawa together, Ontario's lakes, and its rivers. They ate mostly at Mae's table but also at a good English restaurant.

Later, Don's sister, Mary Helen and her husband, and his cousin, Don Simon, the fire chief of Massillon, Ohio, and his wife Mary Alice, came to spend a week. Again they all explored the sights. But for these more adventurous folks, they went for dinner to the Hotel Laurier. Like Mae and Don on their first visit to the luxurious Laurier Hotel, none of these people had ever had such an experience. Don Simon, especially was astonished at the hotel's a la carte menu. "My gosh, green peas cost as much here as a complete T-bone steak dinner does back home!"

Life in the military was many times better, Mae believed than she had ever expected. Moving in the embassy and National Defense Headquarters circle was heady. She had only one complaint. All of Don's work was highly classified and so she could not participate in it. She knew her work at DeRoy Kennedy School was very important. She loved the international parties at the embassies, the cocktail and bridge parties at family homes and of course the perfect outings with her family. But she wanted to know more than that. "Don, it's unfortunately about time to go home. What have you thought of your assignment here with the Canadian government?"

She was surprised when Don just sat, mum. Finally he moved. "It had been a tour I could not sell for any amount of money. The RCAF has put together a small but outstanding group of engineering officers. They are drawing on our super companies for equipment and support, AV Roe's chief aerodynamicist, Jim Chamberlin, is perhaps the best in the world. They have brought in people like the former civilian chief of the Armament Laboratory at Wright Field and Ian Craig who came from England with only the shirt on his back but is as knowledgeable about armament as anyone I have ever known."

Don caught his breath. "Mae, some of what I'm going to tell you is classified. But you have earned that right. I must have your promise that you will never repeat anything I'm going to say."

Mae became totally serious. Inside she was smiling, churning with anticipation. She was speechless. "I truly promise."

In this era of truth drugs Don knew no one could make such a promise. And where was an agent who could suspect his sweet wife of having such information? Further, he intended to cover only information that was not officially classified, but even so it would not do to have it disclosed. "When I went to the mockup approval for the CF-105, it passed with flying colors. I checked every requirement of the avionics and armament system against the contracted specifications. I found only a few minor discrepancies, things that can easily be tweaked up. The CF-105 is a miracle bird. It will be the fastest, will fly the highest, the furthest, and carry the most armament of any aircraft in its class on earth. It can, in fact, make Canada a world power!"

Mae was very tense. All she could utter was, "Wow!"

"Unfortunately, there is confronting the Canadians, a wall which I seriously doubt they can surmount. I have explained my concern to the group captain and now I have a meeting with the air commodore and the air vice marshal in the morning."

Mae knew Don did not sleep well. He tossed and turned all night. Even her hugging him did not seem to help. He did not sing in the shower. He was absentminded at breakfast. Certainly, after her briefing, she knew the cause.

Don was in the air vice marshal's office at 0900. Air Commodore Easton looked at him and asked rather sternly, "Well, Don, the air vice marshall and I are here. What do you have on your mind?"

"Sir, what I am going to say may sound presumptuous coming from a captain in the USAF, but as a loyal exchange officer, I believe I owe it to you and to Canada to say it. I have personal knowledge of the armament systems on all our USAF aircraft. As you know I am system concept trained. As a fallout, I have sought knowledge about the whole development package of each of our weapon systems. There is no doubt whatsoever that your Canadian CF-105 will be the most advanced aircraft in the world. If I am correct, if it becomes available for overseas purchase, it will make Canada a world power. As a personal note, I am very proud to have been a part of its development."

The air vice marshal, a breathtakingly handsome officer, respected internationally, Don could see, was beginning to become bored.

"Captain, where is this recitation leading to?"

"Sir, I also know what it cost our U.S. taxpayers to produce modern aircraft. Yes, as you know, the research and development for such an undertaking is expensive, but it pales compared to the cost of production. I have put together some figures. If I am correct it will require the total national budget, not just the budget for the army, navy and air force, of Canada to produce the CF-105. We must all surely know that such a plan is impossible.

"As the air commodore knows, I recommended in my final exchange report, forwarded through our embassy, that the United States consider buying CF-105s. It has almost identical specifications as the system I was involved with planning before I came to Canada. You know, air vice marshal, our air force sent a team here to investigate. It made the same recommendations as in my report. I have heard of no further movement. Of course, that is you flag officers' business and none of my own. That's all I wanted to say."

The room remained deathly quiet. The bomb drop on Hiroshima had probably not had such an adverse effect upon this senior group. Then Don saw these two most senior officers fidget almost imperceptibly. He suspected this was not their introduction to this subject. Neither officer so much as blinked. "Thank you, Don," said the air commodore. No one needed to tell Don, he knew this disagreeable meeting was finished.

As always happens when a person knows too much about a monumental national effort, Mae's curiosity was rampant and she met Don at the front door. "Well, fearless one, how did it go?"

"Madam, I believe it is safe to say I am no longer fearless."

There was less then a month for the Kipfers to pose as Canadians. They were already considering their next post. Out of a clear Canadian sky, came a beautiful, formal invitation signed by Air Commodore Easton. "With great pleasure, the RCAF invites Captain and Mrs. Donald C. Kipfer to a formal dinner dance that will be held in their honor at the Ottawa RCAF Officer's Mess at 1800 hours—signed John Easton, Air Commodore, Royal Canadian Air Force."

Don was speechless, Mae at first cried. Then she came roaring back, laughing and dancing around their dining room table. "I told you they would change. Such wonderful creatures God had created to share their lives. We women needed only a chance to show what we could do!"

"God!" exclaimed Don, "That air commodore is even more of a man that I ever expected. This took guts!"

The grand formal was just mind-boggling, especially for the starry-eyed RCAF wives. Everyone was in his or her best formal attire. The music, the first time for dancing in the club, the drinks and the food were just another fairyland. Mae was beside herself. "Don, did you notice the women? I've never seen them so happy. Their hubbies will be terribly glad they set their wives free!"

The air commodore always made short speeches. This gala night was no exception. He never mentioned having women in the mess. A stranger would have thought this was a long-established custom.

"My fellow armament officers of National Defense Headquarters: You all know that C Arm's most vital program has been the development of the CF-105 Arrow. Captain Don Kipfer, who we are reluctantly allowing to depart from us in a few weeks, has been an essential part of our program. I have come to know Don well, not only professionally, but in social affairs and fishing trips. Don will, and I can tell you confidentially, that our CF-105 means as much to him as to any of us."

"If you will come forward, Don, we have an engraved drinking mug for you so that you will never forget your tour at NDHQ."

And here this stern man seldom finding anything humorous, smiled, and said, "And bring Mae up with you. We also have a document for her. It makes her an honorary member of the RCAF." And with that this wonderful, strict officer raised his arms, and pumped his fists.

Everyone of these true friends stood and clapped. Mae made it to the microphone for the presentation but could not hold back the tears. Don had to help her to her seat. It was a moment shared by such unusually warm friendship that no one present would ever forget it.

Sometimes the seemingly smallest incident becomes the most memorable. Don had taken his sons on many fishing trips. But a good friend had recommended the Jock River as a sure bet to catch pike. So off went the whole family.

There were no pike. But the cattail-edged banks were simply covered with huge bullfrogs, some eighteen inches long. "Come on boys, I'll show you how to catch these fellows."

Don took one of their poles, put a four-foot length of line to it, terminating it in a treble hook with a swatch of red muslin cloth. "Now, watch what happens when I set this down in front of one of these giants."

Six eyeballs were focused on the red cloth. *Whups!* One huge frog grabbed what he thought was a beautiful butterfly. Another, attempting to eat the same fly also, was bumped aside. Don Jr. hauled the frantic frog up on the bank. After the Kipfers had fifteen frogs in their creel, Don declared, "Enough. Let's pack up."

On the way home, David asked his father, "Pop, what are we going to do with the frogs?"

"Why, eat them, of course, David."

"No way," shouted Mark. God alone saw Mae shake her head in agreement.

The boys played in their basement with the athletic amphibians. Finally, exhausted from the strife, Don declared, "Back to the Jock River for these pests."

Now, the rest of the family members securely stowed in their Cadillac, Don was making a final check of their basement before departing the Giraffe forever. The basement was his last stop. He was astonished by what he found.

When he went back outside to take his place at the Cadillac's wheel, Mae asked with some concern, "Everything all right?"

"I suppose you might say so. When I looked down into the sump pump, there from the dark water, two large eyes blinked at me."

"My word," wondered Mae, "what were they?"

Don said, "Fellows what do you think?"

All three in unison yelled, "A frog!"

Everyone laughed. Mae spoke for all. "What will the next woman who lives in the Giraffe think when she sees those eyes staring up at her?"

Don Jr. solved the riddle. "She'll scream!" he said.

As the Kipfers crossed the border into the United States, Mae sang out, "Canada, Oh Canada . . .

Don echoed, "Canada, My Canada . . .

From the back seat, three small, tenor voices screamed in unison. "Canada, Our Canada . . .

All aboard knew they had experienced an indescribably pleasant tour none of them would ever know again.

Home again! Back to Massillon and reunions around the huge fireplace in Don's mother's backyard. Wonderful, fresh garden produce; and happy meetings with new baby arrivals. Don Jr. was to stay behind in Massillon with his grandmother while his parents found quarters in Baltimore.

Off to Newark for more family reunions at Mound Builders State Park, to Baughmans Monument Farm, and to Black Hand Gorge. Family vacation time had run out. Mark and David were left with their grandparents on Dayton Road in Newark.

Mae reminisced as they hit the Interstate for Baltimore, "Here we go again, Caesar, just we two!"

Don looked over at his unusually sentimental wife. "True, but what a trail we have left behind. Can there be anything else?"

Mae giggled. "By this time, I believe I know you as well as one person can know another. I think you still have a few surprises up your sleeve! By the way, what is the system's command you're reporting to in Baltimore and why is a major military command headquarters located in the middle of a large city?" she asked.

Don didn't take his eyes off the road. "My, you have a lot of questions. The system's command supports basic research and development for building advanced future weapons systems for the air force. More important, it develops far-out subsystems and system prototypes for advanced future weapons systems. When the hardware prototypes are found to be sound in form and perform better than anything in the inventory, they are put into production. Why they are located in an old newspaper building in downtown Baltimore no sane person could explain. Perhaps there was no other location."

Andrews AFB

Mae knew Don had been given the name of a small hotel near the headquarters so they went directly there and by luck they were settled.

"Now what, man?"

"Let's check the local map and go looking in several neighborhoods for our house. We'll have to be south of Baltimore so I can fly out of Andrews AFB. I know only the senior officers can fly out of Friendship."

They had traveled only a few miles when Mae saw the sign LINTHICUM. "Don, I like the sound of that place. Let's take a look."

They found Linthicum was a section of the old Linthicum Plantation. It was just really a residential area. They had only looked down several side streets when Mae squealed, "Look down there, lover. The whole street is shaded on both sides by sycamores. The houses are beautiful colonial style. Let's mosey on down."

Even Don had to admit the street Mae favored was beautiful, beyond any neighborhood he had ever seen. And by glory, one of the nicest homes had a for sale sign in the yard and the name of a Realtor in Severna Park. "Don, God has taken a hand again." Mae added, "And I noticed a school just across the main street. "Driver, let's go see the main man!"

The very last thing Don intended was to buy a home. Why would a sane man who was subject to move orders without notice want to buy? But when the Realtor said, "I like military families. I would recommend buying. I can get that home for $16,500; $2,500 down. You can move in tomorrow."

Don wavered. Don looked at Mae. Mae looked at Don. "But Don, can we afford it?"

"Yes" he smiled.

"Sold!"

The Kipfers soon found out they were surrounded by military families. Don joined three other officers in a carpool so Mae would have the family auto most of the time. Across the street lived Lieutenant Colonel Ralph Hicks and his beautiful and gracious wife, Barbara. Mae and Barbara became friends. More important, Mae told Don, "Can you believe, just as across the street in Canada, the Hicks have twin daughters just David's age. The three just adore each other. David seems to enjoy female company!"

Don told Mae, "I had to turn my personnel records into the personnel people first thing. The head of personnel, a full colonel, asked me to come into his office. My records must have been flagged.

"'Sit down, Captain,' he invited, which of course I did. 'I have had a call from the group captain for whom you worked at NDHQ. He told me what a key role you played in the development of the CF-105. Of course the USAF is proud of such a record. However, since NDHQ is in a foreign station you will not get credit for the mandatory time we require to be spent in a United States National Headquarters. Further, your outstanding officer effective-ness reports were awarded by a foreign officer and won't even be seen by a promotion board.'"

Mae almost fainted. "How can anyone be so cruel?" She knew then that her support would be sorely needed. "This is your welcome home?"

Don, himself wasn't in much better shape. "I always try to see the plus side of my country and my service. But this is a disaster. You and I have known officers who have been promoted for washing out their bosses socks during a temporary duty trip or carrying their golf clubs during a tournament. But there is no doubt that this is the most flagrant mistreatment I have ever encountered."

At the beginning of their second year in Linthicum after all three boys were in school, an event happened that would affect Mae the remainder of her life. Through the Officer Wives Club and the gala headquarters balls at Fort Mead's Officers Club, Mae had met a young wife just her age and enough of a look alike to be her sister. Ducky Henderson was an Osage Indian, unbelievable to nearly everyone, and was listed on the official Osage roles.

She was about as beautiful as God made women. She laughed and bumped Mae, saying, "Mae, let's go to Fort Meade and play golf."

Mae looked at Ducky. She had to laugh. "Ducky, I don't know anything about golf."

Ducky said enthusiastically, "You will, Mae, you will."

Mae knew Don had played golf once or twice at West Point. She knew he was forced to play in an RCAF tournament in Canada. When she reported Duckie's challenge, Don was enthusiastic. "Get the boys. I'll get out my clubs and we'll go to the school yard."

Don had instructed people in almost every type of activity all his life. He showed Mae exactly how to grip the golf club, and how it was necessary to stand. "Now, my golfing friend, most people who never become good golfers, try to hit the ball with to fast a swing and too hard. Don't get trapped. Use a smooth swing. And, my love, I know it's difficult for you to do, but hold still, hold your stance, keep your nose stationary over the ball, especially when you're putting."

Even the great golfers such as Jack Nicklaus, are coached continuously even after an event they've won. However, these were the only instructions that Mae was ever to receive.

Don knew Mae was a natural-born athlete. She could hold her own in almost any sport with anyone. He was too busy tending government business to play golf with Mae nor even to follow her progress. But It was no surprise at the end of the season when his talented wife met him at the door with a huge, silver loving cup.

"Olympus, you are now viewing the Fort Meade nine hole golf club champion. What do you think of that?" she snickered.

Don dropped his hands, then hugged and kissed his happy young wife. "Wow!"

When Don had reported into his new outfit he could hardly wait to tell Mae his news. "My immediate boss is Lieutenant Colonel Jex Brigham. He's top-notch. But I almost jumped for joy when he took me into see the big boss, our division chief, Colonel Harold Tuebner. He jumped up from his desk, stepped across the office and shook my hand. He seemed as glad to see me as I was happy to see him.

"Mae, Colonel Tuebner gave me some really earth-rattling news. 'Don,' he said, 'I have a special job for you starting next summer. I believe you're the most qualified officer to represent our division. System Command Plans is holding a summer seminar near Woods Hole on Cape Cod at the Whitney Estate. They will be inviting the country's most knowledgeable scientists and engineers to help us decide where we should spend our development money for the next ten years in order to make our military forces the best in the world. These men will work in small groups and at the end of the summer they will submit papers. However, we know that often such gab cessions overlook some of the most important information and it falls through the cracks. Your job will be to pick up these crumbs. The command will also have several other listeners at the seminar, and also you will be expected to support these men in anything they request.'"

When Mae received this news, her countenance immediately drooped. "The seminar will last all summer? I don't suppose the fellows and I could go along?" she asked.

"Sweetie, apparently Colonel Tuebner had kept track of us. He told me, right in front of Colonel Brigham. 'Of course, this would also be a nice summer trip for Mae and your sons, Don. Air Commodore Easton has told me that Mae was worth her weight in gold to Canada. She deserves to go along.'"

Suddenly the atmosphere at the Kipfer residence took on a more rosy hue.

Six months later, Don came home bubbling, "Sweetie, this will be the second time I've given you information that perhaps I shouldn't. But I believe you should know what I'm going to tell you and I know now that no one will ever pry the knowledge from you. Today, Colonel Brigham asked me to attend a briefing by a major contractor. You will hardly be able to believe what I'm telling you. They claim an ordinary aircraft crew can take a guided missile aloft, and fire it into a suborbital trajectory. It coasts the whole way around the earth without a power source and can be recovered exactly where it was launched from. What do you think of that?"

Mae was certainly confused. The concept was too complicated for her to digest in such a short time. She knew she was just given some terribly important information, but she was not sure what it was she had heard. She played it cool. "What do you think, Einstein?"

"That's exactly what Colonel Brigham asked, except he referred to me as Don, not Einstein. I told him it's a fantastic event for man even to think about, much less do. But just as it is, it seems more like a stunt than a practical accomplishment. I believe it has only limited use for our military requirement. 'But Colonel, all of us, whatever we believe, have got to know this is a springboard to the beginning of Space Operations. We must nurture it.'"

Mae and Don had heard all their lives about northeasters, lobstering, cod fishing and picnicking on Cape Cod and at Martha's Vineyard. Now the Kipfers had rented a ramshackle cottage twenty feet from the Atlantic waters with a great room, kitchen and six bedrooms. Mae and the boys used their rowboat (while Don was laboring) in their bay and caught scallops, coquina, oyster and fish. The first night when Don came home Mae enthusiastically told him, "Today, we saw scallops jumping through the air just above the water!"

Don would never contradict such a direct piece of evidence, as Mae presented, especially when her three clones confirmed her news. However, he knew he would never believe such a sighting. Still, after he did his homework, he realized that was exactly how the scallops propel themselves.

After his first day at the Whitney estate, Don could hardly contain himself. He was bursting to report to his better half. "Sweetie, just when I believe there are no higher levels for us to ascend, one appears. I'm to sit in a small room at a small square table with three men a few years older than me. But you will never guess who they are. If you hadn't noticed, I'm soaring in the clouds. First is Dr. William Shockley, inventor of the transistor, for which he was awarded the Nobel Prize. His work will totally change how we engineer electronics. It will start a stampede that will change our world. Next is Doctor Kantrowitz. He's the world's expert in magnetohydrodynamics. His work is still awaiting world recognition. And finally Dr. Charles S. Draper, of Massachusetts Institute of Technology, the leader in automatic control. His bones were made long ago. I never believed I would ever meet these men much less spend the summer working with them discussing some of man's future scientific possibilities. These men are saints in the scientific and engineering world."

By and by Mae met all three of these remarkable men. She told Don,

"These men seem simply to be nice gentlemen. They are perfectly normal."

"If you had not made this trip with me I would never have believed what you have just said. Now, however, I do. My dear, I noticed that each one held your hand longer than was necessary."

Never one to waste an opportunity to maximize an opportunity, Mae invited her aunts Glenna and Vada and her cousin Suzanne to visit Cape Cod and enjoy their spacious seaside cottage. The three of them plus Mae, Don Jr., Mark and David explored the local area and hunted fun places to visit and for evening dining.

After their company had left Don told Mae while they were hugging and kissing good night, "Sweetie, the strangest thing happened today. You've met the men I work with. You know how brilliant they are. I expect them to be leading the scientific revolutions. Well, one of the administrators came into our room today and was followed by an academic-looking man. The paperpusher was a little exasperated. He said, 'The wheels believe you gentlemen should see what this man has brought in to show you.'

"The professor stepped over to our table. He sat what appeared to be an eight-inch-long, three-quarter-inch diameter tube in the middle of our table. It had a green light which seemed to pulsate from top to bottom.

"The three geniuses at our table looked at the tube in silence. It was obvious to me that they were upset to be interrupted. I suspected that they had no earthly idea what they were viewing. Nor did I. Finally, Kantrowitz could stand the silence no longer.

"'Hell,' he barked, 'you've got me, professor, what is it?'

"The confident, mild-mannered academician looked these three giants directly in the face, unafraid. 'I call it a laser.' He then preceded to give them the scientific basis for what he claimed it would do."

Mae was well aware by her association with Don of possible scientific breakthroughs. "I'm sure you don't intend to drop this opportunity, meine Captain?"

"Nope. My roommates were noncommital, but I have a contract with MIT. I'm sending the professor and his laser up there when I get back to Baltimore to find out what they think. Now, Delila, one more hug and we're off to Lilly White's party!"

Mae was undoubtedly the first human female to hear about a laser. Few humans have even an inkling that the invention of the laser in practical terms far exceeded the impact of the nuclear or hydrogen bomb on the human race.

The USAF spent countless millions at Wright Field and in Albuquerque on the laser's development. Early in the twenty-first century President George W. Bush proposed its use as a part of his missile defense system. It made the

Smart Bomb possible and enabled not only pinpoint target destruction but the avoidance of collateral damage. It played a major role in the war in Europe, the Gulf War and the operation in Afghanistan.

But the use of the laser for military purposes is but a small part of its story. It can be connected directly to a digital computer and can etch out, in minutes, on a large scale integrated circuit a chip that had taken a draftsman months to complete.

Jesus Christ had been the only man who could enable the blind to see. Now uncountable surgeons, using the laser, can duplicate this feat. Operations done with a scalpel, that left hideous scars and risked patients lives, can now be done avoiding all these dangers.

The value of the capability derived from the laser undoubtedly contributed enough dollars to humanity to have paid for the operation of the System Command throughout its total existence.

For those individuals, both military and civilian, who question the value of research, help them to understand, digest, and contemplate this story.

Now, nothing on earth is permanent. The military research and development organizations are possibly the foremost violators of stability. So it was no surprise for Mae when Don announced, "The System Command Headquarters is moving to the large alternate Pentagon of Andrews AFB. We'll have to sell the house here on 504 Forest View, and find something near the airbase."

Mae came close to being enraged for the first time in her marriage. "But Don, I like it here. I love our house. The school is fine. The shopping is convenient. And we have a livewire Wives Club."

Don shook his head. "And the golfing at Fort Meade is bonny!"

Mae made a snoot, caught in her own façade. "And, yes, that, too!"

"Never mind, learned one. We'll find a house you'll like even better."

It took several trips from Baltimore to Andrews AFB to locate the house Mae thought suitable. She told Ducky, "Ducky, it's a brick rambler. It has a huge, vaulted living room, large dining room and kitchen, two huge bedrooms, a two-stall garage, and a partial basement. It's two blocks from school and the school secretary lives next door."

Ducky shook her head. "Okay, okay. Now the most important point. How about the golf course?" she demanded.

Mae looked around to make sure no one was listening nor watching. She laughed, made a firm right fist with thumb extended, gave a short upward motion and whispered, "It's about a quarter mile through the base's back gate."

Mae never left any grass grow under her feet. She was involved with

Surratsvilles Elementary School. She was the den mother for her son's Cub Scout den. With her sons safely in school, she was now the terror of the golf course. But her most demanding job came as a surprise. The colonel's wife who was president of the Andrew AFB Wives Club took Mae aside, saying, "Mae, Colonel Harold Tuebner and I are good friends. His wife bubbles when she talks about you. She wants me to appoint you as head of our hostess committee. Would you agree to serve?"

Mae knew she was already overcommitted. But she found herself smiling and saying, "Yes." Subconsciously, she knew it was always what she hoped for.

For Mae and Don, the name Surrat stirred memories from the time of President Lincoln's assassination. Martha Surrat's home, boarded up and secure, sat only several hundred yards from the Kipfers' home on Horseshoe Drive. Mae took her three sons to Martha's home and they inspected it thoroughly. She then told them, "President Lincoln rose from very humble economic beginnings. He freed the slaves in the United States and directed the Civil War that retained the United States as one united country. The man who shot and killed President Lincoln at Ford's Theater, was John Wilkes Booth. Booth was injured during the assault and stopped overnight in this very house. I can almost see him stumbling in here. Our government, and most Americans, believed Martha and her son were in on the plot. They were severely dealt with!"

Mae's aunt Glenna and Vada were born and raised in Academia, Ohio, and much of their food came from the family garden. As soon as it was possible they dusted their shoes, polished them and left gardening behind forever. However, when Mae called and suggested that they and their daughter, Suzanne, accompany the Kipfers to the Marlborough County Fair, Glenna laughed, "Sure, Mae, why not? It'll be fun to see dirt stirrers again."

After all eight people in their party had minutely inspected the fair's animals and produce, Mark told the group, "Hey, these vegetables are not so special. Charlie, David and I could do better."

Glenna could be caustic if she thought it warranted. She looked at Mark and with considerable emotion told him, "Talk is cheap, Mark. Why don't you give it a shot?"

Mae had watched hour after hour, day after day as Don spent every free moment clearing roots by the truck full from the area he intended to use for a garden. He had piles of these damnable roots drying, waiting to be burned on the turned-over ground. When Commander Art Hewitt, Eunice, Caren and Richard arrived from Ottawa, Canada, Don told Mae, "Art and I are going to burn the roots."

Art was obliged to help. He noted that Don intended to burn small piles sequentially, rather than start a large fire that might be hard to control. He approved, saying, "Don, I see you've got the water hose, just in case."

But Mae and Eunice were surprised when they saw an official county auto stop and two uniformed men run toward the fires. "What now?" questioned Mae.

Shortly the man left. Mae and Eunice hurried across the backyard. "Don, what did they want?"

"They told my staunch friend Art, here, obviously the senior and obviously the man in charge, that he had to have a permit to burn."

"Then what?" exclaimed a somewhat worried Eunice, knowing a Canadian national had no business being involved.

"I introduced myself, Captain Don Kipfer, USAF. Then, this is Commander Art Hewitt, RCN. We are only burning a small fire and feeding it sequentially. As you see we have hoses here to prevent any spread."

Suddenly the state men warmed like toast. "Okay, Captain. We were just checking. Have a good day."

With roots gone, gardening was in order. Don Charles planted peanuts. Mark planted squash and David planted sunflowers. Mae told them, "Boys, you will be competing against all the professional farmers in the county. They make their living from their crops. Winning will be very difficult."

Glenna, Vada, Suzanne and all the Kipfers went to the next Marlborough County Fair to learn the results of the judging. Mae shouted, "Charlie won first for his peanuts." By now, David squealed, "I won first for my sunflower heads!" Vada added, "David your sunflower seed center is more than eighteen-inches in diameter. No other entry is over half that size."

David added, "Dad and I had to get an axe and use a ladder to cut the stalk down."

Mae, the thoughtful mother, was concerned. "Where's Mark's squash?" She knew it was more than three feet long and weighed more than sixty pounds. "I've never seen one so large."

Everyone looked around and Charlie finally found Mark's squash on a separate table. There was a sign on it HONORABLE MENTION. Mark was crestfallen.

Mae saw one of the judges and cornered him. "Why, oh why, the honorable mention? Mark's squash is obviously the largest and most beautiful one on display."

The judge was rattled. He had never met a woman so beautiful as this tigress who stood before him baring her feline teeth. He would have preferred to be somewhere else.

"I know, ma'am, but the rules state that you must enter three squash to be considered." Having said this, the man protected his face with an elbow and ducked.

Good fathers protect and succor their children. Mae knew Don loved his sons and would give his life to protect them. She knew he spent every minute with them that was free from U.S. government work. She was not pleased at what became her responsibility to report. "Don, please sit down," she said as Don returned from work. "I did not know that Don Jr. was staying after school to take part in YMCA athletic activities. I didn't know he was playing contact football. He wasn't wearing equipment. He was playing with older boys. He's badly injured himself. It appears the major muscle in his right leg has been torn!"

Mae knew Don was trained by West Point to be tough when necessary, but she also knew he was calm and rational with her, especially when large problems arose. "My good God! Why didn't I know? He's only got that kids make believe cardboard play uniform to wear. He's only nine years old! The YMCA boys are teenagers."

Mae thought her rock was about to shed tears but he did not.

"Is Don in pain?"

"He's very worried about what you may say or do. He believes it's his fault. He says he has no pain but that's impossible."

Don went in to examine Don Jr. and his leg. He did not mention football, nor the cardboard uniform or the teenage boys. "Well, Don, we'll just have to have the expert look at that leg and see what can be done. We'll do our best to make it well."

When Don returned from a hellish day of work the next evening, Mae met him at the door. "The specialist at the hospital examined Don Jr. He says there has been only moderate damage. He could do surgery but he doesn't recommend it. That might even make things worse. Unless Don Jr. is un-lucky, his leg should slowly improve."

Several days later, after the boys were in bed, Mae went over and sat on Don's lap. He frowned. "Now what are you up to, my pretty little plotter?"

"You remember the boys and I were going into the officer's club when that distinguished looking man stopped and talked to us. He had said, "I'm General B. D. Foulois. I was once a fighter pilot. Are you boys interested in flying?"

All three boys had chirped. "Yes, sir!"

He told the boys how he had used his army Tom Brown Belt as the first safety belt to keep himself from being thrown from the open cockpit of his plane. He also mentioned what Orville Wright had told him about making a forced landing in case of trouble. "Pick a bushy tree and set her right on top of it."

When I went inside I asked the officer club's manager, "Who was that wonderful man?"

"That was General Foulois, the first commander of the United States Air Corps. His wife is dead. He lives here in the officer's quarters."

Over the next few years, whenever General Foulois saw Mae and her three sons, he continued a running account of Air Corps history. He told of Lieutenant Tom Selfridge's aircraft death on September 1908.

He recalled his and the Air Corps final flight on 30 July, 1909 at Fort Myers, Virginia, to qualify the Wright Brothers Army Airplane No. 1 for purchase. This flight was personally supervised by Orville and Wilbur Wright.

That first flight, with B. D. Foulois and Orville aboard averaged 42.5 miles per hour and traveled ten miles. The aircraft was accepted and then B. D. Foulois and Lieutenant Frank Lahm became the Army's first flight students.

Now Mae hugged and kissed her captain. Don knew something was about to happen that someone suspected he may not appreciate. "The president of the Officer Wives Club has appointed me to be General Foulois' official hostess."

As Mae suspected, Don was not amused. "He may be old, sweetie pie, but no man ever loses the twinkle in his eye. You're an irresistible stimulant. What are you expected to do?"

"The president was vague. 'Make sure he's comfortable, Mae. Especially be sure his martini glass is never empty.'"

Don had been busy ten hours a day, six days a week. Nevertheless, Mae was happy to learn he had agreed to coach the fellows' Little League team. But she knew he had been up to much more important pursuits. She knew he told her as much as he could. So she was surprised when he confided, "Mae, you recall that presentation in Baltimore about the missile that free traveled around the earth?"

"Sho 'nuf!"

"Well, our planners and engineers haven't been sleeping. Our brigadier, even though he is a bit ambitious, understands what is happening. He's sending Hap Haberman and me to survey the contractors on the West Coast to see what they know about space science. If they seem neutral, we're to prick them a bit. He's ordered us on his staff to stop the laboratories from spending money on aerodynamic programs and transfer it all to space activity."

Mae shook her head and said, "That seems ridiculous, even to me. Can he do it?"

Don paused. "He can certainly order it, but he can't really do it. That would be like stopping the QE-II in one hundred yards. You may remember I told you a year ago that he ordered all military and contractor personnel to cease using the English standards of measurement and instead to use the decimal system. Nothing has happened. Nothing has changed. That's impossible!"

When Don returned from the West Coast he was filled with information. After becoming reacquainted with his family and after the household had calmed down, Mae inquired, "How did it go?"

"Well, Haberman and I found that the West Coast contractors, the most advanced in the world, are as ignorant about how to spend money on space research and development as a two-year-old female is about birth control. But we certainly did stir them up. They may not follow futuristic developments, but they understand money. By next year they'll be steaming with proposals. But it was not that experience but side cases that were so interesting."

"Don't tell me I've got some competition?"

"Heavens no. We first checked in with Captain Ray Hill in Atherton where he has his Systems Command liaison office.

"He's a member of the Atherton Key Club. The manager, after learning my name, told me, 'I can't believe it. There's a Mr. Kipfer who comes in here every night for dinner. He's a multimillionaire. He drives a big Rolls. He lives next to Shirley Temple Black. Why don't you give him a call?'

"No way," I told him. "I'm not going to bother such a man. Besides, my father told me there were no other Kipfers.

"But Hap and Ray kept pushing me until I called. E. B. answered. 'Those guys at the Key Club put you up to this. One other time they sent a Kipfer over to see me.' E. B. almost split laughing, for I could hear him even over the phone. 'I gave him ten dollars and I have never seen him again.' There was silence. Then E. B. said, 'I'm coming over.'

"When E. B. saw Ray, Hap and I, he knew he wasn't being conned. He bought our drinks and dinner. We compared notes. We finally found we were both aware of, had met and knew, cousin Bertha Shipman from Forest Hills, Long Island and knew we, in some way, were related."

Mae was enthralled. "Oh my, that's thrilling."

"But, my dear, that was just the beginning. When Hap and I checked into the airlines to come back to Washington, naturally, I had to give my name to the hostess standing in the doorway with her pad in hand. The hostess dropped her check in board and called one of the other hostesses to take her place. She looked just like my sister, Mary Helen. The hostess's name was Helen.

Her brother is a major in the air force. I'm a captain. His name is Charles Kipfer, my name is Donald Charles Kipfer.

"Helen said, 'There are no other Kipfers except for my family,' and asked for identification. The rest of the trip was first class." And with that mouthful, Mae and Don were both silent with their own thoughts.

It wasn't six weeks later that Don came home from work, obviously shaken. "What now, superstar, must you do for God and country?"

"Will wonders never cease? Somehow President Eisenhower has found out that we air force types have been working on space programs and are nearly ready to launch. He's told his White House staff in no uncertain terms. There will be no international warfare in space. I forbid it. All research and development to that end must stop!"

Mae cringed. "Doesn't our president, among all people, know that scientific and technical progress cannot be stopped so easily? If we don't do it, someone else will."

"Our brigadier knows that. Still he must comply. He's ordered all our documentation to be changed so that space words are changed to aerospace. Vaughn Goodman is already looking at a procedure to do that. He's going to call it the Red/Blue exercise. He asked me what I thought about it."

Mae clicked her tongue. "Isn't that a little transparent? Can't heads roll?"

Don nodded. "That may be true but it avoids a court-marshal."

A month later, the Russian Sputnik was tracked by a U.S.-owned Baker Nunn camera, Norwegian operated, located for scientific purposes in Norway. "You know Mae, as I told you, President Eisenhower had declared, 'I never want to hear the word space again?' But you know, my sweet alter ego, he'll hear it now until it makes him dizzy."

Still, as Mae had foreseen, a younger viewpoint was about to emerge. President John F. Kennedy saw an opportunity for the American people to support the world's most ambitious project ever. He set the United States objective as putting a man on the moon. It was an incredulously exciting program, believed by nearly everyone to be impossible.

However, with such backing, progress was mercurial. And as always, Mae was at its center. In the 21 September 1959 *Life* magazine, the prestigious picture coverage of world events in publication, they showed the seven wives of the seven first astronauts on its cover page, beautiful, smiling, and in full color. On its page 143 they again printed the seven gorgeous young women clustered around the Mercury capsule John Glenn would ride into space.

In the *Washington Daily News*, 20 January 1960, these same seven women, Anna Glenn, Rene Carpenter, Louise Shepard, Betty Grissom, Trudy

Cooper, Jo Shirra and Marjorie Slaton, reunited for lunch at Andrews Air Force Base's Officers Club for lunch as guests of the Officer's Wives Club. "Tell me more about your magnificent affair, hostess with the mostess!"

Mae almost burst with pride, not only because of her association with these famous women but because it brought her so near to one of the most exciting projects man had ever conceived. "You devil, you. You know I'm the chairwoman of the hostess committee. I was their hostess. What a thrill."

"And I can tell that was not all."

"You're right, almost major, we hope. Who do you believe was sitting right next to Louse Shepard? The one and only General Benjamin D. Foulois. Yes, as his official hostess I also kept the martini glass filled, but I really don't believe he noticed."

Within weeks the Air Research and Development Command Headquarters was scrambling to keep up with General Bernard Schriever's directions. The headquarters had been reorganized.

Mae asked, "Where does that leave you, apple of my eye?"

"I'm to be in 'plans.' What fun! There are no national objectives established. On the other hadn't, there must be objectives in order to plan a defense program that makes sense. Obviously I'll have to fabricate my own. What a responsibility. Let's hope I'm correct."

"Also they've put a no-nonsense full Colonel Hoskins in charge and his deputy is to be Colonel Lundquist, a national tennis champion. Things are moving awfully fast. You know I've been chosen to go to Command and Staff College at Maxwell AFB in Montgomery, Alabama. You and I have been planning for that. I've already requested leave so that we can go to Ohio en route. Now Colonel Lundquist wants me to cancel leave and finish the plan I'm working on. He and Colonel Hoskins like it. Colonel Lundquist told me on the side, 'Besides that, Don, the command promotion board meets here in two weeks. Colonel Hoskins and I believe you should be on the list. You can't afford to be changing commands at such a time.'"

Mae shuddered. "You a major, me a major's wife, I'm too young! When we were at Goodfellow, Major Heston Daniel, your squadron commander and his wife seemed like demigods to us lieutenants wives and they seemed so old. Again I say, we have moved uptown since Academia and Groves Patch!"

Sure enough, when the promotion list was posted, Don's name was on it. Mae was trembling with excitement. "Sho do feel good, master. It'll be fun to arrive at Maxwell AFB as a major's wife."

As the Kipfer family finally hurried south, without vacation time in Ohio, Don reminisced, "Sweetie, you know we are both patriotic Ohioans. We have boasted of Ohio wherever we went. But somehow going back to Montgomery gives me a warm feeling, also."

Mae was not as enthusiastic. "But surely you remember the despicable conditions of the poor? The black women in flour-sack dresses, the blacks who lived in the destitute sections of town."

Don Jr. came to life. "We read about the Civil War in school. The South lost. That's where we're going, isn't it, Mom?"

Mark interrupted, "Isn't that where they had slavery? I like to do what I want to do."

Mae wanted to avoid such a question, especially since they would be living in Montgomery. "Boys, no one in my family nor your father's family have ever owned another person. No one of our relatives has ever been in favor of slavery. Yes, your father and I have both lived in the South. Neither of us has ever known a Southerner who has owned slaves nor any Southerner who was in favor of owning slaves. We are to be guests in Alabama. We must obey their laws. It will not effect your activities."

Don had planned to stop at Cherokee for their sons to see real American Indians. Now they had arrived. "The Indian chief that you see here at Cherokee is really authentic," advised Mae and all three boys stood examining him and his clothes in precise detail.

After they exited their auto and walked over to meet the chief, he spoke. "Where are you boys from?"

"We've just come by auto from Washington, D.C.," answered Charlie

"Yes, that's the white man's capital. It is not the Cherokee capital. Then looking at Mae, her dark hair over her shoulders, her bright brown eyes glistening, he addressed her. "I do not believe you belong to the white people, Sweet Princess. We have a historic myth that someday a white princess will come and save the Cherokee from extinction. I believe you are that princess. Is that your husband?"

"Yes sir, Chief."

Then the chief finally tore his eyes from Mae and looked condescendingly at Don. "Sir Brave, will you sell this woman to me? How much will you charge?"

Charlie was listening and understood the whole conversation. "Pop, you won't sell Mom, will you?"

"Of course not, Charlie."

Then the old chief roared laughing. All five Kipfers stood next to him, not appreciating his joke. They paid five dollars to have their picture taken with him and were on their way.

Don Jr. wanted to discuss another subject. "Dad, you know how we love to hunt Indian arrowheads. Maryland was once Indian country. You know that we found many arrowheads in the fields. How can we do that living in a house in the middle on Montgomery?"

Don knew he was cornered. He had gone by military plane to rent a house for his family to live in while he attended Command and Staff School at Maxwell AFB. It was on South Court Street across the street from Bellingrath Junior High School, a large Presbyterian Church and not far from Governor George Wallace's beautiful mansion. "Okay, boys, you've got a point, but we'll see if we can't do something about that."

Montgomery, Alabama

When they arrived in downtown Montgomery, Mae almost giggled. "Don, Montgomery is more beautiful than I remember but the parking situation hasn't changed."

As Don drove away from downtown, out Court Street, Mae pointed and explained, "Boys, that's the Alabama State governor's mansion."

David, a third-grader, was impressed. "Mom, the governor must be an important man. That's a large house. Is his name Wallace?"

Mae was impressed with David's interest. "Yes, David."

Almost before anyone could think of anything else to say, Don turned into a driveway on the left side of the street beside a gorgeous light green painted brick home. Mark was ecstatic. "Pop, look at the huge pecan trees. We all love pecans," he said.

"Yes, fellows, this area used to be a huge pecan plantation. All of these pecans are paper shells, not like the hard bullets your grandmother and I gathered in Texas a decade ago. They'll be ripe in a couple of months."

When Mae saw the inside of their new home, especially the kitchen and family room that was bordered with hundreds of potted vines supported on a bamboo cross-latticed structure, Don thought she might cry. "Don, this is the grandest home we have ever lived in. The Tallmans certainly had good taste. He'll make general!"

Mae enrolled the boys in school. She found the teachers to be respectful and knowledgeable. She involved herself in the Base Officer's Wives Club. And of course she began to master the Maxwell AFB golf course.

However, it was not long before their three sons realized there was such a position at their school as substitute teacher. "My mother," Don Jr. told his principal, "is a good teacher. She could be a substitute."

And so Mae was added to Bellingrath's roaster and in that capacity affected the lives of many Southern children with new ideas.

Don told Mae, "They gave us all, nearly a thousand captains and majors, an entrance examination. I'm sure to measure how much we will have learned while we are students in their college. I am in the top one percent. It seems ridiculous to send a recent West Point graduate here. Still there are officers enrolled whose education is so meager you would wonder how they would have been commissioned. Of course, they'll benefit tremendously."

Mae knew Don would also benefit. "You'll also benefit in other ways. Just knowing the other students will be a plus."

As time went on, she found out Don had won the class handball championship. He had helped his section win the class softball championship with a batting average of .750. His final essay, a treatise on magetohydrodynamics was selected the best in the class and was forwarded to the Systems Command for their information. When Mae mentioned this last accomplishment to Don, he gurgled, "I'm sure the people in Systems Command Plans will recognize my name."

The Kipfer boys made many friends. Don took them fishing on the base's prolific lakes and under the bridge at BlueCreek. But all at once Don's academic year had slipped by and it was the exciting time for new assignments.

Don came home that afternoon in a mood which Mae had never seen before. "What on earth is the matter, Don?"

She saw that Don had to catch his breath and control his anger before answering. "I can only believe Air Force personnel is made up of a bunch of sadists. First they con me into getting an advanced degree so that I can be promoted. Then they take me away from operational flying because I have an advanced degree. Now, after I've gotten a sound foundation in research and development so that I can accomplish something for our country, they assign me to a teaching job at the Warfare Systems School, where I can make no contribution to research and development. An Air University assignment, unlike such an assignment in the Army or Navy, is the kiss of death for an Air Force officer. You are considered dead wood.

"I've requested a T-33 for tomorrow morning. I'm going to see the chief of Air Force personnel and see if he won't listen to reason and send me back to the Systems Command!"

Mae listened. When Don hurt, she hurt. She understood. How can anyone consider it rational that because an officer is overqualified that he cannot work at the assignment he's best qualified for?"

The next night Don returned from Washington. Mae heard their Cadillac roll in and met Don at the door. "How did it go, sweetie?"

Me knew after one glance at Don that his trip had been a failure. "The chief of personnel is major general. As you would expect, his opinion is without flaw, unassailable. He told me, 'Major, this is just one assignment. Then you'll be right back in the research and development business.' No explanation whatsoever of my assignments injustice. Why would such a Godlike man need a plausible justification?"

"Now what?" Mae said, realizing Don was beyond just being upset.

"Well, friends of mine have resigned for lesser reasons. Believe me, I've considered it. I've spent thirteen years learning procedures and analyzing the chain of command in the research and development business. I can help make the United States Air Force the most awesome technical power in the world. Now some uninformed air jockey has destroyed this opportunity. Still, as a civilian, I can do absolutely nothing."

Mae hurt from the tip of her head to the tips of her toes. She hugged and kissed her man. "How about you sitting down and I'll fix you a cup of steaming java?"

Don never mentioned his misassignment again. After it was learned by her Montgomery neighbors that the Kipfers were remaining in their city, Mae noticed a complete change in their attitude.

Mae was no longer a transient. She was a resident. She was invited to the locals' lady parties, which her neighbors held at such family homes as the Teagues and Wallaces. She was asked to accept a position on the Base Officer Wives Club. And more exciting for Mae, she told Don, "Hey, my name's appearing much more often in the golf clubhouse on the winners bulletin in the activities room."

Things had changed at Bellingrath also. Mae had faithfully reported to Don. "David has been elected as captain of his Safety Patrol and will wear an appropriate badge. He's proud of that.

"David was also selected as an all-star halfback in the Montgomery City junior varsity football league. He has also won three medals in the Montgomery Junior varsity track meet.

"Mark had developed a new technique for high jumping and the Lanier High School boys were coming by to see what he's doing. Mark was winning all the pole vault tournaments for Bellingrath Junior High and was known as a wonderful sprinter. Don Jr., Mark, David and Billy Newhouse have won every 440-yard relay they've entered," said Mae.

"Yes," agreed Don, and of course I was really surprised to see the full-page picture of Mark in the Sunday paper, winning the city kite contest."

"All that is true," agreed Mae. "But the exercise you have Don Jr. when he was a baby must have been important. Mark told me Charlie set a new Bellingrath record for the rope climb the first time he ever tried it."

"Yes, yes, yes! We will never forget that giant who gave Charlie such a fit the first two years he ran in the Montgomery County track races!"

Mae laughed. "Of course, it was almost humorous. It looked like David and Goliath. But I thought that rivalry was ended when Charlie finally beat him for the city dash championship and then went on to set a new record in the 100-yard dash for the Southeast United States."

"Not so, according to Mark," added Don. "Those two were back fussing and tussling during football practice. The coach told them. 'Tomorrow, boys, in the gym, we'll have a takedown wrestling match. That will be the end of these needless confrontations.'"

Mark really smiled. "No one thought Charlie had a chance. How could he? Goliath is nearly six-feet tall and weighs in at about 180 pounds. Charlie is five feet seven inches and weighs 145 pounds. But these unindoctrinated people did not understand the tremendous advantage of speed. The fast-draw western gunfighter killed his opponent before he could clear leather. Napoleon destroyed the enemy before he could pull his lanyard. Charlie, from his middle linebacker spot catches the opposing halfbacks before they get the ball. When Charlie, as a halfback, gets the ball, he's on his way before any of the defensive players knows who has the ball."

Mae could stand the suspense of this dallying no longer. "Well, what happened, Mark?"

Mark slapped his hip and shouted, "Charlie pinned Goliath in ten seconds. Everyone present was speechless. The gym was deathly silent. Now Charlie's an icon!"

All three boys trained on the Bellingrath fields. The first time they saw the tall, handsome, giant of a man run across their practice area they knew he was a unique athlete. A true Southerner, he stopped to talk with them in a friendly exchange. "I'm Richmond Flowers. How would you guys like to do a few laps with me?"

When they got home and told their parents about meeting Richmond, Mae almost became hysterical. "That's Governor General Flower's son, boys. Richmond is the best white sprinter in the world. Also he's beaten most of the best black sprinters. He's a leading candidate for our Olympic team. He may be the United States' last great white sprinter!"

When Richmond was offered a four-year scholarship at the University of Tennessee to play football, Don came close to tears. "Talk about two-star generals doing foolish things, this takes the cake. What fiendish thoughts go through the minds of supposedly intelligent men. By the sword of King David, couldn't they wait a year so Richmond could run in the Olympics? He may get hurt. There are thousands of football players. Any strong, tolerably fast man can play end. But of all earth's men there can be only one world class sprinter!"

Mae, having quickly read the front page on the *Montgomery Advertizer*,

was the first to learn of what the Kipfers considered a national tragedy. FLOW-
ERS INJURED IN FOOTBALL ACTION AT TENNESSEE. EXPECTED TO MISS THE SEASON.

My God, thought Mae, calling on an expletive she would never think of
using vocally. *How will Don and the boys handle this one?*

After having heard the news, dinner seemed like a wake at the Kipfers.
Don had a cup of coffee. The boys went to their rooms to attempt to come to
grip with this tragic news. For the rest of their lives, none of them ever
recovered.

The Kipfer family made innumerable friends while they were at Maxwell AFB. A classmate from West Point played handball and golf with Don.
He had two daughters and a son the same ages as the Kipfer boys. They just
loved Mary, Hal Eberle's wife. The two families spent many weekends together at Maxwell AFB's recreation area on Choctohatchee Bay and often
traveled the few miles to the Gulf of Mexico to spend the day.

About the second time they went down to the Gulf, Don noticed Hal
Eberle had bought Mary a $1.98 rod and reel because she loved to fish. Don
got Mae aside and whispered, "Heaven help Mary if she ever catches a fish
on that rig, Mae. It's a toy!"

Mae just turned her head to look at Mary fishing in the surf when she
heard Mary scream and saw her rod bent like a willow branch. Mae yelled at
Don, "Mary's caught something. Go help her."

Don knew if this fish got away he would be persona nongrata with five
Eberle's and four Kipfers. He grabbed a landing net and raced into the surf,
following out Mary's singing, taut line. He saw the huge fish, witnessed it
snap her line. By some miracle he had gotten the net under the fish and it
dropped into the net, helpless!

Everyone gathered, even strangers, on the beach in awe at Mary's huge,
beautiful specimen. "What in the world is it?" asked Mary, shaking.

Don, who was exhausted from the situation's tension, swore. "By hem-
lock, Mary, you are some fishing person. That's a pompano! It's the largest
one I've ever seen. They're considered by many the best-eating fish in the
ocean." Then looking at Mae and Mary who were hugging each other, Don
challenged. "Hope you two ladies are up to preparing such a bonanza for our
dinner. I'm sure there'll be enough for everyone."

But such perks did not make up for his assignment. Mae knew Don was
not a happy warrior. She feared he may never again be one. She did her best
to make life easier for him. She watched him on Montgomery's local television, explaining to an as yet uninformed civil audience the nuances of space.
She read the base newspaper and noticed with approval that there was almost always an article quoting some phase of space that Don was teaching.

Nevertheless, she queried him about speeches he gave to local lady clubs and civic meetings. He had one story he told her with roaring hilarity. "Mae, you remember I had four distinguished-looking ladies visit me quite some time ago. They were responsible for writing the *Air Force Quarterly's Religious Guide for Sunday School Teachers?*"

"Yes, I remember."

"Well, I told them after they had inquired, 'No, ladies, I have not lost my faith in God because we are exploring space. To the contrary, it has intensified my belief in god to know that He has created such a perfect universe!'

"All of the ladies smugly smiled and politely applauded. Their leader requested. 'Major, would you write an article saying just that for publication in our quarterly?'"

Mae interrupted Don, "Yes, I remember it well. You told them a resounding 'yes' but that clearing it through channels the whole way to the Pentagon was beyond the time and energy you could afford. They were welcome to the article but could not use your name on the byline. 'One of you must agree to be the ghostwriter!' you cautioned."

"*Exactamente*. Your memory is perfect. They had all nodded and all agreed. Now, today, I receive a copy of their quarterly and what do you think I found in it?"

Mae pursed her lovely lips, "It beats me, Shakespeare."

"Look here. It's the article I wrote. Not a word has been changed. And there at the top in bold letters is the byline, 'By Major Donald C. Kipfer.'"

Mae's expression changed. "Now what? Will all hell break loose?"

Don laughed. "I believe I'm safe. Do you really believe that any four-star generals really read this quarterly?"

But these pleasant episodes about space were but interludes. There were many more serious facets to the Warfare System School. That was one reason it was surrounded by an eight-foot storm fence.

There were some of the earth's top experts housed inside. Don had helped rewrite and edit the Air Force manual on the effects of nuclear weapons. During the Cuban Missile Crisis he had told Mae, "I am not at Air Force headquarters level nor on the president's staff, but you know I keep up to date on the world situation.

"Few persons know that we have short range Jupiter ballistic missiles surrounding Russia. The Russians do not like it.

"Nor do we. Nevertheless, the Russians do have missiles in Cuba. It's a similar situation. Would you be surprised if we removed our Jupiters and the Russians went home?"

Mae took only a moment to reflect. "And so, ipso facto, a political solution. Neither side pushes the other. And so a crisis is not faced, but avoided. And in fact, everyone won."

When, during the same crisis, Don began departing for work earlier and returning just in time for bed, Mae had to inquire, "You don't love me anymore, oxbow?"

Don grabbed his beautiful young wife and kissed her until she struggled for breath. She didn't need to ask her question again. "Sit down, sweetie, and I'll talk. Same rules. No talking to anyone. But again you've earned this. The United States built Cuba's primary airfield. We've had all the engineering drawings of that base stowed in our Air Force Library here at Maxwell. We have computed the nuclear effects of any weapon we have upon that base when exploding at various points and heights. If this confrontation were ever to become serious, Cuba could simply be a memory!"

There was little doubt that Don had been unhappy at his teaching job. So it was unexplainable when his three-year obligatory tour was ended and he so unexpectedly volunteered for another year.

"Why, oh why," coaxed Mae.

"I'm not a crybaby nor even a complainer, you know. But I have to face reality. My own service has destroyed my career. Nothing can save it. But our sons deserve a chance to finish junior high school at one place. So we're staying."

Nearly a year later when the promotion list came out, for which Don was a first-time eligible, he was not on the list. "Why?" asked Mae. You have done everything for the Warfare Systems School."

"When I first arrived here I beat the boss at golf. I knew he was ticked. When I invented the Dynamic Orbital Trainer, saving the Air Force hundreds of thousands of dollars and had it patented, although all the generals at Maxwell came to observe it in action, the boss never came near. When I developed the first accurate graphics of satellite ground tracks, before the Rand Corporation published theirs, for satellites oriented variously in orbit, and made training films of them at Orlando AFB, he wasn't interested. When I developed the equations for deorbiting a weapon from an orbiting satellite to a target on earth, or fabricating graphical solutions for the ICBM's trajectories, and graphical depictions of nuclear effects that lay students could understand, he missed the point. When I told senior officers that they would never be able to make 90 degree turns or maneuver in space like they do in sensible atmosphere until we developed more efficient fuel he convened a study group to prove I was wrong! Not me, but he! Even the command personnel center returned my last officer effectiveness report saying the writeup supported a much higher rating than I had been given. I have never seen such an extraordinary administrative action.

"Officers promoted on this list did none, could do none of the things I'm relating. Two of them gave only one lecture per class during their tours. I've given every lecture in the curriculum. I helped establish the course curricula, write and edit texts. I can say no more!"

Mae could say no more. Their last year in Montgomery went fine for her sons. Midway of the year Don disclosed another thorn in his pincushioned side. "Every year, our Deputy Commander Colonel Carter has been urging me to go with our technical team to the Royal Air Force Technical College north of London to give lectures on our programs. Each year I've declined. I really don't want to go and there are so many who do. This time he gave me a clear order."

When Don returned from Europe, Mae, as always asked, "How did it go, Mr. Franklin?"

Don seemed to have practiced his answer a number of times before he spoke. Mae was suspicious. "I don't often admit I've been wrong, sweetie. But I have been wrong about Europe. It is bonny. Especially Paris. It's a city beyond description. We must go and live there."

"How are you going to arrange that, Rogers?"

"The same way I invented the Dynamic Orbital Trainer. By being inventive. The last time I tried to alter my assignment I went to the top. You know what a mistake that was. This time I'm starting on the other end! I know the senior master sergeant in the Pentagon on the personnel staff. I'm going to call him in the morning."

As Don stepped out of his auto that evening, Mae was waiting. "Well?"

"Bonjour, Madame. There is an opening in Brussels, Belgium, for a physicist, preferably with a pilot's rating."

Mae's mouth twitched. "But your specialty doesn't include being a physicist. And what about the fellows schooling?"

"After the despicable leadership I've endured here any skill I claimed would fall within the bounds of acceptability. But have no fear. My best friend from Command and Staff College is a wheel in personnel, *here!* He can convene an appropriate board of scientific officers, incidentally all from the Warfare Systems School, and make me a physicist overnight. The European Office of Aerospace Research (EOAR) has its own C-47. I'll check out in one during the next few weeks."

It was all done. Done smoothly. Done as any good operation unimpaired by over-supervision. Don was now an Air Force Code 2636 physicist. Don's friend in Pentagon personnel told him, "You've got it, Don, you'll soon receive official orders. They'll appreciate and love you, Don, and especially your wife, Mae, whose background they have obviously already checked out from Brussels!"

The Warfare Systems School announced a farewell party for the departing Kipfers. Don had paid the final rent, saw the household furniture off, and cleared the various offices at Maxwell. Mae asked, "What about the party, my fearless leader?"

"What party, my faithful helpmate? I find it difficult to believe they want me to attend. I feel they would only enjoy rubbing salt in my gaping wounds. Salt in a wound never did feel good to me! But Colonel Ed Mazac is having a smaller group of people just from our division and we'll go there to say good-bye to the people we love and who love us!"

Mae wasn't finished. "Whoa, better think it over. Won't such rudeness, the like of which I have never heard, ruin your career?"

"My dear, that is incidental. These fiends have already taken care of that. I already had my resignation written. Now we're going to have some fun. First off to Newark and Massillon, then to the Old Sod we go!"

A visit back to both Mae and Don's roots restored a bit of Don's drive. Mae was happy for that. Then off to start a new fantasy.

Mae and the boys remained in the Visiting Officer's quarters at Charleston AFB while Don checked the family in for their overseas flight and parked the car with the navy for overseas transport. On his return to quarters, David, thirteen, wondered, "Pop, what's going to happen to the new Cadillac?"

Don grimaced. "David, only God knows. The Navy will transport it by ship to Europe. We'll have to pick it up at the port."

It was dark before the Kipfers were aboard the Air Force contract aircraft. Mark roared, "Well, folks, we're on our way."

But it was not that easy. The weather was bad and the aircraft, which was scheduled to refuel and put food aboard for the overseas flight could not find an airport with weather above minimums. It kept scuttling from airport to airport until it landed, late at night in New Hampshire. Everyone aboard was starving.

On the ground the flight crew told everyone, "You'll eat here. Anything on the menu is on the company. Then we'll be on our way."

Don asked the captain, "How long do you estimate we'll be down?"

The captain seemed unconcerned. Don later realized the captain had lied to him. "Perhaps an hour, perhaps two."

No one hinted to the passengers that the dining room staff had gone home, or that the restaurant manager would have to call them back. Nor did the aircraft commander say that the crew was over their legal crew flight time and were being replaced by a crew from New York City.

Normally polite passengers rudely jostled each other to get a seat in the inadequately sized dining room. After the Kipfers were seated, Don said, "Well, we can order anything we want from the menu. May as well order T-bones or lobster!"

It was nearly two hours later before anyone was served. Mae had looked the passengers over. She saw a young black woman with two children about two and three years old, waiting impatiently for food. She puzzled. "I wonder what these two small children will order."

When the mother and kids were served, all three had huge T-bone steaks. The kids just sat and looked at them in wonder. Don shook his head at what he saw. "Those kids have never seen anything like that. They have no idea what's on their plates. I suppose it doesn't even look like anything to eat!"

Everyone hurried through their dinners and skipped dessert. Everyone tried to sleep. No chairs. Only bare floors. It was four hours before they were airborne again. Mae made one of her very rare complaints, "If they had been honest and told us we had such a long delay we would not have had to skip dessert."

Just before sunup the hostess served everyone brownies, the only food on board. "We're going to be in terrible shape to make our first appearance in Europe," groaned Mae.

Brussels, Belgium

Major Ray Hill, Don's sponsor, the very same officer who had hosted Don and Hap Haberman in Atherton, met the Kipfers at the airport in Frankfort with a driver and minibus.

After introductions, Ray grinned and welcomed everyone to Belgium. "I phoned the airport and they knew you would be late. I'm taking you to the Belgium Air Force Officers Club, the Maison des Ailes for temporary housing. There are plenty of good restaurants in that part of Brussels and the Office of Aerospace Research is just down the hill a few blocks, halfway to the Grand Place," he said.

"Don, you can walk to work in ten minutes. We Hills will be in our chateau another week, then you can move in."

With those helpful instructions the Kipfers were left at the House of Wings where they were shown to two remarkably lovely rooms. Mae appraised their situation. "Don, these rooms are so wonderful I don't know why we would need a house."

As soon as the three fellows saw their room they whooped. Charlie shouted, "Wow, I want the bed near the window!"

For dinner they went only two doors down the beautiful, wide Avenue Chasei des Arts to a place where chickens were being roasted in the front window and where the help spoke English. "Just like home," nodded Mark.

The next morning they all went exploring. Through the National Park, halfway down the hill to the Grand Place in an arcade they chose a beautiful restaurant. Don wanted to display his knowledge of the French language, learned on his one week visit to Paris nearly a year earlier.

In what he believed was fair French, he ordered soup, scrambled eggs, sweet rolls and fruit. All the requests were made in what he considered French. When the food came everything seemed in order except one dish. Mark curled up his nose and pointed at a nondescript dish, asking, "Pop, what's that?"

Don had to laugh. In fact he had to roar. "I suspect one of your father's mistakes. I ordered soup; *potage*, I thought. But what has been delivered is *paté*." Don later learned the elite referred to it as *paté de foie gras*.

David squirmed. "What is that? Do we have to eat it?"

Don called the *garçon* over. "Monsieur, I ordered potage, soup. This is paté."

The waiter replied in perfect English, "Yes, sir, that is paté. That is what I believed you ordered."

Mae wanted no disturbance so soon after arrival. "Don, it's okay" she spoofed. "I like paté."

For dinner the Kipfers went to and beyond the Grand Place. Mae was totally astounded. "I can hardly believe these buildings surrounding this huge central court. The Hotel de Ville is the most beautiful building I have ever seen. And I can hardly believe that it was built in the twelfth century. Columbus didn't discover America for another three centuries! Why did Europeans ever leave here for dirt-floored, primitive log cabins in America?"

Don knew the answer for that. "My dear, not all the Belgian people lived in accommodations like these!"

Though the Kipfers did not know it, every Sunday a market was held in the Grand Place and this Sunday this whole, huge area was jammed with cages filled with exotic birds of every description, for sale. The three fellows were totally engrossed. Mae watched her fascinated sons as they examined every cage.

"Don, I don't believe those garçons will have any trouble adjusting to Belgium!"

Don was reluctant to break up the fun. However, he finally told his gang, "Folks, tomorrow is my first day at work. I want to be ready. I'll need a good night's sleep. Let's find a good restaurant and eat dinner. Mae suggested, "Don, there seems to be plenty of restaurants just here around the Grand Place."

Don nodded, "True, but let's take a look on some of the side streets."

It was Charles who realized the layout first. "Pop, every street here is lined with restaurants. It must be that all these people do it eat," he said, and everyone joined in the laughter.

Perhaps it was just luck. Perhaps it was the *marquise*, which announced Chez (Charles) Leons. Perhaps it was because Mae lingered longer than she had at other restaurants. Mae found she was surrounded by so many interesting people and businesses that she was overstimulated. Still, she liked this particular restaurant. So all ascended to a table on the second floor from which they could watch all the people strolling by.

Mark rated the place at once: "Mom, this place is cool!"

Everyone except Don ordered steak, french fries, salad and apricot tarts. Don explained, "I always like to try something new. I'm going to try 'moules'!"

Mae, Charlie, Mark and David recognized their food. Don was served a peck basket full of what looked like Ohio fresh water mussels. Don had read on the menu that *moules* were the house specialty and that they were specially fed for two weeks before being cooked and served. David took a bite of his steak and pronounced, "This is the best steak I've ever tasted!"

Mae moaned with epicurean pleasure. "I agree, David, it's wonderful!"

Charlie was more interested in his father's reaction. He could not believe anyone could eat such disgusting-looking food. "Pop, how're the moules?"

Don had been easing the bivalves open with another open shell, using it like a pincer. He was nearly halfway through the large serving. "I want you to know I love these moules. I'll eat them whenever I have the chance."

And so it was. Don ate moules whenever the opportunity presented itself. The others never ate any.

When Mae saw the chateau she was to spend three years in she almost burst with joy. It was a real pleasure to see anyone so happy. She could not help describing it to Don even though he was inspecting it with her. "My Lord, Napoleon, it really is a chateau. It has a common wall with the chateau to its left, to make it appear like a huge royal palace. Counting the basement, it's four stories tall. It has a huge dining room, living room and kitchen on the ground floor, three large bedrooms on the second floor and a commodious room on the fourth floor. The floors are completely tiled. It is simply beautiful. Is there no end to our movement uptown?"

Charlie spoke up immediately, saying, "Pop, I want the fourth floor. I'm going to paint it bright red and black!"

Don had reservations about that. But Charlie was an artist in his own right. "Okay, Charlie, but you may have to repaint it when we leave, if Monsieur Renvoir insists."

Don was glad to see everyone satisfied. He had only one concern. It didn't hit him fully until he had recovered his Cadillac from the port. "Mae, you can see now why I was worried and made a scaled model of the Cadillac to glide down into the cellar garage on the house plan while we were still in Montgomery! Let's see if the car will actually fit into this garage."

Don was the only one in the car. He took it very slowly. The other four Kipfers were especially apprehensive as they watched what appeared to be an uncertain operation. Still Don did not hear the scrape of metal on concrete. When the Cadillac was safely in the garage he asked, "Well?"

No one wanted to give an opinion. Don Jr. was the first: "Pop, it cleared by about one inch."

Mark added, "Don't ever eat a large meal before you drive in, Pop."

David clapped. "Don't let them scare you, Pop. It was a breeze!"

Mae was still breathing heavily. After all the others were just kibitzers. She would have to drive the beast into its lair. "We'll never make it with passengers or a loaded trunk. Promise me, paisan, that you'll keep the tires at full pressure."

Mae had just begun to unpack when the French lady from across the street came visiting. She introduced herself as, "I'm Madame Provence, from across Hetres Rouge."

"Yes," cooed Mae, "we are the new Americans. I am Mae. This is my husband, Don. These are my sons, Charlie, Mark and David. We are pleased to meet you and to be in Belgium."

Mae was surprised at Madame Provence's first request. "Mae, I know you Americans have large, wonderful appliances. When you leave Belgium to go home, we would like to buy them all from you; the refrigerator, dishwasher, stoves and any other appliances you may have. It would save you transporting them back home."

Mae, far beyond the comprehension of most, understood politics. She replied at once, "Certainly, Madame." Later, when Mae saw in Belgian stores how terribly small most appliances were, she understood her French neighbor's request.

Madame Provence talked on, saying, "I hope we will be good friends, Mae. Undoubtedly, since you share the chateau with the Hughes, you will come to know them very well, also. You must know that we are Wallons and they are Flemish. We do not mix socially. In fact, two years ago, there were tanks here on Hetres Rouge Avenue to keep the peace between our two groups."

"Oh my," answered Mae. "We Americans love everyone."

It was only an accident if anyone came close to being created equal. Mae knew that everyone was not created equal. It was only opportunity that should be equal. The road to international fame could certainly be painful for some people. For her it was a glorious experience.

Next on that menu was a two week submersion in the Berlitz course in French. Mae knew she must do well because some of her social activities and all of her shopping had to be done in French. When Don asked her how it was going, she made a snoot, rolled her large brown eyes and replies, *"Bon oui!"*

Mae's next item was to get her sons settled in the International School of Brussels. That was very easy. When asked, Mark told her. "It's okay, Mom, but the English used by the teachers is not American. It's English."

On Don's first temporary duty away from Brussels, Mae and the boys went for a fun trip of exploration downtown. The Thirty-ninth Street trolley was jammed. When Mae started to pay for their first small purchase she noticed her billfold was missing! Obviously she had been jostled and the billfold lifted on the streetcar. What to do? All her identification, cards, and money gone in a strange country.

Of course, she could not, as a newly arrived Yank, afford to cause a disturbance. She immediately recalled that Don told her in such an emergency, "Call Vera," and he had given her Vera's number to keep in a very private place.

Vera Alexander was an American free spirit who had married a Frenchman. She was now a secretary at EOAR. Vera had connections with every embassy in Western Europe. She spoke uppity and gutteral French. Even the local gendarmes respected her knowledge and power. When Vera understood the theft she told Mae. "Don't worry, my madame. I'll take care of it."

Unlike the sometimes callous response from the police back home over such a minor incident, Mae received a call at her chateau two hours later from Vera. "My madam, Mrs. Kipfer, I am happy to report the lost is found. Your billfold was spotted by a gendarme. It was lying on top of a public trash can downtown Brussels. I believe it is intact except for the money."

Mae was pleasantly surprised to say the least. She could only whisper, "Heaven be praised. Thank you Vera!"

Mae again became the unofficial driver for meetings within Brussels for the American ladies when they assembled. One colonel's wife explained, "Mae, these Belgians honor *priorité à droit*. That means they are free to enter the main stream of traffic from the right without making sure that it is clear, even from a meadow or cornfield. Some people, especially jolly Belgians, say you can tell an American because he is so terrified of priorité à droit that his neck and head are always canted to the right.

"The Belgian driver is the most aggressive driver in Europe. He can be identified by the big B symbol on the back of his car. When other Europeans see this Belgium symbol, their courage departs them."

Mae learned this the hard way. Soon after her arrival she had finished her shopping at the market in Stockel and she was adjusting her seat belt prior to backing from her parking place and departing. She happened to glance in her rearview mirror, just in time to see a Belgian driver back into her at full speed. The man made known that he was leaving. Mae shouted, "No! Polizei! Polizei!"

The man pleaded, "No polizei, please, madame."

However, the policeman did come and took all the particulars. Little damage was done to Mae's large Cadillac but much more was done to the Belgian's car. The accident's information was sent to Mr. Krumps, Mae's Belgian insurance agent, and nothing more was ever heard of the affair.

Another incident happened after Mae had picked up Mark to transport him to Casteau to take an examination for an ROTC scholarship. Mae and Mark had stopped at a traffic light that also had a gendarme under it to make sure the light was obeyed.

When the light changed to green Mae realized that there was an aggressive female driver determined to pass her on the left, so she dropped back perhaps a car length. Ninety degrees to Mae's left a Deux Cheaveau, an auto much like a sardine can with huge wheels and no safety glass came streaking through the red light. He hit the Belgian woman's car, turning her car ninety degrees and knocking her through her side door like a projectile through the air. He then hit Mae's front left fender lifting her car off the pavement perhaps eighteen inches. During this instant the Belgian woman slid under Mae's car and as the Cadillac came down, the Belgian lady was pinned.

Mark told Don later, "Pop, that wild Belgian driver came flying through the Deux Chaveau's windshield. I will always remember the spider-web-like cuts squirting blood from his face as he flew over our hood. Of course his windshield is just ordinary glass and it shattered."

Mae called Vera immediately. It so happened that Don had returned from a trip and when he was alerted, jumped into the car with Vera.

Many of Brussels' streets have roundabouts. Arriving at the first two, Don realized there had been major accidents. He pointed out to Vera, "There they are Vera, pull over."

"No," calmly replied Vera. "My, colonel, those are not your accident!"

Finally, they arrived at the proper accident. Mae ran over to them. "I am indeed glad to see you."

There were two gendarmes, several witnesses and of course the two bloody victims. "Somehow," explained Mae, "some of the bystanders lifted our car and pulled that poor woman out. I felt so sorry for her. Don, I don't know how badly our Cadillac is damaged. Mark and I are on our way to Casteau for his examination. It's imperative that we get there.

Don took a look at the damage. He pulled the bumper jack's handle from the trunk. Mark helped him. "I'm pulling the front left fender away from the tire. Mae, I believe the old boat is okay. Start her up and let her roll forward a few feet. That done, Don pronounced, "Yes, it's safe."

And just like nothing had happened, Mae and Mark hurried to Casteau.

It was not long after meeting Mae that you understood she was someone who knew how to get things done properly and efficiently. Colonel Jack Deets, the EOAR commander, understood this more quickly than most. He knew that NATO and the European Common Market Headquarters were coming to Brussels. He had long festered about not having an American high school in Brussels. He knew this was his chance. He had the help of ten full colonels, four ambassadors and the U.S. Secretary of State. He knew he had less than a year to build the campus he wanted, equivalent to that of a small college, with grand buildings and immaculate playing fields. Anyone else would have thrown up their hands at such a task and such a demanding schedule. But he didn't understand the meaning of "No."

When the U.S. Army Engineer's colonel responsible for building Colonel Deets' campus buildings showed little sign of haste, Jack Deets went through his ambassador to the Secretary of State. The surprised Army colonel received the following official message from Washington: "Urgent, that the construction of the American high school in Brussels be finished with God's speed. Our students need to register and attend there for the coming school year. I expect a personal daily report from you on your progress. Signed: The United States Secretary of State.

Several highly placed persons had told Jack Deets: "It is ludicrous to believe that the College Board of Education will accredit an empty building. They have very strict requirements for accreditation." Jack Deets knew this. But he had his own fiendish plan. He had an ace up his sleeve that no one else knew about and he was primed to play it. He went to see Mae.

"Mae, a building is not enough for accreditation of our high school. Our Brussels American high school must look like its professional. It must have a library that's first class and all the other supports a teacher needs." Colonel Deets looked hopefully at the only person who he could trust with such a mission and asked, "Mae, can you do it?"

Mae didn't even hesitate, "Yes, sir. But please, I don't need any messages of encouragement from the United States State Department!"

Jack Deets was nobody's fool. He shook hands with Mae and laughed. "Mae, just call me Jack!"

Mae caused the fur to fly in Brussels. She called for help from all the American families in Brussels. She sent each family a list of the type books she would need. They couldn't be just fillers. She knew every book would be examined. They must be creditable reference books suitable for high school students' needs. Then with the backing of the U.S. Secretary of State, four ambassadors, and Colonel Deets, she called on mechanical engineers both from EOAR and Casteau.

Don twirled his bonny lass around and gave her a gentle hug and kiss as soon as he learned of her assignment. "Sweetie, you've taken on a big and important job. You're really international now. Hallelujah! I know you understand the décor of the library and books must pass a rigorous muster. It's the only roadblock that could keep the high school from opening. Success will make you a heroine!"

Mae didn't even flinch. "Mano, you have your job and I have mine. I've lined up all the help I'll need. The school will be accredited and will open on time!"

Don was ashamed of himself for even harboring such thoughts. When the rather stuffy, conservative board arrived, Mae had arranged lodging for them at the best hotel and twenty-four hour, comfortable transportation. She had a special welcoming banquet at their hotel at which Jack Deets and each of the four ambassadors gave brief comments. Finally, Jack read a telex from the Secretary of State according them best wishes. Mae had laid a firm groundwork!

Of course, Mae and her crew had cataloged and arranged the 15,000 books. They were equivalent to any high schools in the United States. She had appropriately decorated the classrooms. Then the agony of waiting began.

Only Mae was unshakenably confident. She was correct. The visiting Board of Accreditation was pleased. Everyone of them would always remember the female whirlwind who eased them so pleasantly into and out of Brussels. Brussels American High School would open on time. Everyone knew that its opening was a miracle facilitated by God, and of course, God's helpers!

Mae attended all the embassy and Woman's Club of Brussels meetings. She enjoyed the international flavor she found there. There were many misunderstandings about the United States that she diplomatically corrected. Once, when one of the ladies, the wife of the president of an international airline, told Mae, "The United States certainly is always there to help some-one in trouble." This lady followed up her compliment by amplifying her position. "But you know Mae, you Americans are too good to be true. We all believe you have some ulterior motive." Of course, for the United States such an attitude was dangerous. However, it was just one of many erroneous ideas about the United States.

Mae replied diplomatically, "The United States is basically a Christian country. Since the time the first white men set food in North America, we have had to help each other. It was a necessity. There was no one else. So you see, giving and being helpful is an old habit with us!"

But the time one of the ambassador's wives, he from the Midwest was asked in the question-and-answer session after her very well-delivered speech, "Madame, we all know how large, sweet and delicious the Belgian strawber-ries are. Some of us were wondering if you have such strawberries in the United States?" This ambassador's wife, who had a strong dialect to her voice, and had probably never lived in the United States, was prompt and positive with her reply: "I'm glad you asked that question, dear. I am sorry to tell you we do not grow strawberries in the United States!"

When Mae told Don the story about the strawberries, he shook his head. "It was the strawberries I grew and you devoured that drew us together, ruby lips. I sincerely hope our diplomats' affairs are more accurately accom-plished!"

Mae knew her husband supported and loved her. She also knew that he did not want her to miss anything that was possible to experience on earth. So she was not surprised when her hubby came home from the Middle East with his incredible, impossible proposal: "Mae, the Middle East, Greece, Turkey, Lebanon, Israel, Jordan, and Egypt, are just an experience beyond anything an American can imagine. For example, the Old City Bazaar alone, run by the Dakaks, is worth the trip. I've told you the old man runs the bazaar. Ali runs all the trips through the Holy Lands and Salami guides the larger international trips. He looks and acts like Humphrey Bogart."

Mae began to suspect something big was cooking. "Yes, I know. Why are you telling me again?"

"Well, unless something is done you may never get to see these things. I've talked to Salami. He can bring a big, first line jet into Brussels, pick up thirty to forty ladies, take them all those places. Guides, sightseeing, accom-modations, food, etc., are all included. He knows how to get the very best prices. The cost per lady is so reasonable that even I can afford to sponsor you. You would be in charge. What do you say?"

Mae giggled, then laughed. "You devil. What would you expect any defenseless woman to say. But what of you and the fellows?"

"Mae, you know our sons are almost men. All of them know how to cook and surely I can supervise."

Mae went to work. She put together a flier. She solicited adventurers through EOAR, the U.S. Embassy, the European Common Market Head-quarters and NATO. She was relieved when Colonel Bill Woodyard's wife, Ruth, signed up. Soon there were thirty-five excited ladies available. So Don sent a telegraph to the Dakaks in the spring of 1969. A week later, thirty-five beautiful, tailored, wealthy, ladies boarded their shinning jet airliner and, like Lawrence of Arabia, were off to the Middle East!

When Mae returned, it took days for her debriefing. She squeezed her sons and nearly broke Don's ribs. "I'll tell you all, I'm truly glad to be home!"

The boys treated their mother like a visiting messiah. David asked, visu-alizing treacherous men from the Arabian Nights, "Mom, did you really see some Arabs?"

Mae laughed, "You bet, David. There were Arabs everywhere!"

"My," Mae exclaimed, after she had caught her breath and looked around. "All the food I prepared is still in the Frig."

Silence. Finally, Charlie had the bravery to break the trance. "Mon, we ate down in Stockel at our favorite restaurant. We had steak and french fries every night. No cooking. No dishes to wash. Pretty smart, wasn't it."

"Pretty sly, I'd say. Who thought of that?"

Silence.

In bed, after their long-neglected personal life had been tenderly nur-tured, Mae began a debriefing that lasted half the night.

"You know, Don, your suggesting and arranging this stupendous tour really made me its leader. Everyone believed they were my responsibility."

"Yes, but still Dakak was really in charge and should have been respon-sible!"

"True, but our preconditioned women could not really put their full trust in an Arab. Not even Dakak. Still everything went well, nearly!"

"We had wonderful food aboard the aircraft and could snack whenever we pleased. We went first to Beirut, Lebanon. Dakak took us by auto over the dangerous mountainous, narrow road, which had been used for centuries by invading armies to and from Baalbeck, Lebanon. Most of us were terri-fied by the seemingly reckless tactics of our Arab drivers, I'm sure they were performing for our benefit. But my, Baalbak was worth it. It seemed to chronicle man's history since its beginning and was just as colorful today as then. No one in America could imagine that such a city still exists today.

"We ladies personally visited the Temple of Jupiter, the ancient city of

Heliopolis with its wall, and Constantine's Arch, and Bajdas Pass. It was difficult for us to conceive of such mind-boggling artistic buildings from such ancient history.

"We learned that Augustus, two thousand years ago named the city of Baal, Heliopolis. Its ownership has been a pendulum. In 1175 it surrendered to Saladin. In the fifteenth century, the Arabs considered Baalbeck one of the finest cities in Asia. Today, we could see its remains are an astonishing record of past centuries!"

"Egads, Mae, Baalbeck is the only city I've never gotten to visit!"

Mae liked her advantage of one-upmanship over Don. "Then we went to Beirut. We first visited your favorite jeweler, George Mansour at P.O. Box 3603. When he rolled bushels of gems onto the carpeted floor in his shop for his American visitors to see, their eyeballs popped and their well-heeled pocketbooks snapped open. It was a scene I expect I'll never see again.

"Dakak took me aside. 'Madam, can't you control this carnage? These women will not have any money left when they get to my father's Old City Bazaar in Jerusalem!'" Mae tried.

It was Ruth who noticed their one Jewish lady disappeared every night to a room not her own. "Mae, I can't believe my eyes! The Jews and the Muslims hate each other. What in the world? She knows he is Muslim!"

"Don, I couldn't help but roar; silently, of course. I told Ruth, 'Maybe they're going to continue the shooting war!'"

Even Ruth, her morals offended, had to laugh.

The American women went by chartered bus to Jerusalem and directly to their fine hotel. Next morning first thing, before any more money could be wasted, they were off to the Old City Bazaar where they met the one and only, the handsome, suave, Mr. Dakak.

From a man who supposedly preferred his women to be covered from head to toe came an unexpected compliment. "Mrs. Kipfer, we are honored to host so many beautiful ladies from the United States. If there is anything you wish to see or any way we Dakak's can help you, let me know."

Salim had voiced a real concern. The Jewish woman who had celebrated the nights so mightily in Beirut kept asking all the ladies as they shopped. "I'm nearly out of money. Can anyone loan me some?"

"Ruth asked Mae the first chance she got, while examining a solid-gold crusader's cross, 'Say, Mae, I'm curious. I wonder where and for what you know who spent that huge roll of money we saw her with?' And then we two military wives had another sidesplitting roar!

"As you know, all the holy sites in Jerusalem are under the control of Jordan so the Dakaks have a unique product to sell tourists. And that was very clear when the American flotilla sat off, four ladies and a driver to a car.

"We went to Saint Stephen's Gate, the seven stations of the cross, the Dome of the Rock, the Dead Sea, and the sweet-smelling market where most of the ladies could not look at the sheep carcasses strung up nor the plucked chickens hung by their necks, to the rock where Abraham nearly dispatched his son, to the Dead Sea and to the excavated old city of Jericho."

Don squeezed his one and only. "And so you've seen it all in the Holy Land. And yet you've come back to me!"

Mae tugged back. "Oh, yes, Salidin. It was like being transported back to the time of Christ. Nothing, their dress, their shops, their homes and mosques had changed!

"Next, as our schedule commanded, we went to Egypt. Of course, at the ridiculously low prices the Dakaks charged us we could not stay at the Nile Hilton as you do. But we stayed across the street and ate once at the Hilton.

"We toured Cairo. We saw the rich and the desperately poor. We visited several mosques and inspected one large minaret. Then we were off to the Pyramids and the Sphinx. Ruth and I rode in a cart much like our racing sulkies drawn by skinny horses. What an experience. Those ancients required superb civil engineering, exact celestial mathematics, and the consideration of long-extinct religious beliefs. Don, how could men construct such imposing structures?"

Mae sensed Don was getting tired. He mumbled, "It sounds like you ladies saw it all!"

Mae wasn't a bit sleepy. "Not so fast, house-husband! You may recall that just at that moment the Greek dissidents chose to try a rebellion in Greece, our next stop!"

Don had temporarily forgotten the timing was so exact. "What did you do, my political strategist?"

"Well, the American women did not trust the economically oriented Dakak. They came to me and pleaded, 'Mae, you're military. You're our leader. Please go to the American Embassy and see if it's safe for us to go to Athens!'"

"And?"

"I took Ruth with me and we went to ask the embassy for their recommendations. We saw the first secretary."

"What did he say?"

"Well, you always told me how helpful the Canadian Embassies were to traveling Canadians. I expected the same treatment. The secretary told us, 'I really can't recommend a course, Mrs. Kipfer. If I tell you to go, it will mean the U.S. government believes the rebellion is over. If I tell you not to go it will give credence to the insurrectionists.'

"And as we started to leave, Ruth seethed, 'And why, pray tell, are we paying that man's salary?'

"But a young man, perhaps an aide came hurrying after them. 'Ma'am, we just received a message from our U.S. ambassador to Athens. The Greeks know you are coming. They welcome you. Our ambassador there is non-committal.'"

Everyone noticed their Sabena plane had disappeared. In its place was a United States carrier. Once airborne, the music was loudly playing the familiar song, "Lawrence of Arabia."

"When our plane landed in Athens, Salim told us we were the first commercial plane to land there since the insurrection had begun. 'But, Mrs. Kipfer, be sure you caution your ladies, as I will also, no pictures of military vehicles or military men. Greek jails are very unsatisfactory.'"

Don was starting to slip away. "And did the ladies stow their cameras?"

Mae pecked her husband's mouth before answering. "Of course not, my dear. They are all free souls. Cameras were popping like popcorn!

"That night the hotel had a special party for our tour group. They could afford such a luxury because we were the only guests there. Their Greek wine was free. The ladies, after several glasses, could hardly pay enough compliments for the Zorba the Greek music, the exotic food and the special service.

"The hotel manager went to the microphone about midnight with this announcement: 'Ladies of America. I am pleased to announce that the Greek government has agreed to extend the curfew on all cabarets for one hour in your honor. Enjoy yourselves!'

"Ruth whispered to me, 'See Mae, America's influence is pretty strong!'

"I answered, 'No, Ruth, it is not America's influence. It's Dakak's palm-crossing that's so powerful!'

"The next day we toured Athens. We visited the ancient outdoor theaters and government ruins. And finally, as a finale, we went to view the Acropolis and the Temple of Athena."

"And how did you like your tour, my dear?"

"I almost cried. I hope that someday our brilliant, modern civilization will have the money and energy to restore all the miracles I saw. It certainly demonstrates the best architecture, beauty, art, morality, and capability that man has ever possessed. We were all entranced!"

"And so," murmured Don, "back to life's reality."

"Yes, but I wouldn't trade for what has been! Still, I thank you, oh holy man, for such an unforgettable experience. No one on the tour with us will ever forget what they have seen, heard, and felt!"

During Mae's three-year residency in Brussels, one of her favorite things was her overnight visit to London. She would board the red-eye flight from Brussels to London and have a late-night dinner with Don at the Columbia Club. She could shop all day the shops of London. They caught a theater performance, had dinner at Simpson's on the Strand and then she returned to Brussels to resume her duties.

She was a frequent-enough visitor at the Columbia Club that the help came to know her. Don once heard one of the maids whisper to another, "I wish there were more guests as kind as Mrs. Kipfer."

While Mae was working her own magic, her sons were busy as well, All three were doing well in academics at the International School. Their real problem was the lack of the full sports program they were accustomed to in the United States. However, the International High School did have a soccer team and all three Kipfer men were out to make the team and play. Charlie was like his mother. Neither liked to practice. They both reserved their best effort for competition. Thus, Charlie, at first blush, was not a favorite of his Belgian coach who doted on preparation. In their first match in Paris against a French team, after a few minutes, the Belgian coach, puzzled that his team was being outplayed, in a break, asked his team, "What's the matter, boys? We're going to loose!"

Mark, who feared no one, spoke up loud and clear, "Coach, put Charlie in. You'll see that things change!"

The coach pretended Mark's comment was nonsense, but he did say to Charlie. "Kipfer, go in."

Charlie was not huge. But he was made of steel and he was as fast as any man alive. He was totally objective-oriented. The Frenchmen had never encountered such a maniac. Of course, they knew that tackling was permitted in soccer. But they had never seen anyone tackle like Charlie when he was in action. Less than a minute later, two of their best players were sidelined. Brussels won the match!

The coach got Mark aside, "*Merci beacoups*, Mark. *Je comprende pas!*"

Before Mae would even consider a tour in Europe she wanted to be certain her sons' education would not be stunted. College after college, professor after professor, institutions such as Georgetown University assured her, "Mrs. Kipfer, three years in Europe are in itself a college education. If your sons have that opportunity, go for it!"

Now, the whole International School was going together for a week's vacation at Spain's Costa del Sol. Mae knew the three sons were excited. She told Don, "Hey, mano, you went to Saginaw, Michigan, for your summer vacation. I went to Uncle Will's farm in Peoria, Illinois. These guys are going to the Earth's number one vacation spot. What a time they'll have!"

Mae knew Don was no spoilsport. He loved a good time as well as anyone. Still, he was not as enthusiastic as all the other Kipfers. He told Mae, "Those three boys are pressurized like a cooker. I hope that whole bevy of gorgeous girls doesn't come back impregnated!"

Mark was born with an irrepressible drive. It mattered not what the objective, sports, academics, socializing. It was no surprise to Mae or Don when Charlie told them, "Mark Kipfer and Ken May are running for president and vice president of the International High School's Student Council!"

Mae, and educator, was flabbergasted. "But Charlie, I thought only seniors could run for such an exalted office!?"

Charlie roared, "No, Mother. It's an International School; they are determined to be democratic. Anyone can run. Mark's slate's slogan is: Tall and slim, Vote for M & M!"

Mae was silent for what seemed like a long time. "Charlie, do they have any chance?"

Charlie squirmed. "I'm sure they have a good chance, Mom. I'm their campaign manager. No one else is running!"

David was listening. He added, "Mom, he means he's the enforcer."

And so it came to pass, Mark and May, as juniors, the first-ever at the International High School, were elected president and vice president of the Student Council.

It was well-known wherever they had traveled that the Kipfer young men were athletes. But they were certainly prevented from much activity by the nature of the International High School of Brussels. That was about to change. Colonel Deets' American High School changed all of that! Each boy lettered in bowling, baseball, basketball, soccer, track and football.

In 1967 Charlie, for the American High School ran the 220-yard hurdles, the pole vault, 100-yard dash, 800-yard relay, and 1,500-yard relay. He ran in two meets in Germany, one in London, and one in the West Berlin Olympic stadium where Jessie Owens deflated Adolph Hitler. He won four medals in the district meet.

In 1968, Mark, for the American High School, ran the 180-yard high hurdles, the relays, threw the discus, and did the high jump. He performed in two meets in Germany, one in London, and one in West Berlin's Olympic stadium where as noted, Jessie Owens had set his remarkable records! He won four medals in the district meet. He was selected outstanding athlete of the year for the American High School.

In 1968, David, for the American High School, ran the 220 high hurdles,

888-yard dash, 880-yard and 1,500-yard relays and threw the shot. He won two medals in the district meet.

But of all the sports, football was the Kipfer boys' favorite. When the American High School of Brussels became a reality, these miracle believers were thrilled to believe their school would have an American football team. But Don told them, "Fellows, there is no field! There is no coach! And there is no team!"

Don was baffled about what to do. His sons were crestfallen. Mae almost demanded from him, "Husband! Father! You must do something!"

No fool, Don replied, "Of course, dear." Don convinced Colonel Deets to have a football field prepared at the high school. He convinced him to appoint linesmen and referees from his staff. He himself arranged to get uniforms and equipment from Casteau. Mae told Don, "Get them a practice field here in Stockel, even if we have to pay for renting it ourselves." And rent it herself she did.

Don called the practices at Stockel. He ran the conditioning exercises. He gave each boy a chance to practice the skills he would need at his preferred position. The team anxiously awaited the arrival of their coach, Mr. Paul Kalkbrenner. It was Paul's first year coaching and he only partially understood he had a tiger by the tail.

The American High School "Brigands" played a full schedule against other American teams in such exotic places as England, Germany, France, and the Netherlands. Don roamed the sidelines, during every game since his three sons played both ways as running backs and line backers. Mae sat in the stands biting her fingernails. Charlie ran touchdowns. Mark caught passes, and David won one game single-handedly by catching a long pass in the end zone. Meanwhile, Coach Kalkbrenner was frequently seen kneeling on the ground, chewing grass directly from its roots. Still, Brussels American had a winning season!

The United States Military newspaper for Europe, the *Stars and Stripes* headlines proclaimed: OH, BROTHER, and went on to include Mark on both offensive and defensive All Star Teams, Charlie on the defensive All Star Team and David on the offensive All Star Team.

Mae danced and pranced again around the dining room table. She shouted at Don, "Well, macho, I guess we can sprout and raise something more than peanuts, squash and sunflower seeds!"

Until this point in their married life, Don had always dealt with highly classified material. Mae had always felt excluded from his work. Now, however, Don told her, "Sweet patootie, nearly all of my work from Brussels is basic research. It's mostly unclassified. I plan to take you with me when I can and let you see behind the Green Door!"

Mae hugged her flyboy. She could not answer because of the tears running down her cheeks.

Major Billy Green was EOAR's flight operations officer. He owned a very important person (VIP) C-47, furnished in plush fashion. He had two outstanding master sergeants supporting him, and three crew vehicles. He caught Don in midair almost before he had first hung his hat in the House of Wings! "Don, we only have three pilots besides myself. Our aircraft is in the air five days a week. You won't be home much!"

Billy was right. Mae wrote home, "Both Don and I always wanted to be international politicians. This is our chance. He's been in thirty different countries in our first three months here. But don't despair. The boys and I are just as busy!"

Throughout his three-year tour Don related his experiences to Mae each time he returned to Brussels: "Professor Rosseland in Oslo is a wonderful gentleman. It was the Baker Nunn camera he and his son operate for us that first picked up the launch of Russia's Sputnik. Otherwise we would never have known about it. He deplores what he considers the immorality of the young USAF officers who come to visit the Baker Nunn sight, but play havoc with the young Norwegian girls.

"Finn Lied is United Nation chief's brother. He himself is Norwegian Air Defense commander. Each year he takes several senior officers (and so far I've been included) on an inspection of Norway's defenses. On our last visit, we were all-night fishing guests of the mayor of Bodo on the city's boat during the midnight sun period."

Mae was not especially pleased to have been excluded. "What fun!"

"Don't despair, my pretty little maid. I'm the pathfinder. You will be going!"

Mae lighted up. Then Don went space-bound. "Sweetie, Sweden has a somber appearance but they have the best engineers in the world. You know my interest in Thor, Wooden, and Bodin, and the other Nordic gods. They are not yet dead. We have a contract with the University of Uppsala, the capitol of the ancient Vikings. Professor Harald Norinder at Uppsala University has a laboratory you couldn't believe. He has electronic tubes forty feet tall and all sorts of other devices for generating high-voltage electricity. It reminded me of the ball lightning we sometimes saw when I was a boy in Ohio as it danced along the rail fences. When Westinghouse was stringing high-voltage transmission lines and having crippling accidents because of electric energy out of control, they went to see its master, Dr. Professor Norinder. He went to the United States and solved their dilemmas. I asked the professor, "How much did Westinghouse pay you? Did they make you rich?"

Dr. Norinder rolled his head backward, then shook it sideways. "Can you believe it. The price of a roundtrip ticket on an airplane to the United States!"

Don told Mae, "The first time I met the doctor he invited me to take dinner with him. We two sat at a small dimly lighted table in the corner of the restaurant. He told me many stories of ancestral Uppsala but I believe his prime reason to have me to dinner was to introduce me to the snowberry!"

"What in the world is that?" coaxed Mae.

"It looks like a red raspberry, but it's yellow. It has various flavors all wrapped into one. It was remarkably good and it does poke its head up through the snow and produces this delicious fruit. Naturally, I have never tasted such a fruit before and perhaps I shall never do so again!

"The Swedes are ingenious engineers. They took me into one of their mines. You go down by bus along a well-lighted boulevard. It's like a city. And despite their fascination with socialism they have their work crews organized in about twelve man groups, each with a quota. To make any real money the crew must exceed their quota. No man can shirk. It is an ingenious way for such devoted socialists to sweat their laborers!"

Mae shuddered. "I know that system well. Our naughty Americans used it against me one summer while I was working in the war effort to make clothing for our GIs. I hated it. It drove me to other pursuits, perhaps even marriage!"

Don shook his finger. "That's a lie. You know you couldn't resist me. Still, I knew within months of arriving in Brussels that the United States was getting not only a bargain on the basic research it was sponsoring but on goodwill in Europe, Asia, and Africa."

"And what, my oracle, leads you to believe that? Isn't that a bit of wishful thinking?"

"Well, one of our projects in Sweden is the observatory at Kiruna. It is a jewel and a window for the United States on far northern activities. Now Swedish Prime Minister Palme has been accused by many of being a pinko who is in Russia's hip pocket. Whatever. Nevertheless, Palme tried his darnedest to push our basic research efforts out of Sweden. The Swedish scientists revolted. They told their government, 'The Americans supported us when our own government either could not or would not support us. Better that Palme should go then our generous friends!' And the matter was dropped!

"As you know, I really wanted to visit Finland, that small country, among all the others, which was the only country that paid its World War I debt to us. Providentially, or perhaps Colonel Deets knew of my wish, I was tasked at the eleventh hour to make a visit to Helsinki.

"When I checked into my hotel, I saw a hand-printed sign on the desk: MASSAGE $2.50. SCRUB WOMAN $2.00. Never having had a massage, I felt this was the place. I did wonder about the scrubwoman, but I realized someone has to clean up. Yup, I was really surprised when after the most agreeable massage, a much older, all business woman strode in. I found out she was a tough, rough, ruthless, scrubber and her target was me!

"The Danes are probably the true representatives of the Viking civilization. They are smart, energetic, and proud. We have many key projects with them. But the first time I visited one of their research laboratories, I felt I had to educate them about we Americans!"

Mae became alert. "I hope you didn't get to wound up, Thor baby!"

"Oh, no, not me! We Americans, not Brussels EOAR, had a team in place building the Danes an anechoic chamber. It's a tricky job that only a few engineering teams could tackle. However, I could tell immediately there was friction between the two groups."

"What in the world did you do?" grimaced Mae.

"I simply asked Professor Lundbah and his Danish engineers, who all wore custom-tailored suits with white shirts and ties, what the problem was.

"The ranking Danish engineer told me, 'Major, as you can see, we Danish engineers all dress well out of respect for our profession. You Americans have sent us a group of street fellows. We tend to resent such apparent riff-raff!'"

I understood at once. "Sir, we Americans are proud of our citizens, including those from Denmark. We honor your country. We have sent you our best engineers to supervise our project here. You must not judge us because our men wear short-sleeved shirts and casual slacks. We Americans are, not only free, but for better or worse, we are very informal, especially in our dress."

Mae was surprised. "Do you believe your explanation did any good?"

"Their chief engineer took my hand and shook it warmly. 'Thank you, Major. What you have said will help us to understand.'"

Mae went with Don to Briesack in Germany, where Ray Hill, on behalf of the USAF, had given Briesack engineers the largest radar antenna, now surplus, in Europe. She went with Don to the Technique Hoscule in Munich where Herr Doctor Professor Meinke was completing his phenomenal antenna work, which would assist in so many applications, including the assisting of wiping the ugly rooftop antennae from the homes of Americans and from the face of the Earth!

Mae went with Don to Italy's Research Complex where the EOAR's investment was quite large because post-World War II Italy had very little money. The scientists there put on a show for Mae that was male Italian-flavored. Of course, the Italian men were famous for their tender treatment of women. No woman had ever been into their inner sanctum before. When they saw how beautiful and congenial Mae appeared, they simply went bananas.

Mae was totally aware that the United States' most-advanced television sets showed scenes only in two dimensions so that except for X and Y movements the images appeared as Kodak pictures.

The handsome man who headed the show at the Institute Nazionale di'Atalia was also an Italian dandy. He wore a tailored suit, splendid Moroccan leather shoes, had manicured nails and a shinged haircut. His performance was so directed that Mae need not have been shown a scientific breakthrough to be entertained. "This, señora," he began, "is television in three dimensions. Come here, my lady," he said, putting his arm around Mae's tantalizing shoulders, "and you will see not only a lady's face, but by moving your own head you can see totally around hers. Features behind her are not made to look distant because of size reduction but because they are actually behind her."

Mae put her hand to her mouth to cover her surprise. "Professor, what you are showing me is just miraculous. The people of the world will be startled and gratified. When do you believe we'll have such television?"

This handsome, perhaps irresistible Italian smiled. "My lady, we are just scientists. You have seen that three-dimensional television exists. I must depend upon the wealthy manufactures to determine its fate."

And so it went: Ireland, England, the Low Countries, France, Spain, Austria, Israel, and Lebanon. "As you can see, Mae, we have touched them all and they have touched us!

"Mae, our sponsors back home, the American taxpayers, should know that we EOAR scientists touch not only technical problems. Dr. Jules Aarons from our Cambridge Research Laboratory is one of the world's foremost optical scientists. He understands that it is vital that the Earth's 'E' layer must be mapped. A critical part of that scientific effort are collection stations contracted and administered from EOAR. I want to give you a feeling for the strange twists we run into."

Mae was getting restless with all this undecipherable information but she lied, "I'm all ears, Theodosius."

"Well, Professor Anastasiades is one of my favorite personalities. He holds two chairs at the University of Athens. He has a direct line to the heads of the Greek government. His hacienda has its own vineyards and wine factories. He has sketched my likeness during Joint Satellite Studies Group (JSSG) meetings and seminars. However, the Scandinavians despise him!"

"Why? How can that be?"

"Well, I was present for one of the professor's outdoor banquets. There must have been two or three hundred people gathered around a table several hundred-feet-long groaning with all the good things of Greece. Greek music was playing. A man who looked like Zorba the Greek, was entertaining. Everyone was having a wonderful time."

Mae was sure she was about to be Shanghaied. "I'm certain I would have enjoyed such an affair. But *so*?"

The professor's grounds were protected by a high, sturdy, metal vertical barred fence that no one could enter from the outside. But we could see, lined up along the fence, their faces jammed between the bars, were men, women, and children in disreputable clothing, hoping only for smells to sustain their wretched bodies!"

Already booby-trapped, Mae groaned, "And?"

"The Scandinavians are socialists. They believe everyone deserves at least a share of food, shelter and clothing. I share that belief. But this is not only their belief but their practice.

"They were enraged. Our Norwegian professor told me. "I will never attend a JSSG meeting again if it's held in Athens!"

"What, oh miracle worker, can you do about such things?"

"Little. An example, perhaps; persuasion as well. But Kenya was a different problem. I arrived there shortly after Kenya had gained their independence and stayed at the New Stanley Hotel on Delmere Avenue. The small, but vital contract to be initiated with them I thought would be taken care of at a low level of government because it involved such a small amount of money. No, not so!

"I was ushered into the black deputy prime minister's office. He stood, hurried over and warmly shook my hand. "Major, our country is happy to enter the space age through this contract. We want to know only one thing: Is this effort a part of an active military project?"

"Now, my sly one, that took some fast stepping. I simply told the deputy that the contract pertained only to basic research, the results of which were openly available to anyone. I further added, mistakenly, I must admit, that our work was as pure as the driven snow. I immediately realized what a *faux pas* I had committed!

"The deputy's face lost some of its color. "Major, that's an unfortunate comparison to use in Kenya."

"I knew I was trapped, but fortunately, God had given me a brain that was fast acting and agile. I pointed out the deputy's window at Africa's pride, Mount Kilimanjaro. 'Sir, don't you agree that the snow on Kilemanjaro is at least as pure as any other on Earth?' Now, the deputy knew I had him! He laughed, returned to his desk and our business was over."

Mae was warming to the conversation. "Well, do you always run into situations like that?"

"Sometimes they are worse. We needed very badly, and with dispatch, a contract with South Africa. To do so, we needed our embassy in South Africa's approval."

"Oh, no!" howled Mae. "I can guess the rest from my experience in Egypt!"

"Yes, sometimes we are is forced to believe our embassies are deaf, dumb and like Lot's wife, have been solidified in salt. Laboratories back home expect EOAR in Brussels to move *tout de suit*! Knowing that, I decided to go south on my own and sign the contract."

"Is your future worth that, generous one?" asked Mae.

"At first it seemed that my experience would be even worse than I had anticipated. Bobby Kennedy had arrived in South Africa a week before I did. Apartheid was still a condition in South Africa that was unimaginable to Americans. He gave his 'freedom for all men' talk to the locals, the newspapers, the magazines, and the radio. By the time I, an American, arrived at immigration, I was not sure I would be allowed entry into South Africa. Because of the many situations faced from different countries, some of which I have described to you, you know I carry plenty of different, but legal passports.

"After a long, long delay the immigration officers stamped my passport and smiled. 'Have a good visit,' they wished me. My neck now in the noose, it was my problem to make sure someone did not kick the scaffolding from beneath my feet!"

When Mae had first seen her new chateau, she realized that there was little room outside the house for teenage male activities. Of course their high school demands kept them very busy, but she had her own agenda for their family's weekends.

"Don, we can't wait for months for our Cadillac to arrive before we begin seeing Europe. I'm anxious. Your sons are pacing. How about renting an auto?"

When Don came home with the Volkswagon, Mae was stunned. "Hey, treacherous one, I requested an auto, not a bug!"

Their first weekend the Kipfers went to tour the Netherlands. In Amsterdam the parking was scarce, the autos parked on both sides of the street up on the sidewalks. They found parking spaces almost nonexistent. At one point, they found a spot only one foot longer than the Bug. Unable to maneuver the onery Bug into position, each of the four men went to a corner of the auto and lifted it into parking position!"

"Let's go to the zoo," propositioned David.

"Cool," added Charlie.

But it was Mae, as they sat down for a riestaffle dinner at a lantern-lighted, smoke-filled Indonesian restaurant, who opened a door for them all. "When I was a girl in Newark, Ohio, no one would imagine going to Europe. When air traffic arrived a few wealthy families were able to go and their trip was given fabulous coverage in the newspaper. I never dreamed I would not only visit but live in Europe. Here we are, as authentic as though we were sitting down to a meal in Indonesia!"

Charlie looked up from his menu in surprise. "This menu says there'll be thirty-two courses!"

Strange as this menu appeared, the Kipfer sons, their horizons raised by travel, took a chance. After the first course of braised bananas sprinkled with chopped nuts had been served and devoured, Mark, a diplomat, summarized for them all, "Mom, of course this is not as good as your cooking, but until then, this'll do!"

With the arrival of the huge, white, Cadillac DeVille, the Kipfers could take longer weekend trips. First to Weisbaden, where they could stay at the Von Stueben Hotel and eat American food. Then a second trip to Munich where the boys could see the Black Forest and the um-pa-pa bands at the Haufbrau House.

For their first two weeks vacation, Mae pleaded, "Hey, tour director, you've been there, but what about fixing us a tour of Scandinavia?"

And since that was one reason the Kipfers had come to Europe, their tour director obliged. Naturally, they had to travel through Denmark. "Can you believe these farms," observed David. "They're all trimmed like a wealthy person's lawn back home!"

Mark loved the old government buildings. "They're almost as old as the Grand Place. They remind me of the stories I've read of the Vikings."

Charlie agreed but had other interests. They all had dinner inside the Tivoli Gardens while they watched all the carnival activities going on around them.

While Mae and Don lingered over their desserts, the fellows went out exploring. It was Mae who happened to notice that Marlene Dietrick, the electrifying actress and songstress of yesteryears in the United States, was appearing in the Tivoli's theater.

"Don, let's go!"

Marlene never disappointed anyone. This night was no exception. Gorgeous in a sheer white evening gown, she sang all the old songs to thundering applause. Just before she finished she took the mike in her hand and stood completely still. She spoke to utter silence: "Ladies, and gentlemen, I would like to pay a tribute to the United States, a country that is much maligned these days for doing no more than what it believes to be right. Many of the most unfortunate people of Scandinavia for whom there seemed to be no place here have found salvation in the United States. Whenever, wherever there has been trouble in the world and need of help, the United States has always been there. For myself, a poor lost soul, America welcomed me and gave me a life that no one could ever hope to enjoy. In its time of stress, I wish to offer it my best wishes."

As the lights faded and the house lights came on, Mae announced to Don, "I must go and thank Marlene. It took guts to do what she has just done."

It was easy to find Marlene Dietrick's dressing room and since the door was unlocked when Mae knocked and Marlene responded with, "Come in," the Americans obliged.

Mae could hardly believe how beautiful Marlene was up close. She introduced herself and Colonel Don Kipfer. "Marlene, we had to come backstage and thank you for your defense of the United States. Now we know that you are much more than a wonderful actress and singer. What you have just done, takes guts!"

Marlene got up from her dressing bench and, smiling, came over so that she and Mae could tightly hug each other, and Marlene purred, "Mae, when I was down and out, America took me in and loved me. I can only hope to do something in return today!"

The Kipfer boys were waiting. Charlie had the floor this time. "Mother, their girls are all like models. I danced with several of them!"

Sweden was even better. They went to the National Museum of Stockholm and saw and touched the Viking warship *Wasa* in Djur garden. David laughed. "Hurrah, I've seen the great warship. I've touched it. It makes me feel like I've been on a Viking raid."

It was both Mark and Charlie this time who appreciated the beautiful girls at Skansen Park. Mark reported, "Mom, they really are beautiful. Charlie, David and I all danced with them. They seem to like Yankee boys."

Mae appreciated the superb shops. "Look, Don, hand-carved trolls. And can you believe the teak furniture? Absolutely chic!"

The final destination: Norway, Mae felt their hotel in Oslo was a little primitive. "Don, what's the purpose of that rope tied to the radiator and coiled so neatly?"

Don roared, enjoying one of his best moments so far in Europe. "My dear heart, that is an escape device in case of fire. Throw one end of the rope out the window and down you go!"

"Ugh. tell me, wizard, that we'll never have to use it!"

Almost on cue, that first night, sirens screamed, lobby doors banged open and stomping boots ran past Mae's bedroom. "My God, Odin, what's that?"

Don looked out their door. "They're firemen climbing one floor up. One told me, 'Don't get alarmed!'"

Mae, the picture of efficiency, was already uncoiling the rope, one end out the window. "Don't get alarmed?!" she shouted. "Get the boys."

But before Don could get dressed, and out into the hallway, a fireman on his way downstairs, said, "All okay, sir. Nothing to worry about."

The Kipfers loved the Norwegians. Mark said at their first breakfast. "Not like the French! A smorgasbord for breakfast. Now I know where my ancestors came from!"

At night they went to the Bygdoy Gardens. After viewing the young women at the Bygdoy, Charlie announced, "They keep getting better!"

After the evening meal at the Grand Hotel, Mae was able to finally relax. "Meine concierge, I knew you stayed at the Grand Hotel in Oslo. I thought our very own tour director had somehow passed it by. Not so. Now I'm satisfied that I have experienced Norway. It is scrumptious!"

The International Route 1 from Oslo to Stavenger was a one and one-half lane gravel road. Mae exclaimed, "This is an international road?"

Mae had hardly uttered these words when four long, hairy legs appeared with a thump on the road just in front of them with two legs straddling their Cadillac's hood. Don slammed on the brakes in an effort to stabilize the portion of the hood between the two legs. Mae was so startled she didn't even become terrified. "What the heck is that, Tarzan?"

"By Jehoshaphat, folks. As I live and die, that's a moose. He's slipped down the steep cliff we've been following. Sit still."

The moose quickly recovered his own surprise and extracting himself from the Cadillac, climbed rapidly back up the side of the cliff. "Get your camera, Mom," Charlie screamed.

Mae moved as fast as she could but the moose moved faster. It was to late. When Don related this incident to Professor Norinder, he wrinkled his nose. "You must be mistaken, Don. We have no moose in Norway."

Of course, Don knew the Kipfers were not dreaming. When he checked the encyclopedia he found "What the Americans call the moose is referred to as the Elk in Norway."

Because of the slow travel the Kipfers arrived in Stavenger late, but since Mae announced, "I'm really hungry," they went immediately, after checking in at their hotel, to a local restaurant. They found it lighted and alive with music and dancing but the door was firmly locked.

The manager at their hotel explained the custom they had observed: "We close the doors so that people who may have drunk to much liquor at another establishment do not enter and cause trouble." The next night the Kipfers were at dinner early and took part in the revelry! It was vigorous entertainment!

Stavenger was a storybook seacoast town with a snug harbor that produced most of the world's canned sardines. The fellows caught many fish, all of which they returned to Neptune's empire.

The drive from Stavenger to Bodo was one of the most dangerously thrilling and at the same time the most beautiful that any of the Kipfers would ever see. In Bodo they rented a boat and fished very successfully where Don had fished with Bodo's city fathers on their boat under the midnight sun. They cleaned enough of the fish for a meal and toasted them over an outdoor fire with a view of the North Sea!

Mae sat looking out over the sea, completely happy. She pulled Don over and smooched him. "So, exalted one, this is how you've been spending your time working here in the North Country?" But she received no answer.

And so the Kipfer family's visit to the northern land of the fabled Vikings was ended. The return trip to Brussels was not nearly so exciting!

However, another expedition was about to begin. France! A dichotomy. But historians recorded and Americans appreciated the support France had given the revolting American colonists more than two centuries earlier. No military student could deny the moral support and military advise of LaFayette. When many Americans doubted the friendship of DeGaulle and rejected his heavy handedness, Don told Mae, "Yes, Charles does tend to become theatrical. His reserve doesn't sit well with Yankee brashness. But France has had so many incompetent governments since World War II that its future has been in doubt. Charles DeGaulle has stabilized the French. Now they will be okay. And further more, from my own selfish viewpoint, on TV, Charles is the only French-speaking person who speaks slowly enough so that I can follow his every word."

Paris is only an hour by Trans-European Express railroad from Brussels.

That trip is in itself a great reward for one's soul. The *clap, clap, clap* of American rails is damped on the TEE by rubber tires. The ambiance of its cars is precious. And the food is deliciously French. Mae, always available for short notice adventures, traveled by TEE on business trips with Don. "My dear," explained Don, "you can shop the Champs Elysees. That is the home of the marble palace of Guerlains. It alone is worth the trip to Paris. The sidewalk cafés serve superb onion soup. And the world of fashion originates there. But please do not talk to strange men!"

When the Kipfer family visited Paris on their weekends, they stayed at the Princess Caroline Hotel just a block from the Arc de Triomphe. The family went to the top of the Eiffel Tower, to the spires of Notre Dame, up the Seine River in a sightseeing boat, to the Follies Bergere, the Louvre, the Statue of Joan of Arc and all the other famous places.

Eventually Mae, herself, grew to know Paris quite well. "Don, once Paris was to me like hoping to walk on Mars. Now its just like down the road from Newark, Ohio!"

The Kipfers had company. Colonel Sullivan was stationed at the American Military Advisory Group (MAAG) in Brussels. Mae met his wife, Dottie, at a Brussels Woman's Club meeting. In their conversation, Mae disclosed that her mink coat had been removed from the Kipfers' high-value household goods shipment somewhere between Montgomery, Alabama, and Brussels. On the other hand, Dottie's solid silver tureen, tableware and ancillary silverware had been taken from her household goods and obviously it had been used to replace Mae's coat. Naturally, Mae returned Dottie's silver but the fur coat was never located.

Also the Sullivans' daughter was as cute as girls are made, and the same age as Mae's sons. Mae asked Dottie, "I know you love Paris as much as I do. Let's go down for a weekend together."

"Good. Sullie has contacts there. He'll plan it."

So, again the families traveled to Paris. Everyone checked into the hotel. They took advantage of the Metro to go to the West Bank. Then on a dark, narrow side street Sullie looked at his written instructions, and matched his address to that of the building. Sullie told them, "Don't get excited, folks. This place is safe. But it's Basque. The Basques believe in having a good time. So do we!"

A jocular, heavy-set man with dark hair and drooping mustaches, dressed in a white apron, showed them to their table. "Messieurs, madames, garçons, be seated."

Mae whispered to Don, "This place is a madhouse! People seem to be sitting on top of each other. Everyone is talking loud or singing. The noise is damaging my eardrums. But the music is super."

Don laughed. "These patrons have been here for hours stimulating their appetites and drinking. Soon they'll eat. Then they'll continue the drinking. They're Basques!"

Almost before Don had warned Mae, a dancer, singer, playing a mandolin sprang from the top of a neighboring table on to their own, played and sang a few bars and floated away. Now, waiters began to bring food—tubs full. Charlie asked Colonel Sullivan. "Colonel, is this food fit for humans to eat? It looks like it's for animals!"

Sullie had by now consumed his first drink. His fingers were thumping on the table and his feet stroked the floor in time with the music. "It better be, Charlie, the American Embassy approved of it." And so their marvelous night ended, tears of joy in everyone's eyes.

When Mae learned Don's sister, Mary Helen, her husband, Louis Soldatis, and their two children, Gary and Betty were coming to Brussels, she predicted, "Gosh, this will be as much of a shock for them as it was for us. Let's have something planned. But be sure we give them a little slack!"

As soon as the Soldatises arrived in Brussels, Louie announced, "I must see the cemetery where my brother is buried. He was in the Battle of the Bulge!"

Mary Helen added, "Then the rest of us want to do Paris!"

The Soldatises were on their own to navigate the European transit system. They returned from the cemetery, enthusiastic. Louie told the Kipfers, "I was very impressed with the beauty and care taken of the cemetery. I was able to see my brother's memorial stone."

Mary Helen added, "True. And we learned more about the public transportation system than we cared to know!"

Mae and Don both agreed the Basque restaurant was a little too much for the Soldatises short time visit to handle. So they went to a more conservative restaurant the Kipfers had used several times. Mae whispered to Don, "You know Betty is only twelve years old. She's seen and has identified the chien roasting in the window. She knows, with that long, long tail that it's a dog! Needless to say, she won't be able to eat!" And Mae was correct.

One afternoon, after an exhausting morning of sightseeing and a late lunch, everyone except fourteen-year-old Gary retired for a nap. Gary roamed the Champs Elysees.

That night, everyone except Gary was assembled in the lobby anxious to get to dinner. Suddenly Gary appeared, no longer a fourteen-year-old, but a grown man. His clothes were immaculate, his hair shinny, his voice controlled and speaking a salutation none of them had heard before, he proclaimed, "Well, good evening, Uncle Don!"

Gary, in one afternoon, had transitioned from boy to man! No one would ever know what had caused this transformation.

Mae and Don wanted to take Mary Helen and Louie to the Follies Bergere. They felt Betty and Gary could watch television for a few hours.

The four of them enjoyed the dinner and champagne. But when the men and women began to appear on the stage without their clothing, Don's sister went ballistic. She, of course, noticed Louie's eyes protruding, popping around, and his tongue hanging out. "Let's get out of this place, you'all!" she demanded. But Louie didn't budge.

When they took the train up to Amsterdam, they visited the tulips and windmills. Then they headed for an Indonesian restaurant. Mae whispered to Don, "Oh-oh, the ambiance is too strange for the kids. And of course they've never seen an Indonesian waiter. What now?"

Based upon Mae's recommendation, the adults all ordered the classical Indonesian meal of thirty-two entrees. Betty and Gary, petrified, ordered a simple American steak. When the first Indonesian entree of roasted bananas and grated nuts was served, Betty and Gary intercepted and split it!

"My gosh," whispered Don to Mae. "Those kids are going to eat all my Indonesian food!"

Brussels seemed to attract visitors. And Don knew mothers needed to be loved, too! And he was aware of his mother's love of travel. So when she arrived in Brussels, Belgium, Mae told Don, "I know your mother. She'll want to see everything we've seen, even though we've been here years and she is a short-timer. And you know, she's eighty-three."

Mother Kipfer found that Paris was a ball. She loved the Eiffel Tower, the Louve, Notre Dame, and the Champs Elysees. "She has to be tired," Mae told Don.

He replied, "She'll never give up. But you've noticed the boys are helping. Mark and Charlie have their arms under her armpits and are nearly carrying her, even onto the Metro."

But on one of the outings, Don heard his puritan mother shouting, "No, no!"

Now in Paris every block has a large, green, round, metal enclosure, which houses a latrine for males. Perhaps that's from Napoleon's time, when he cleaned up France. Don's mother told him, "Those boys were trying to take me into one of those green things."

Don knew his sons were making a joke. He laughed, "Don't worry, Mother, I'm sure you're mistaken!"

I suppose like many sisters-in-law, Mother Kipfer and Aunt Glenda Kipfer had always been friendly competitors. When both ladies decided to come to Brussels and visit the Kipfers, Don volunteered to meet them at LaGuardia Airport in New York City, and escort them in their commercial plane to Brussels.

Don met the two ladies' plane, which came in from Canton-Massillon at LaGuardia as scheduled. He told Mae later he had suggested to them, "Ladies, we have four hours before our plane takes off. Let's relax, get some dinner and then we'll check in."

Mother Kipfer had written to Mae, saying that both she and Glenda had their passports. Aunt Glenda, so she wouldn't forget, kept hers on her kitchen table in Brooksfield, Ohio. So, at immigration Don knew both his charges were all set. Aunt Glenda was first to face the ordeal. The immigration officer, in his no-nonsense manner, asked Aunt Glenda, "Passport, please, Ma'am."

Aunt Glenda's mind suddenly clicked in. "My lord! Passport! I don't have my passport!"

Fortunately, Don was very accustomed to solving irritating problems. He did not panic. He spoke to the airport manager. The airlines put Aunt Glenda up in a nice motel room at the airport. Don called his sister, Mary Helen, in Massillon. She went to Brookfield, got the house key from Aunt Glenda's neighbor, retrieved the passport from Glenda's kitchen, took it to the Massillon-Canton Airport, gave it directly to a hostess and shortly after midnight the errant passport was at LaGuardia's immigration desk, waiting!

Don, Mae, and Aunt Glenda's nephew on the Grable side of the family, together with his wife, all met Aunt Glenda at the Brussels' Airport. Aunt Glenda had been a high-ranking officer in the Republican Party in Stark County and was a fine vocalist who sang all over Ohio. But if she had been Chinese, the pain of stepping down from the plane by herself to meet her relatives who knew the reason for her tardiness would have caused her to lose much face!

Aunt Glenda was to have a grand tour. A tourist agency had planned her solo trip. By the time she returned to Brussels she had been in every country in Europe and to the holy sites in the Middle East. Don knew where she was staying in London after she departed Brussels, and left a message for her to meet Mother Kipfer and the whole Kipfer family for dinner in London at the Columbia House in London across the street from Hyde Park.

There, all six Yankees sat, vibrating at a table in the Columbia Club, assembled, waiting to order dinner as soon as Aunt Glenda arrived. Mae whispered, "Don, I see Aunt Glenda in the lobby. She looks totally in charge. The manager is bringing her to our table."

Aunt Glenda gave Don a warm kiss and he helped her into her chair. She was certainly out of breath. "Donald, it's been a grand and glorious vacation but I'm worn out. I had decided not to come for dinner I was so tired, but the hotel manager told me, 'Mrs. Kipfer, the Columbia Club is one of our best restaurants and it is private. Few people get to go there. You must go. I'll get you a cab. And so as you can see, he bullied me. Anyway, I'm here!'"

Yankees all, they ordered American food. Aunt Glenda beamed. She graded the food as excellent. "This is the best food I've had since I left Ohio!"

Don teased his aunt, a widow. "Did you meet any interesting men?"

Aunt Glenda stonewalled his question. "None in the same class as your uncle Kip." Then she gave Don a more questioning look, wondering if her question was appropriate. "In Jordan, my young driver asked me to take him back home to the United States with me. I didn't think he would ever give up the hope. Do you think he was serious?"

Don laughed. "Aunt Glenda, you are beautiful. You are wealthy. He was just as serious as Uncle Howard was when he drew a bead on a pheasant!"

Aunt Glenda was warmhearted, but certainly in control of most situations. She truly loved Mae. When Mae laughed and told her, "Aunt Glenda, you certainly lost a great chance." Aunt Glenda asked, "My dear, what on earth would I do with an Arab driver in Brookfield, Ohio?" and almost split herself laughing!

The Kipfer party had been up early and checked out of the Columbia Club. They started, minus Aunt Glenda, for New Castle on Tyne. Suddenly Mae shouted, "Don, that sign says ''Newark.' England's Newark is an official sister city of Newark, Ohio, my hometown. Please stop."

Could Don do otherwise when his sweet wife was so determined? Don had never been bashful. Mae knew all Don's military discipline had reinforced his forcefulness. He went right to the mayor's office and introduced himself and the whole Kipfer party. The mayor, a jolly, congenial Englishman, invited them to lunch. His fascinating attraction to Mae was inconcealable. Recording all the blarney recited by Mae and the mayor about their two cities would be too time-consuming for inclusion here.

Then they rushed off to Newcastle. The Kipfers toured the town by auto. They walked up the steep hill and toured Newcastle's Castle. Don and the boys went into the deep, dark dungeon below ground. David told Mae, "Mom, the old torture tools are still there. I'm glad I was never a prisoner there!"

On the trip south, Don's mother seemed rather quiet. Mae noticed this and she was concerned. "Mother Kipfer, are you all right?"

Laura managed a small, crooked smile. "I suppose I'm pouting just a bit,

Mae. My mother, who was born and raised in Newcastle, never told me there was a castle on the hill!"

Everyone except Don's mother burst out laughing at this admission!

For Laura Kipfer, her visit to Belgium, to France, and over a great deal of England was a dream come true. She knew her mother, her father, and all of her many sisters and brothers had all lived within sight of the castle in Newcastle. Now she had also been there. But Laura was ready to return to her home. Further travels could be left for the younger members of her family.

¡*España!* Mae shared her thoughts with Don. "I suppose for most Yankees, Spain is not first on their list of places to visit. For me, even with an English and German background, it is different. I think of Columbus and Queen Isabella. Certainly they were vital to all we white people coming to the New World. Hemingway was not ever really happy unless he was surrounded by Spanish culture in Spain. Ava Gardener, one of our most beautiful, fascinating females, was totally involved in Spain!"

Don nodded, "Yes, Ava also favored the matadors! Be careful for the safety of your reputation!"

Mae ignored Don's chauvinism. "What am I really to find there? What is Spain really like?"

The Kipfers, in their new Cadillac DeVille drove south through the spectacular French countryside. They stopped for the night in Bordeaux. The hotel's doorman directed Don to the parking garage a block away. "Mae, you stay in the lobby. I don't feel secure in this neighborhood. I'm taking the fellows with me."

Even at fifteen, sixteen, and seventeen, these males were in superb physical condition and trained athletes, capable of rugged combat. When the four men returned, obviously a little excited, Mae questioned them, "Well, señors, what happened?"

Don was not an especially happy traveler. "We ran into four seafront ruffians. They shouted anti-American slogans. When one of them shoved Charles, I could stand no more. The four of us took boxer stances and when their leader stepped forward to taunt us again, I decked him!"

Mae was aghast. "I'm glad none of you were hurt. We have not had such an incident happen anywhere else. What stimulates such hatred? Are they jealous of our religion, our free country, our democratic political system, our capitalistic economic system, our obvious confidence?"

Don was tired. "Who knows. Perhaps all of the above!"

Nudging south across the border of Spain, in sight of the Bay of Biscay, they stopped for oranges. David was the first to taste the fresh orange's juice.

"Pop, we have oranges in the United States, but none like these. They are heavenly!"

On to Madrid. Of course, it was necessary to stop for gasoline. In the small village the refueling point was usually difficult to find and often no more than a pipe protruding from the ground. "It's a male routine between the Spanish conquistadors and our Cadillac, it seems to me," Mae said to Don. "The men and boys have never seen such an auto. They cannot believe the size of the engine or when you show them the trunk, that it is large enough for three six-foot men to sleep in comfortably!"

Don agreed, "But also the women come to see you and to rave about the cars' interiors. And how they love and envy you. You look enough like a Spanish woman to be one of their own!"

In Madrid they ate paella at the best Spanish restaurants and enjoyed the Spanish music. One of the female flamenco dancers pulled Charlie onto the floor. She had no idea what a dancer Charlie could be. Charlie had been voted Mr. Congeniality in his senior year book at Bellingrath Junior High School in Montgomery. He was no shrinking violet when it came to the ladies. Charlie sat down. Mae told him, "Not bad for a Yankee!"

"Mom, she asked me what I was doing for the rest of the night!"

Mae was aghast. "What did that mean? I hope not what I suspect! What did you tell her?"

Charlie laughed, "I told her her invitation was a great honor, but that I had to leave early in the morning!"

Everyone wanted to see a bullfight, except for Mae. She remembered visiting Bob Mathis at his mother's home in Eagle Pass, Texas, of attending the fights, and that she could never again comfortably eat steak.

Still, Don told his sons, "We'll go. We'll get seats on the shady side of the arena. Be prepared for manly sport." Then looking at his woebegone but feisty wife, he inquired, "Mae, are you in or out?"

Mae gave Don a look he was not soon to forget! "I'm in!"

The three boys were fascinated by the military-type music, the picadores, the bulls and the matadors. And as the fights were ending, they jumped into the ring and purchased pics from the picadores. "Some keepsakes!" allowed Charles.

Mae looked away but pronounced the whole situation, "Awful!"

Everyone had done their homework about Spain. They knew about Salamanca. Still, Mae reminded them. "Salamanca is a university town, during the Middle Ages it was the repository for much of man's western European knowledge. It is country. If we are to feel and know the real Spain, it will be in Salamanca."

Salamanca appeared almost unexpectedly from the surrounding tan-colored countryside. Its buildings and those of Salamanca's University were all built from the same buff-colored stone. David observed, remembering the difficulty his father had identifying San Angelo from the air. "Pop, you'd have a difficult time finding this place as an emergency field from the air!"

At their hotel, the concierge gave the Kipfers their first lesson in the Spanish culture. "Our habits are much different than those in the New World. Because we party until morning hours, we start our daily business very late. We break for lunch quite late and then enjoy a siesta. About five o'clock P.M. we're back at work. Then some of us take a short nap before dinner. Our restaurants do not open to serve dinner until eleven o'clock!"

"Oh, my," concluded Mae.

Feeling very Spanish, all the men cheered and shouted, "*Viva el toro.*"

They all visited the city's museums and walked the ancient university's halls and classrooms. But in the evening the Kipfer young men participated in the time-honored promenade about the Salamanca square by the young men and women of Salamanca.

"These girls," apprised Charlie, "are beautiful and curious about we Yankees!"

"One even squeezed my arm, supposedly to test my strength, as their cute threesome passed us," agreed Mark!

"But the local boys do not appreciate the local girls being so interested in the Yanks," David added. "I heard several of them say, 'Damned Yankees!'"

As the Kipfers crossed over the Trás-os-Montes, they saw fields no larger than a small American yard and little sign of even the most modest income. But the view of the Atlantic was breathtaking. In Lisbon one knew immediately that Portugal had once been a world power. Mae, awed, said to Don, "These old buildings are substantial and beautiful. Even the sidewalks and streets are decorated with white and black marble mosaic patterns!"

Mark, an artist like his brothers, was impressed, "Mom, we've never seen anything like this!"

Mae asked Don, after they had checked into their hotel, "The desk told us the cost will be five American dollars a piece per day. That includes lodging, meals, our own table and our own waiter. How can that be, señor?"

"Dubious one, I arranged all our stops through the American Embassy. They have some connections. Enjoy!"

The Kipfers' waiter loved the American boys and was interested in their actions. "Señors, you may have as many steaks as you can eat. And sure, all the desserts, too!"

"It seems to me," summarized Mae, "that Portugal has more castles than all of the other countries of Europe and that we've seen them all!"

David had something to add. He liked a little danger for spice in his life. "I liked it best when we went up that narrow steep road with the cliff on the side. That wagon and donkey had to be maneuvered at a steep angle and it fell aways off the cliff for us to pass!"

Mae shrugged, realizing the danger to the Spanish driver that incident represented. "That was not my most memorable moment!"

Mark chimed in, "Then what was, Mom?"

"Of course I enjoyed everything in Portugal, especially the castles and our food. But your father always talks about Mr. Cork's Store when he returns from Portugal. And so I wanted to go there, perhaps more than anywhere else."

Charlie burst into the conversation. "I will never forget Mr. Cork's Place. He recognized Dad as soon as we went in. What a memory. I saw pictures of our most famous American generals and admirals hanging on his shop's wall. Better still, he handed each of us a glass of port wine, just like we boys were real men. That was we offsprings first. I saw you slip your glass to Pop, Mom! Mom, Mr. Cork gave you a small fortune in cork gifts. He's another Spaniard who thinks you are dulzura!"

"He was indeed generous, Charles. Everything in Mr. Cork's store is made from cork. Also he is an American patriot. But then, too, I have purchased many things from him!"

On the way southeast from Lisbon to Gibraltar, Don stopped the Cadillac at an isolated spot that had immediate access to a forest of cork trees. Mae guessed what her roommate was up to and cringed.

"No, please, my well meaning criminal, what you are about to do is stealing!"

Don pretended he never heard his cautious wife. He knew his sons would probably never have this opportunity again in their entire life. He jumped out, opened the trunk, and retrieved the bumper jack handle. He handed it to Charlie. "Go get it, boys!"

A few minutes later all three fellows returned. "We got some nice pieces of cork bark, Mom," David showed his mother.

"Yes, David," agreed Mae, "but I don't want to see it!"

The boat trip from Tarifa to Tangiers was perfect. Don told Mae. I've briefed the fellows on everything I know about Morocco. I'm glad they listen. Because of that we can take them anywhere. But for you, my pretty little maid, it's a clean canvass upon which you can print your own impressions!"

When they stepped into the Riff Hotel, the one the Americans used, all the Kipfers, but especially Mae, were amazed at the spectacular Moorish interior decorations. Mae told Don, "I begin to believe this little girl from Academia had seen everything. But now I know I have not. Now I finally realize that the marvels of our Earth will never end. This hotel is beyond beauty. It is incredulous!"

The Riff's rooms matched the lobby's decor. Their food was perfect. One could either indulge in Arabic, North African, or American food. And for the next decade the Riff Hotel sent each member of the Kipfer family a card on their birthdays.

The next morning, these wary, suspicious Americans began their walking tour of Tangiers. Up the steep highway they hurried. On the left side of the rather broad street was a solid-board fence. Before they had gone far, out stepped a boy no more than eight or ten years old, with mournful eyes and his palm extended. In perfect English he implored, "Alms, please, for the poor. My mother and sister are sick. Please, Americans, Please."

Mark dropped back saying, "Pop, what do you think?"

Mark, you know what I told you about the professional beggars. Look at that boy. See how fat he is. Still, I want you all three to learn something. Be generous. Give him a pound note. Then let's slow down and watch what happens!"

The boy grinned, stunned by the large gift. "Bless you, Americans. Praise be to Allah!"

But as the Kipfers watched, the boy disappeared behind the fence. They heard a slap and a shriek. Then they noticed the head of a tall man appear momentarily above the fence. Mae laughed, "Sahib, we get the picture!"

They went by sidewalk shows put on near the street by Arabs with cobras and mongeese. Don and Mae became so engrossed in window shopping that they didn't realize that their three sons were gone."

"Yikes," choked Mae and then, "that's them way up ahead!"

When Mae and Don caught up, Mae asked, "What were you three talking to that Arab man about?"

Mark fielded this question, almost bursting with laughter. "You know Charlie. He was having a ball. He believed Pop's briefing. That Arab man in long robes hailed us. He had hundreds of small items sewn inside his cloak, which he flashed at us. He pulled out a ring. 'Effendi, this ring is very valuable. It belonged to my mother. But she died. Now her young daughter, my sister, needs money. It's a bargain at fifty dollars. See how the diamond shines!'"

"Charlie remained serious. 'Is that your best price? I have spent much money for the poor and at the cobra shows. I must be careful how much I spend!'

"The con man smiled, came closer to Charlie and whispered. 'For you, effendi, fifteen American dollars.'"

Mark could hardly contain himself. "These negotiations went on until the price went down to two dollars at which time Charlie motioned to us and we all started to move on.

"The hawker quickly turned mean. 'Allah, curse you. How about fifty cents?'"

Mae was not so amused as her sons. "Be careful, men. These fellows can be bad actors. Twisting their tails is not a good way to remain healthy!"

The stores were full of wonderful bargains and the Kipfers all got outfitted with Moroccan shoes. Charlie had studied his geography. "Pop we're right near the magical city of Casablanca and Marakech. Can't we go there?"

Mae knew her sons had experienced so many outrageous places and events that nothing seemed impossible. She answered so Don would not loose face. "Not this time *muchachos*. We've still some of Morocco and Tangiers to explore!"

The second day, the troop started for the fabled Casbah. In doing so they passed the world-famous heiress, Barbara Hutton's home. "Unbelievable," reasoned Don.

Mae was certainly shaken. "For a moment I was certain Barbara's face was looking out through that steel-barred gate."

Don was even more certain. "If she had seen we Americans passing by she may have been curious. If we had not been in such a hurry, she may even have invited us in!"

When Don announced, completely unexpectedly, "Tonight we transplanted Moroccans go to and dine in the Casbah. It is an opportunity that none of us may ever have again!"

Mae, the reasonable traveler from Ohio, was horrified. "Don, is that wise? How can it be safe?"

"Relax, dear. I've checked it out with the ambassador. He said his wife and he sometimes eat there."

The Hotel Riff Concierge put them into a taxi with a driver who didn't speak a word of English. Mae was truly frightened. "Don, he can take us anywhere. We can't even protest!"

Don squeezed his trembling mate's hand. "Relax, this is purposely to be an exciting experience." Their taxi came to the stone wall and gate into the Casbah and immediately everything outside became black. There wasn't a single light to be seen. After several minutes, the driver stopped and into the headlights appeared a terrifying man. David said it all: "Pop, he's huge. He's in white robes and wearing a red turban!"

Mark butted in, "See that huge, curved sword on his hip. It's used for cutting off infidels' heads!"

Mae pleaded, "Don, we're infidels. Let's go back to the hotel!"

But out they scrambled. The taxi departed and there the Kipfer lineage stood, in the middle of the Casbah with a huge armed man who spoke no English!"

The guide motioned for them to follow him. As best the group could tell they were led down a totally black alley, up some stairs and into a large room.

There was only a faint candlelight and the shadowy but gorgeous Moorish decorated room, copious, with low tables surrounded by seating cushions, that became visible only slowly as these suspicious infidels eyes accustomed to the darkness. The prime waiter lead them to their cushioned seats at a large, round beautiful appointed table. Still everyone was disoriented. "What happens now?" asked Mae. "Are we to be the only victims in this place of horror?"

However, even as she spoke, a waiter brought them a large wooden menu, perhaps, three feet long by one and one half feet wide with the menu inscribed. David's eyes had already opened to their maximum size. "What does it say, Pop?"

Fortunately the menu was in English and everyone ordered something they understood they could eat. Suddenly a spotlight went on, lighting six men with single-stringed instruments sitting on a low platform just a few feet from their table. Talk about tension! The tendons in the five infidels bodies were tight as iron bands!

Mae finally recovered her breath as the show began. "Eerie music," she whispered. "And look at that young boy in Arab clothes performing what appears to me to be a belly dance!"

Don was also perplexed. "Don't try to understand, my sweet infidel. Just enjoy it."

Mae groaned. "You've got to be kidding!"

But gradually more people arrived. Gradually the lighting improved. Suddenly Mae could see. "Don, this place is just devastatingly beautiful. It seems each day we see something more startling. The show was amazing." Mae knew from their clean plates that everyone enjoyed the food.

But when it was time to leave David looked at their waiter, dressed just like the fearsome guard outside. He whispered to Don, "Pop, you're going to give this waiter a big tip, aren't you?" David realized that the Kipfers were up a creek without a paddle. "Pop, we don't even know where we are. We don't know the language. We don't have transportation!"

Don wasn't concerned. He stepped to the front desk. He paid his bill and returned. "They have our taxi waiting for us. He'll take us to our Riff Hotel."

In unison, Mother and sons chorused, "Praise Allah!"

"Traveling in foreign lands provides a thrill a minute for everyone," Don said to his troops as they left the Riff Hotel and hailed a taxi to catch the one boat a day that sailed to Gibraltar. But he had no idea how true his prophecy was! "Morocco requires us to turn in all our Moroccan money, before we depart. I hope we've all done that," said Don.

At the dock, it was apparent the Kipfers were the only infidels there to depart. But there were hundreds of porters to serve them. Don didn't intend to hire a porter to carry their luggage twenty feet from the gate to the ship's gangplank. Little did he suspect that he would have no choice about hiring a porter!

The Kipfers waited for the immigration officer to come to the gate and admit them. Nothing happened. Don told his sons. "Boys, protect your mother from these bastards. I'm going to see what's wrong."

Mae saw the immigration officer appear, say something and disappear again. Don returned. "You know the Moroccan official in Tangiers forced us to turn in their Moroccan money. Now immigration officials won't process us unless we pay the departure fee in Moroccan money!"

"What now, brave and wise sultan?" asked Mae.

"I'll be forced to bend to their system!"

Mae saw Don turn to the baggage handlers and shout, "Who speaks English?" She also heard the chorus. Every porter of the hundreds present, shouted, "I do!"

Don gave the selected porter ten dollars. The porter slipped easily into the immigration office into which it was clear he had slipped many times before. The immigrations officer came out and marked each piece of luggage with a piece of chalk. Don shook his head left and right. "Yup, I had to pay. Yup, we have to carry our own luggage through the gate over to the ship. Mae wasn't reassured. "You mean the one that's been holding the departure for two hours!?"

Still, Mae was relieved. "Well, you've climbed that mountain but now we'll be late in arriving at Gibraltar. And I know we'll have to travel a mountain road from Tarifa to Granada!"

"So be it!" After the experiences they had just been through, Mae and Don were a little surprised that their Cadillac was still at the dock. "Now we've got to hope that the Washington Irving Hotel held our reservations," worried Mae.

The boys were asleep in the rear. Don was concentrating on clinging to the narrow mountain road with cliffs on one side and a shear drop into the sea on the other, in total darkness. Mae, on the other hand, was terrified. "Don, it seems the sea is pounding the cliff directly below us, almost under our Cadillac."

Finally they arrived safely at the hotel where Washington Irving had stayed and had written about one of the worlds most romantic cities, Granada. Late, though it was, Spanish hospitality provided them a light, but tasty dinner before they turned in.

Grenada was everything that has been written about it. Mae visualized its total concept. "It seems impossible that each new wonder we visit and explore is more beautiful than the last. Can that be or am I imagining it?"

Don concurred, "Those Moors had hot and cold water, baths and underground plumbing while Christians were still wearing untanned fur and living in caves!"

Their three sons, each of whom were award winning artists, were breathless. "These men who built Grenada must have been the world's best artists."

Don was more practical. "I wonder how these people who were so advanced fell behind in technology?"

As they started the long drive north toward Brussels everyone thought they had seen it all. Not so! Spain had always been governed by autocrats. During the Kipfer's visit it was no different. They found that an armed soldier, his rifle at the ready, was almost unbelievably, stationed about every hundred yards the whole way from Grenada to Madrid. All the Kipfers were incredulous. Each soldier came to attention and saluted with his rifle as they passed. Mae understood this phenomenon first.

"These men have never seen a white, Cadillac DeVille. We know it's impressive, even to us. But it's especially wonderful for the Spanish citizen to see. These soldiers believe our car is carrying their dictator!"

The three boys sat back and enjoyed this unexpected protocol. Having seen Spain, Portugal, and Morocco, they were now looking forward to Brussels. And Brussels, their adoptive home, was still there, awaiting their return. But Mae knew her family must take advantage of their opportunity to travel together to all of Europe's special places. So she reminded Don in advance of each vacation he was afforded by the Air Force.

So, barely remaining in Brussels long enough to repack their suitcases they were all under way again with Mae remarking. "Don, I cannot think of Rome as Italy. It is simply Rome to me. The Roman Empire I read about stretched in the east beyond Israel and to the west through England. It stretched from Egypt in the south to mid-Germany in the north. Perhaps more has been spoken and written about Rome than any other Empire's capital. Its armies, government, language, science, art and literature have totally changed the course of the human development. None of we modern-day Americans have escaped its influence. Rome has always been a far away place to me. Not even in my dreams did I ever visit there!"

Don kept his eyes on the road. He was to drive through Belgium, Germany, Switzerland, Monaco, into Italy. And yet the amazing fact was that it was not very far. "True, Mae, but now you are on your way to that grand place!"

Mae still had sort of a dazed look in her eyes. "Yes, here I am in a New Cadillac DeVille, with my family, driving through countries in two days that took Rome years to conquer!"

"Don't get carried away, my dauntless voyager. First we must stop in Monaco. Certainly we will at least see where Prince Rainier lives and touch the earth where Princess Grace walks. Did you know when she was simply Grace and a starlet in New York City she sometimes dated cadets and came to our Saturday night dances at West Point?

Mae gave Don a questioning glance.

They found their hotel room in Monaco to be beautiful. The boys soon disclosed Monaco's secret. "Dad, Monaco is no larger than a small farm in Ohio!"

Mae collected sterling silver souvenir spoons from each country she visited. The one from Monaco was the most expensive in her fifty-spoon collection.

Mae told her sons, "Boys, you cannot enter the Monaco casinos. Even your father cannot arrange that!" And after Las Vegas, Don and Mae pronounced the casinos in Monaco a bit disappointing!

"Still," summarized Mae, "Monaco is truly beautiful. It's covered with beautiful flowers and trees!"

The Kipfers soon tired of driving up and down the mountains on the squiggly *laceted* roadways. But once through the Mount Blanc tunnel, everyone had hopes. Pisa was their first stop. Don had been there many times, stopping each time for purchases at its Alabaster Shop. "First," he had said, "the Leaning Tower!" Mae was astonished. "I thought it would be built out of rather plain stone, but it's beautiful. Almost like precious jewels!"

Charles was the first to notice his athletic mother's unsteady stance on the top floor. "Are you all right, Mom," he asked, going to her aid.

Mae was embarrassed. Her equilibrium had been disturbed. "Of course, Charlie. But this floor is really tilted. It's really deceiving!"

Everyone went and admired Don's favorite alabaster factory where he had previously bought stone bowls, stone fruit and many other alabaster items.

Then on to Roma! The hotel was near the American Embassy so they went to the small Post Exchange in its basement for breakfast. Scrambled eggs, sausage, and toast! "Viva la Roma," whispered the three sons!

That first day they visited all the ancient ruins. The next day was Easter so they went to the Vatican. Mae again noticed it first! "The pope is coming out on his second-story banister!"

"Yes," observed David, "they're dropping his royal red drape over the banister's edge."

"Quick, whispered Mae, "let's get our picture taken with him!"

While they were at the Vatican, they went to see Michaelangelo's art in the Sistine Chapel. Mae told them all, "It is hard to believe that man, one very special man, could create the art we see in this Sistine Chapel. I never dreamed that I would ever see such beauty."

There was only silence. There was only admiration! "To think that most Romans of that day abhorred Michaelangelo's work here," cautioned Mae. "Only his pope fed him and understood his work!"

That night Don had to repel a revolt. Everyone demanded, "We want to go to the Coliseum at midnight and hear the Christians crying." Don did not. But he was too weary to resist his troops any longer.

At 11:00 P.M. MAE shook him. "Don, we've ordered a taxi. Surely, you're not going to let your loving wife and your three sons go to that bastion of agnostic combats alone, are you?"

Mae had reached Don! He arose and dressed. Nothing more was said. When they got to the Coliseum, and approached the entrance down near the stage, sure enough there it was. Mae, whose hearing was excellent, heard it first. "My holy father, it's true. The long-dead, tortured Christians are crying and screaming!"

Everyone stopped in their tracks. No one could believe it was possible. Finally David, who loved and lived with animals broke out in laughter. "Hate to disappoint you folks. Those are not Christians. Those are love struck Tom cats!"

And with that, the spell was broken. Also the silence.

The next morning they drove up to and along the Appian Way. Mark thought about it. "Folks, this road has been in operation nearly 2,000 years. It's in the same condition as when it was built. It endures the same temperature changes as our roads back home. Why do our roads fail in just a few years?" It was a puzzle not one of them wanted to attempt to unravel!

Next on their list was Sorrento. Their hotel on the cliff facing the Mediterranean Sea was built so that a tunnel through solid rock connected the two halves of the establishment. Here, they discovered that America had indeed improved upon Italian pizza! "Hey, Mom," complained Charlie, "This pizza is just like pie crust with a little ketchup on it!"

The next day, in daylight, looking down the cliff on which their hotel perched, they could see a small beach with boats turned upside down on the shore. Charlie proposed to his dad, "How about we three boys go down and rent a boat for a trip on the Tyrolean Sea?

Don anxiously questioned Mae, "Is that really safe?"

Mae was undecided but answered, "I believe so."

Then he said to his three sons, "Here's ten dollars in U.S. Get what you can."

Off went the three brothers, Mae thought, perhaps never to be seen again. The uncertain parents watched their sons hurry down the winding roadway to the marina. Out came the Italian who obviously was showing his customers various boats. "There," said Mae, pointing her index finger, "that man turning a boat over and the four of them are scooting it into the water."

Half an hour later Don and Mae watched in horror as the small row boat disappeared around a two thousand-foot-high promontory. "My good God," shrieked a nearly hysterical mother. "What do we do now?"

The terrified parents waited for more than an hour and a half. Finally, Don could stand it no longer. "Mae, I'm going to alert the authorities!"

Don had already stood, ready to leave on his mission when Mae shouted, "Don, I see something. I believe it's the boys!"

Sure enough, the spot grew larger and finally they could see three figures, thankfully, all upright. "But why are they turning the boat around in the opposite direction? For Ned's sake, come on in!" pleaded Mae.

When the sons rejoined then on their high perch, the voyagers were unable to understand their parents' concerns. "We had a wonderful time," reported Mark. "We saw some out-of-this-world grottos!"

Mae's curiosity was killing her. She surely did not want to hear about some dangerous grottos but she did want to know, "Why did you stop and turn around when you were coming in close to shore?"

Now Charles had to burst out laughing. "David was the only one who had a billfold. We gave him the boat rental money for safekeeping. Some how his billfold fell overboard without him realizing it. When he discovered the loss, we turned around as fast as possible and went backward. Can you believe it, there was David's billfold, bobbing on the waves, just ready to sink. But we got it!"

The manager at the hotel told them there was to be a holy reenactment at the church that night that they should attend. So out they went not to the church, but along the walkway from the church downhill to a platform that looked out over the sea. David, as terrified as the rest of the family, gave a running commentary: "Look at the men in the scary costumes out front pounding the drums in that annoying cadence. Then there's what looks like a statue of Jesus on the cross. Next come the many priests. After that there are dozens of men in costumes that remind me of Boris Karloff!"

Mae was totally impressed. She was totally absorbed. "Don, if our religious services were like this back home, I could never handle being a Christian. They're scary!"

"Italy is such a varied country," Don explained to his sons. "It is difficult to grasp. You have the military and government of Rome. Then there is the religion at the Vatican and what we have witnessed at Sorrento. And of course the art in the Sistine Chapel. But now on our way northeast you will see more splendid art and craftsmanship."

As the Kipfers approached Florence, Don told them, "Florence houses some of the world's best art. I had a government contract here and when all of central Italy was flooded I had to go into Florence in a jeep for a visit. The mud was up nearly to the jeep's hubcaps. Water and mud had reached into many of the city's museums. It was a world tragedy!"

As always, their hotel and food was excellent. They were anxious to see Michaelangelo's *David*. All five of them stood, with no other humans sharing their view for nearly half an hour viewing this mind-boggling work of art. Mae was the only one to really recover and the first one to utter a word!

"Can you believe this sculpture stands in this huge room, illuminated by natural sky lights and yet its magnificence totally fills the room! How could any stone be so white or translucent? And the statue of *David* is huge, huge, huge. I was unprepared for his size. He is so lifelike I almost expect him to move. And though he is totally naked, I take no offense at that!"

Don had been to see *David* before. "Michaelangelo never ceases to amaze me!"

Charlie had spent all his viewing time in analytical estimates. "Mom, Michaelangelo's *David* looks exactly like our David!"

David blushed.

Mark could hardly stop looking at the statue. "You're right Charlie, but our David is warm, alive and is here with us!"

The Kipfers visited all the other museums in the city, but though they were exceptional, after *David* they seemed somehow meaningless. What they all enjoyed most was the Pont de Via, the bridge spanning the Tiber River, lined on both sides with curio shops containing merchandize the Kipfers had never seen anywhere else. Each boy bought a small reminder. Don took Mae in tow. "I'm buying you gloves to last your lifetime. Some cover only your hands. Some go to the elbow. And others go to your shoulder! These are made of the finest Italian leather in the world!"

Turning to a clerk, Don directed, "I want you to fit madam with your finest gloves. Two pair wrist length, two pair elbow length, and one pair shoulder length. All black, please!"

Mae was astonished, "Don, you know very well I never wear gloves to social affairs!"

Don almost choked in laughter. "I know, my dear. But that is the kind of gift a lover gives to his beloved!"

Don had planned their trip so that Mae and their sons would visit last the most unique, most fun-provoking city in Italy. He briefed them all: "It was no accident that Marco Polo launched from here on his journey to far away Cathay (China). The City State of Venice was peopled with craftsmen, businessmen, and traders. Little has changed today."

The Kipfers, no different than all the other visitors, were requested to leave their auto in a public parking lot outside the city. Actually, since there were no roads, they had no choice! A gondola took them to their grand hotel, where steps disappeared below the surface of the canal. The Kipfer boys, and Mae, having seen so much of Europe, Asia, and Africa, were difficult to amaze. Still, Charlie, least impressionable of all, in all seriousness showed his utter disbelief in what he saw when he complained to his father.

"Pop, this isn't real. These people have just staged this for our benefit!"

"No, Charlie, this city with its water avenues has been here since the time of Marco Polo. Venice was then one of the world's most wealthy city states!"

That evening they wandered out to St. Mark's Square, toured its cathedral and then selected one of Venice's best restaurants for dinner. Mae was usually just one step ahead of the men. She knew what paella was. She ordered braised lamb, her favorite. The men were braver but terribly uninformed. They searched the menu and finally all ordered the restaurant's specialty, paella!

Mae's dinner arrived first. She pronounced, "It's ravishing. It's prepared just the way I like it." Then, with tongue in cheek, she waited for the fireworks she was sure would erupt!

In came the four plates of paella. Charlie almost turned white and was light-headed. "God, Pop, what are they doing? This looks like a basket of minnows we seine from Rock Creek to use for bait back in Ohio! They even have their little heads and tails still on. And no one has cut off their fins or cleaned out their guts!"

Charlie's brothers just sat there, stunned!

Don called the waiter. "Señor, how does one eat these small fish?"

The waiter was no help. He showed no surprise. "As you like, sir."

Charlie tried one small fish. The other ninety-nine remained on his plate. "I'll settle for dessert, Pop!"

Mark and Don managed most of their meal. David moved the petit fish around on his plate. When they had finished, Mae, full, and very pleased with herself, chuckled, "Gentlemen, my meal was outstanding. And whatever else you may say, I'm sure you will never forget your paella dinner in St. Mark's Square!"

That night Don hugged and kissed his beautiful confident. "Mae, I know you did not bring your sons, or perhaps yourself to Europe, Asia, and Africa, just to be entertained, but to be educated as well. Tomorrow we are going by boat to the Island of Morano. It has changed little since Marco Polo's time. The men there are artists. The people of the Island of Morano make their income from their products and by trading with the rest of the world."

Mae played it cool. She had also done her homework. She knew what she would see on Morano and she planned to be a buyer!

In the morning, as they boarded the capable looking power boat, everyone was eager to get underway. "What a boat," observed Charlie.

"Venetian," agreed Mark.

"Old World," added David.

No one, not even the cool, prepared American Princess, had anticipated the astonishing Morano Glass Works. The artisans heated their glass cubics to white, glowing color and then twisted, turned and blew the molten mass into any shape they imagined. Mae raved, "These men are magicians. Simply by using their hands, and mouth, they are creating bottles, cups, plates, decanters, sets of every shape and size of creature on Earth!"

"True," agreed Don. "And see your sons. They are memorizing the whole process. No machines, no computers, no dies, no grinders, just hands and mouth!"

All three boys had purchased small animals to carry back to the United States. When Don and Mae came to the sets of decanters, glasses, and trays, Mae, understanding that a wife of necessity, had to encourage her husband occasionally, suggested. "We need a decanter set, concessionaire of alcoholic beverages. What say we purchase one?"

"A good choice, from among all these thousands of choices," agreed the unsuspecting groom. I vote for the green. It gets its color from the inexpensive bronze dust mixed with its glass. The expensive red is colored with gold!"

Mae had never forgotten Don's promise to pay for anything she truly wanted. But she was an unusually sensitive wife. "Sold!" she agreed. The Kipfers were quiet on the long trip back to Brussels. Everyone was analyzing what wonders they had witnessed. It seemed to Mae that her family had surely seen all of Europe. She was more than satisfied. But then when others in the EOAR talked of skiing in Kossen, Austria, at Christmas time, she again got the travel urge.

The musical, and also the movie, *The Sound of Music* had captivated all ages of citizenry in the United States. Few Americans believed there existed in Austria such a place as Innsbruck or Salzburg. If there was, it was certainly impossible that it offered the lifestyle the Von Trapp family lived. An infinitesimally few Americans ever expected to see, feel, or enjoy Austria for themselves!

Now, in Brussels, at EOAR as had been hinted, the American Woman's Club, Mae among these leaders, began to lobby for a group to spend their Christmas in Kossen, a nearby sister city of Innsbruck and Salzburg. Kossen had wonderful pensions, food and a first-class ski school!

Before Don, who had had uncomfortable experiences on ski slopes, could catch his breath, Mae had softened him up and he had agreed to go. "It was one of the best decisions I've ever made," he later told Mae."

Looking at the winter fairyland, Don exclaimed, "Kossen is a picture-postcard beyond belief. The falling snow has already made our Cadillac look like a giant loaf of white bread. I won't dig it out nor attempt to move it until we're ready to leave!"

Mae dressed in her beautiful ski outfit, looked out the back of their pension the next morning, almost vertically upward and could see nothing but snow until it disappeared into the sky. "It's clear that everyone here skis. Even the kids on their way to school. I don't know what they're saying but everyone smiles and seem to say, 'Christ gut!'"

"I believe that's a greeting, my dear," guessed Don.

That next morning everyone went to the ski school. There they got their skis and ski poles and were introduced to their instructors. "Please," requested Mae, "don't give Don and I the same teacher as our sons!"

"Okay," agreed the majordomo. "You two adults will have Stephanie. She has been an Olympic champion!"

Don grinned, "I guess that's good enough for us, eh, Mae?"

Mae was exuberant. "I don't know. I used skis Uncle Fritz made and skied on the hill at his farm in Marne, Ohio. But this will be different." Of course, Mae couldn't cover her joy. After all she was an athlete!

All the EOAR people soon learned the routine at Kossen. Up early, down to breakfast at their own table, with their own waitress and their own linen. Up to the slopes for two hours of teaching. Back to the pension for lunch and a nap or whatever. Back to the slopes for free skiing. Back again to the pension. Down to the lower floor for zither playing, gluvine, and if you wanted, a few rubbers of bridge before dinner.

"Whew," conceded Mae, "this schedule is killing me. My legs tingle. But I love it!"

Still Mae was not to tired to travel by bus to Innsbruck/Salzburg and inspect the location where *The Sound of Music* was made and to imagine herself playing the lead part and singing "Edelweiss!"

As dusk approached on Christmas eve, the whole Kipfer family was out in the quiet, snow-covered, fog shrouded Kossen Square, watching the local Austrians prepare for Kris Kringle. "They don't spend months getting prepared as we do," observed Charlie.

The fog had begun to lower and a light snow was falling. Suddenly they all heard sleigh bells. Mark was first to comprehend. "Folks, those are sleigh bells," and almost before his words were spoken, everyone saw a sleigh, driven by two men come out of the fog and snow.

"But what's on their sleigh?" worried a skeptical and angry environmentalist named Mae.

"Then don't look my dear. But it's a huge stag with a large pine tree beside it. We would call it an elk. Of course, different folks have different ways of celebrating Christmas."

After dinner, at the request of the boys' instructor the family went to his house just off the Kossen Town Square to enjoy a real Austrian Christmas Eve.

"My heaven," whispered Mae to Don, "they have real candles on their tree and they're lighting them. Sit near the door. If the tree goes up inflames, you get Charlie and Mark and I'll get David. We'll be out of here!"

The instructor's family exchanged a few simple gifts. "Not like home," Charlie whispered to his mother. Then the instructor gave each of the Kipfers a Kossen Ski Schule badge. Mae did the honors for her family. She called each of the small children up to her and gave them an envelope. The envelopes each contained an American five dollar bill. The envelope for the instructor was perhaps too ostentatious. The evening was capped off with gluvine and cookies.

When they left the instructor's house, late at night, Mae asked, "Look at all the people going to the church. Let's join them!"

Inside the simply huge place of worship, Don groaned to Mae. "For Lord's sake, these folks must be immune to the cold. There is no heat in this huge stone building and the outside temperature is below freezing!"

Mae smiled a Christianly expression. "True, but can't you feel the touch of God!?"

"Perhaps, but I don't understand a word they're saying!"

"Graduation from the Ski Schule was to be celebrated with a regulation downhill slalom. Don covered his performance in advance. "Mae, you know Colonel Deets is short on pilots. One has already broken his leg skiing. The colonel told us all that he'll take action against us if he has another accident"

"Sure, snowman, that's a good excuse," laughed Mae, knowing her hubby had no choice.

The ladies were first to challenge the difficult downhill. Mae never entered a contest that she didn't intend to win. But she neglected to remember that nearly all the other contestants were Austrian who had been skiing since they were infants. When the ladies appeared coming down the last hill to the finish line it seemed Mae was in the lead. "Way to go," screamed all the Kipfer men. But in the last twenty yards an Austrian edged her by a nose and she had to settle for the silver medal.

In the men's giant slalom, there were four Kipfer men entered. Mae watched for the final downhill dash. She could see the three Kipfers out in front but she couldn't identify who was first. As they passed she could see Mark was leading. Just yards behind, Charlie and David were neck and neck. Mark crossed the line first, David and Charlie in a dead heat second. Then a strange thing happened. Apparently the toe of David's ski got caught just as he crossed the finish line. He flew into the air fifteen feet high, did a flip and lay motionless in the snow on his back.

Mae and all the supervisory staff flew to David's side. Mae whispered gently to David, "David, are you all right?"

No answer.

One of the staff moved David to his side. "Whew," moaned David. "Some ride, Mom. I'm not hurt. It just knocked my wind out of myself!"

So, when the medal count was made, Mae won second and got a silver medal, Mark won first and got a gold medal. Charlie and David tied for second and got silver medals. Mae laughed, "For the life of me I don't know how they determined when David crossed the finish line!"

Charlie was a joker. He asked his father, "How did you do, Pop?" Of course he knew.

"Well, anyway, I got a bronze medal. I'm pretty sure that was for finishing." And everyone laughed!

Occasionally, as one passes through life they meet someone casually, perhaps never to see them again and yet they feel friendship which remains with them the rest of their lives. So it was with Mae and her ski instructor, Stephanie. It is true that Stephanie rose to the top of her profession in one sport, but Mae set records in a great many. Stephanie invited Mae and Don to her chateau. Her husband, a ranking official in the Austrian government had died but his presence was everywhere in Stephanie's home. He had been a sportsman and stuffed heads of every animal native to Austria was mounted on his wall. While Steffanie was in her kitchen preparing gluvine Mae whispered, "Can you believe this chateau? It's huge. It's absolutely beautiful and furnished with the best of everything."

"Only too true" agreed Don, still in his heavy, warm outfit worn on the ski slopes. But I'm sure you noticed that there is no heat in this chalet and it's below freezing outside!"

"Yes, Mr. Snowman. But Stephanie hasn't mentioned that. Sure, and I'm not going to, either!"

Back in Brussels, Don rubbed his hands and smiled. "What a tour we've had here in Europe. I know our presidents get to make diplomatic visits here but you know they only see the interior of a conference room. No, I suspect that no one has ever seen Europe in exactly the way we have been privileged to do. Still, though no one will probably ever believe us, we've done it.

Mae smiled in a way she had that told her husband he has not yet seen it all. "Whoa, whoa, meine backslider. You are not yet finished. You have not quite seen it all. And by gosh, there is still time."

"What now, princess?"

"You remember when we were thinking about this tour while still in Montgomery, your friend in the Pentagon gave you two choices."

"*Jawohl.*"

"Well, the other choice was Garmish, Germany. I'm curious!"

Don wiggled. "I'm not!"

There was little doubt about the outcome of this friendly difference of opinion. The Kipfers found Garmish very much like a United States Military Base set down in Germany. It had officer's quarters, an officer's club, a post exchange, a bowling alley, and of course, American food.

For three days everyone skied the Zugspitz. They ate lunch at the Eagles Nest, set on the very top of that magnificent mountain from which one could look down into Germany, France, and Switzerland.

On the morning of the fourth day the snow was falling in such profusion that one could barely see their hand held out in front of their face. "No," the concierge told Don, "we don't close the ski lifts, but it will be difficult to ski, perhaps even dangerous. You will not see any Germans on the slopes!"

Don and Mae were undecided. Charlie heard their conversation.

"Hey, Pop, we're grown up."

Mae replied softly, "Almost!"

The three young men made their way up and down the slopes at their own pace. Don and Mae were more cautious. Suddenly, out of the grey unknown, Mae saw a figure at standstill. She stopped immediately. How strange she thought. A skier in khaki trousers, a very light jacket, no hat and wooden handled ski poles. Suddenly the man turned and faced Mae and Don.

Mae knew immediately the man staring at them was wondering if these two Americans would recognize him. Both Mae and Don did immediately. Don said, "Hi."

The no-longer stranger replied, "Hello!"

Mae managed to speak out. "We are so happy to see you!"

The new acquaintance replied, after giving Mae more than a casual evaluation. "Thank you, sweetie!"

Then he disappeared into the mist, never to be seen again. Don roared, "Mae, you know who that was, don't you?"

"Doesn't every woman in the modern world, foolish one. That was the one and only Richard Burton. I read in this morning's paper that he's here making the movie, *Eagle's Nest* up at our restaurant on top of the mountain!"

"But where, oh where, is Elizabeth?" sighed Don.

By late afternoon, Mae told her sons, "We're leaving. But we're skiing down the trail that leads directly into Garmish."

Mae, Don and Charlie saw the sign to Garmish, and left the main trail to turn and end shortly in Garmish. Mark and David, the two explorers, missed the sign. Mae was frantic two hours later as it neared dark and the temperature began to fall. "Please, Don, ask the authorities to get out the emergency patrol!"

"Okay," agreed Don and started toward the patrol building. He had only gone a short distance when Charlie came running, shouting, "Hey, Pop!"

Don stopped and Charlie, out of breath, reported, "We think we see Mark coming up the hill, but he's still far away."

Sure enough, almost ready to drop, Mark was still trying to make it back to Mae and Don.

"What happened," asked his father?"

"We missed the turn and wound up in a small village. We tried to call but we didn't have any money and no one would give us any."

"Where's David," shouted Charlie.

"He's coming, but he's really bushed. I came ahead to tell you what happened!"

An hour later, rested, warm and eating American food at the Officer's Club, everyone was especially gay and happy. "Now, determined one, have you finally seen Europe?"

"I believe so, patient one. Now I know Garmish is wonderful. But Brussels is better!"

But back in Brussels, relaxed on a sofa, with their fireplace blazing and their sons in their rooms, studying, Don wanted to add something to Mae's memory of Europe. "Sweetie, before we close the books on our travels in Europe, I'd like to remind you of the less astonishing things we've seen and done."

"OK, partner, shoot."

"Could anyone ever forget Brussel's Grand Park? How about the splendid Cinc Centenaire; our tour of Waterloo? Who could describe Volendam. What about our exploring the Autonium? Who has waded in the Jordan River or smelled the flowers in the Garden of Gethsemane? What American has toured within the Walls of Jericho, Jordan? Have they sat in a classroom at Hebrew University in Israel? Who has walked among the lion prides in Kenya or sat at a desk in the University of Nairobi. Who has been to the festival at Binch, Belgium, to understand the relationship between the Spanish nobility and the American Indian nobility of South America?

"How many people have been in the Running of the Bulls near Rodrigo, Spain? How about my mother's joy at seeing the White Cliffs of Dover?

"We could feel the presence of Ann Boleyn at her house in Staines when we stayed there. And all of us loved the ambiance of Robin Hood in Nottingham. Could any of us forget the huge, but austere Officers Club in Prestwick, Scotland? Is there an American who has stayed with the head professor at the University of Maseru in Basutoland, South Africa? Could anyone claim to have visited the Kimberly diamond mines? How about traipsing through Lapland with Fin Lied? Standing at the Battle of the Bulge memorial at Bastogne one could almost hear General McNaulty utter his reply to the Germans, '*Nuts!*'

"How about my mother and all the other Kipfers bathing at Spa, Belgium! And the glockenspiel at the Marienplatz in Munchen, Germany, was worth the whole tour. Ulm, Germany, the tallest cathedral spire in the world reminded me of the marriage of my relatives, the Hornbergers. What about the impressive old ruins at Trier, Germany? Could anyone forget the *Mermaid* in Copenhagen Harbor? How about the Red Palace in India, which only I saw of course, and all the many other places such as Calcutta, Madras, and the Ganges. How about my trip to Helsinki, Finland, or Aux-en-Provence,

France?

"None of us should indeed, not forget such wonderful experiences. They are truly a part of our tour in Europe."

Vietnam

Mae knew that Don's failure to be promoted under the zone to lieutenant colonel while at the Warfare Systems School was a backhand he would never forget nor forgive after all the accomplishments he had given to the school during his tour. Now he was serving a different command. His commander obviously saw in Don something he himself believed in. They had hardly arrived in Brussels when the orders had been published. Mae shouted, too excited to maintain self-control, "Wonderful. Now I'm a colonel's lady. And it seems to me it was just yesterday that I left Academia!"

Of course there was a huge party. Colonel Jack Deets congratulated all the promotees. He even gave Don a set of his own lieutenant colonel leaves. But Don was not happy. *He probably never would be again concerning the military*, Mae thought. When she congratulated him he was despondent. "What on earth will I do with it, he demanded?"

Don never wore his silver leaves designating him as a lieutenant colonel. EOAR people wore civilian clothes!

But now back in Brussels from her latest triumphant tour Mae could hardly contain herself in the role of colonel's lady! "So, Colonel, has your exalted rank gotten us a reservation to return home on the last voyage of the USS *United States*?"

"You bet your life, helpmate."

"And so the promotion was good for something," beamed Mae.

Not one of their sons had wanted to leave their friends in Montgomery and go to live in Europe. Now, not one wanted to leave Europe and return home. Each had managed to get employment at the U.S. Embassy and planned to stay in Brussels!

Don told Mae, "We just can't have that!"

Mae grinned. "My dauntless leader, have no fear," she explained as she held up three small grayish colored books. "As you can see, I have their passports!"

Still, the night before their scheduled departure by bus for Le Harve and the voyage home, there was no sign of their three sons. "What now," implored Don.

"Don't worry, Colonel. Sleep tight, cooed the confident plotter.

When Mae and Don arrived at the bus pickup spot, sure enough there the lost were standing at the bus with three beautiful girls. Both they and their distraught parents were sobbing.

"Again we have lucked out," crooned Mae. We are departing Le Harve on the Fourth of July. God is good! Look at the USS *United States* shooting fireworks!"

Long before Mae and Don had gotten settled and went topside, their sons had gone exploring. Mae looked up and out onto the fantail of the ship. "There's something familiar about those three men firing skeet from the fantail," she joked.

Don could hardly believe his eyes. Sure enough. "They should be familiar, kiddo. Those are your three bewildering sons. And I believe those three gorgeous creatures with them are not the same three girls they just left in Brussels!"

"True, but as the sages incorrectly say, 'Absence makes the heart grow fonder!'"

Life aboard the USS *United States* was luxurious. The affluent could call at any time of the night and order almost anything they could imagine from the kitchen or bar and have it delivered free by their steward. Charlie confided to Mae, "One night we had a T-bone party!"

Don aired his concern to Mae. "Those wild adventurers can probably get drinks from the bar, also!"

Mae grimaced. "I don't want to know!"

Debarking from the USS *United States* was one of Mae and Don's most special occasions in their lives. Their three adult sons, touching American soil again in tailored slacks, expensive letter jackets covered with sports letters and medals, healthy, in top physical condition, were truly all-Americans. People were following them, taking pictures wondering who they were.

Don kissed Mae, "Sweetie, we're home."

It took two hours before Don had completed the paperwork and recovered their Cadillac from the ship's hold. All the Kipfers carefully stowed their gear in the Cadillac and sat back to rest until they arrived in Washington, D.C. They had not removed the big "B" from the rear of the Cadillac. "I suppose," mumbled Don to anyone interested, "It's just that carrying that 'B' is rather nasty!"

At this point, Don told Mae. "I'm fiendishly proud of the 'B'"

Mae, the participant in two accidents she had not wanted, did not agree. "Proud to have survived it, you devil!"

"It really is good to be home," admitted Don.

They had hardly cleared the fence surrounding the airport and started south when they all heard the police siren and saw the police car's flashing lights."

"What the hell, now," moaned Don. "Now, I know I'm home."

The officer pulled up in front of them and got out. "See you've been overseas, folks!"

"Yes, officer. What's the problem?"

"None, really. Just wanted to remind you, you must get U.S. license plates within ninety days."

"Thanks!"

After the officer left and they were once again under way Mae could not help herself. She had to push a little. "Yes, as you said, Don, we're home! But relax. Tensions are not good for anyone. Give him the benefit of the doubt. Perhaps he was attempting to help."

But Mae knew Don was still upset. "It's not about anything that policeman said but at his insensitivity. My dear, we uprooted our family, separated our sons from their friends, underwent considerable inconvenience. I worked fifty hours a week, mostly separated from you and the boys. All of this to help make our 'Sweet Land of Liberty' more secure. I really didn't need an American policeman to get his jollies by harassing me within the first minute of my return!"

"Should Auld Acquaintance Be Forgot and Never brought to Mind" was to be a sentiment that brought the terrible hated shadow of death to the Kipfers. Mae went first to the Washington Sanitarium to see her beloved aunt Glenna, whom she knew was terminal with cancer. Both she and Don went into Glenna's room and sat on the edge of her bed. Mae was simply terrified. Don was certain Mae was about to pass out. Glenna attempted to smile. She used all her strength to reach out for Mae's hand. "Mae-Mae. I'm so glad to see you. I've held on until you got back home so I could tell you how much I love you!"

Mae hugged the one who had shared herself, her time, her food, shelter and advice when she was just a young girl trying to find her way. Before her now lay a person she did not even recognize even knowing her so well. How could my God allow a deadly, unwanted terror, vicious and cruel beyond understanding destroy this honest, truthful, helpful Christian? "Aunt Glenna, I love you as much as anyone can love another person. I am thankful to you for all you have done for me."

Don kissed this poor soul he did not recognize. Only her voice was unchanged. "Glenna, may God bless you. He made very few humans your equal." And Don could handle no more. He left Glenna, Vada, and Mae to their own thoughts.

Glenna's terminal illness utterly destroyed the Kipfers' visit to Washington, D.C. However, Mark and Mae's visit to Casteau for a shot at an ROTC scholarship had been successful and Mark had been accepted at Georgetown

University. So Mark, Mae and Don went to see the dean of students at Georgetown to make certain all the administrative details of Mark's entry were complete.

Then off to Newark and Massillon. Huge family reunions were held in each town. "It's wonderful to visit friends and relatives again" exclaimed Mae, "and to realize that not much has changed here. They all certainly accept that security is not only a rock for the families but a condition they can rely on!"

Mae had good reason to be concerned with security. She had told Don in Brussels, "They won't send you to Vietnam, mon Beau Brummel. I hate to remind you, but I'm sure you're to old to again fly combat. And besides who ever heard of receiving two overseas tours in a row?"

"Don't be so sure you, camp follower. The Air Force has justified keeping us pilots on flying status with flight pay for just such an occasion. Politically, they must make use of us. Besides I'm a professional. If they need me, I'm prepared to go."

So here, regardless of the sudden shock, this sweet, helpful Air Force wife found herself the father, mother, commander, defender of what was to be left of her family. Charlie, whose alma mater they stopped to see in Athens, Alabama, near Huntsville, would be gone. Mark was to be at Georgetown. Don was to be a combat pilot in Vietnam. Since there was no one else to consult she prayed, "God give me the strength to do my duty!"

When Mae asked David where he would like to live, he didn't even hesitate, "Montgomery, if that's all right with you, Mom."

"Certainly, David," agreed Mae. She knew that officer's wives had been threatened because of many American's hate for the Vietnamese War. She knew such a thing was almost unheard of in the patriotic South.

Driving again out South Court Street in Montgomery brought back many memories. The terrible epidemic during their assignment at Squadron Officers School in 1953. The marches by Martin Luther King and his freedom demonstrators past their home in the 1960s. "Now here we are again," commented Mae, "turning into our old driveway on South Court Street!"

It so happened that Mr. and Mrs. Hodges were in their front lawn next door. They shouted, "Mae and Don—glad to see you back. Come on over." After handshaking and the exchange of a few pleasantries, the Hodges popped the question: "The Mrs. and I have built a new home in the suburbs. This house is for rent. We would be overjoyed if you would take it!"

Mae bloomed. Its location was perfect. She knew the neighbors. The rent, the same as they had paid three years earlier, was ridiculously low. "Sold," she responded. So off went Don. Off went Charlie. Off went Mark. A very closely-knit family smashed to smithereens, never to be put back together again!

Vietnam

Don was back in ten days, knocking at the door, nearly scaring Mae to death. She joked with the combat pilot, "What's the matter, honey bun? Didn't they want such a senior command pilot?"

Don picked her up and kissed her soundly. "On the contraire!" You know I expected to be assigned to jet fighters because of all my jet flying time. But the Air Force has a need for prop jockeys. None of the young guys have ever flown props. I just came from three years of immersion."

"Understandable, now what?"

"You'll never believe this. Bill Terrell and I have been selected to ferry an EC-47 from New Hampshire to Pleiku. Bill's junior to me so he's the co-pilot. We're on our way to the West Coast, Alaska, out the chain, island hopping and then into Don Muang, Vietnam."

Mae was a tiny bit relieved. An EC-47 sounded safer to her than a jet fighter. Don did not tell her that of the six modified EC-47s sent on their way from New England, only one so far had made it to Vietnam. "How long will you be in New Hampshire, Don?"

"That depends on how fast they modify our aircraft. It must have new, larger engines. It must have new, larger control surfaces. It will carry millions of dollars of electronic equipment. And it must have a large, supplementary fuel tank for the ferrying."

After he departed Maxwell AFB, headed north for his aircraft, Don wrote every day. A month later he called: "These guys are really slow, I'm not sure we'll beat the snow! How's everything there?"

"Charlie and Mark are doing okay. David is wonderful. He's the man in charge. He runs this place. It's a tight ship!"

Two weeks later, Don landed at Maxwell AFB en route to Vietnam, his bird painted in full camouflage.

Mae told Don, "It's just like we had never left. I'm head of a subcommittee of the Officers Wives Club and playing golf. When David appeared in the halls at Sidney Lanier High School, his old athletic mates asked him, "Where you been, Kipfer?"

The antiwar protestors were not concerned that the military had been sent to Vietnam by the protestors own civilian associates. It did not concern them that the Kipfer household had been ripped asunder. It did not concern them that Don had missed all of Dave's high school senior year of playing football. However, while Don was home this few days, Sidney Lanier High School was playing for the state championship in Birmingham. Mae and

Don were listening on their radio. Don told Mae, "This is a critical down, Mae. If Lanier stops them, they're the champions."

The announcer came on loud and clear. "Here comes their halfback around right end. It seems he's loose. No, no, no. David Kipfer has just made a bone-shattering tackle and stopped their halfback at the line of scrimmage. He's also made Sidney Lanier Poets the State Champions!"

Needless to say, departing from Mae and David was a very difficult task. Still, Don knew, if he also planned to join them again, he had to stay focused. Before he left the United States, he called Mae one last time. After all the normal pleasantries, Mae bubbled over: "Don, I was at the base post office today, and guess what?"

"I suppose you needed some stamps?"

"Oh, yes, and that, too. But the list of promotions to full colonel is out and you're on it! Hurray!"

"That's hardly believable. Thanks be to God for a fair-handed officer like Colonel Jack Deets. The promotion will change our lives for the better!"

The next time Don called was via the MARS military communications net from Alaska. "We had a time getting up the West Coast of Canada and Alaska, sweetie. Really bad weather. Had to stop a few days on Vancouver Island. The weather was even worse at Elmendorf. But now we're at Adak ready to fly to Midway. The weather will be getting warmer. How's Montgomery?"

"David and I are okay. People help us all they can. The college boys seem to be doing all right. We miss you, my dear!"

"Don't make me cry, babe!"

From then on until Don's first letter from Pleiku AFB in the highlands of Vietnam, Mae kept track of Don's progress by letters from Midway, Wake, and Philippines. The Plieku letter simply said: "I arrived safely and am living in what the locals call menopause manor. Bill Terrell stayed with a buddy in Saigon. There are several officers here I've known at other places. The food isn't bad. It's going okay. Love you, My Dear!"

Don did not tell Mae that Pleiku's Big Voice came on at midnight his first day of arrival and 30mm shells destroyed the hobby shop, a hundred feet from his barracks, one barracks and three EC-47s. He did not say that there was essentially no protection from Vietnamese Soldiers with satchel charges coming through the hallways of their barracks that were unprotected in any way.

He could never have mentioned that the EC-47 missions were low level, essentially right on the tree tops. The Vietnamese soldiers communications had no hard wire to connect units. Their orders were all given electronically, air-to-air. It was easy to intercept these messages and learn all the battle orders for the next day.

After seventeen missions, someone apparently found out that Don and a half-dozen other lieutenant colonels had been promoted. No one, except Mae, had ever officially notified him until that date. Since the Squadron Table of Organization called for only one full colonel, change in assignments had to be made. Don wrote to Mae: "Seventh Air Force discovered my promotion to Full Colonel." My next letter will be from Nakhon Phenom in northeast Thailand as Deputy Base Commander. Love and Sawaddee, my Colonel's Lady."

Nakhon Phenom AFB had been a ranger's base. Don's job, among many others, assigned to him by Group Commander Colonel Tom Owens and Wing Commander Ed White, was to turn that rough and tumble place into a first-class U.S. Airbase. Not really easy. Mission accomplished!

That required a complete drainage plan; air conditioning the enlisted men's mess, installing a movie theater, and base beautification, among other tasks. There was also the support required for the Air Force while it installed its first self-constructed runway to replace the corrugated steel one which had floated away in the monsoon!"

Don's next letter to Mae from NKP was upbeat: "We have a good mess. Individual Squadrons have their own rumpus rooms. Colonel Owens, with my help, has set up good relations with the Thai Governor and his wife to substitute for the non existing 'Status of Forces Agreement' which is normal between nations. I am flying the C-47 quite a bit to deliver High Value equipment and rest and recuperations troops from place to place. Towns like Udorn, Ubon, Utapao, and Bangkok are as familiar to me as our own towns in Ohio. Ching Mai is a Changri La. Hope everything on the home front is going okay."

Don did not tell Mae that one captain and two major friends of his and handball partners at Plieku, had been killed on the runways in aircraft accidents and that he had supervised the removal of their remains. He did not tell her, as disaster control officer, among some eighteen other responsibilities, that he had supervised the retrieval of two crashed F-4 crews who had crashed, one on the airstrip at NKP. He did not tell her that he helped lift the nearly lifeless body of a full colonel, his heart visible through his severe chest wound, from the F-4 that pancaked on the runway at NKP!

Through the five hundred Thai guards assigned to the base for protection, the three hundred young women serving in the Officers Club, and the many other Thai people with whom he came in contact, Don came to respect and love these Asiatic people.

Midway in everyone's tour came the event that all the combatants looked forward to. They were given two weeks Rest and Recuperation. Don wrote to Mae: "Since our family is split into so many locations, I know I could not visit everyone in such a short time. Transportation snafu's have kept many of our troops from even making it home. Please check on the price of a round-trip ticket from Montgomery to Bangkok. If you would like to come here, it is perfectly safe and I can make all the arrangements!"

In record time, back came a letter from Don's loving wife! "Dear Colonel, I have always wanted to come to Asia since I read Pearl Buck's novels. I have dreamed of Thailand ever since I saw *The King and I*. I must admit to you, I have my ticket!"

As in Europe, Don's business for the Air Force had taken him to nearly every town of any size in Thailand, the land of the free, the home of the brave, so that when Mae arrived, her itinerary was all set.

Don had expected, when he went to the rather ramshackle terminal at Don Muang, that he could easily identify Mae when she stepped from her jet by her coal-black hair. Not so, for every female who debarked was nearly as tall as Mae and had the same lustrous black hair. But when she appeared, his remembrance was perfect!"

"Sawaddee cup, Mae, how was your trip?"

"Wonderful. Singapore Airlines kept three seats available for me and I could sleep anytime I chose!"

Walking into the Chaa Phya Hotel, Mae was astonished by its beauty. In her room, she examined the further surprises arranged by her husband. "Don, you must have collected every type of fruit that grows in Thailand! I recognize the pineapple, oranges, grapes, and persimmon, but what are all the others?"

"Darned if I know. Try them."

The next morning Don had arranged to have a rather large boat, handled by one Thai man who never ceased smiling, pick them up. "Our trip today," explained Don, "is referred to as the water market. We will be gone about three hours. Believe me, you are going to be treated to sights few people will ever see, including the Thais!"

"Look," pointed Mae, "those people just come out the back of their home on stilts, onto their floating dock, step down to the canal and perform their toilet! My gosh, they also brush their teeth and wash their dishes in the same water!"

Shortly Mae found out why she was visiting the water market. They came to an area where thousands of peddlers were chanting. "Don, they are selling everything here . . . food, medicine, furniture, and almost everything one could imagine."

"Yes, my adventurer. But enough of this. Now for lunch and some real shopping."

At the fancy Thai restaurant, Mae began to appreciate the Thai culture. "Don, my food is really beyond description. It even surpasses the Indonesian food in Amsterdam!"

"Ah ha," laughed Don, "it is so. But I have promised to take you shopping. Thailand is the source of much of the World's precious stones. Johnny Jems store is the best. He maintains an outlet at Nakon Phnom Airbase where he knows me well. Carole is his Chinese manager here in Bangkok, and she will wait on you."

When Mae and Don stepped into Johnny Jems, Carole recognized Don at once, dropped what she was doing and came to wait on them. "Carole, this is my wife, Mae, visiting from the United States."

Carole bowed appropriately. "I am pleased to meet you, Mrs. Kipfer. Thailand welcomes you. I would be honored to help you select anything you are interested in."

To select from thousands of wondrous stones was not easy!

Mae finally was able to settle on a bronze, buffalo-handled eighteen-place setting of dinnerware. And when Don pointed her toward the jewels her eyes shown like the black opals she seemed most interested in.

"Pick out what you want, my dear," urged Don.

"This gorgeous black opal ring is just what I want, if it isn't to expensive, director."

"A colonel's wife should not have to dwell to long on an items cost, Carole. Wrap it up."

That night Mae and Don went to dine at Bangkok's Eriwan Hotel. Everyone, of course, were in their finest clothing. The service was superb and the food delicious. Throughout this fantastic experience Thai music filled the air. Then a theatrical company began the saga of *The White Monkey*. Don and Mae soon realized that they were being led to believe the White Monkey was a sex deviate. Don rose to leave. "Please," said Mae, "ignore him. The music and costumes are splendid!"

But almost as if the White Monkey sensed Don's hatred, he came scampering to their table, jumped up in the air and landed rump down on Don's lap! "You bastard," yelled Don, jumping to his feet and dumping the creature on the floor.

Barely in time, Mae grabbed Don's raised fist. "Don, control yourself. Knocking him senseless will solve nothing. Sit down!"

Don simmered. "That troupe is lucky. They almost lost their number one pervert!"

The next day the Kipfers toured the sights of Bangkok. They went to the market, the standing and reclining Buddha's and the many temples. "Their temples," concluded Mae, "are not only religious, they are works of art. They define the Thai people!"

"Absolutely," agreed Don. "Now you have been to Central America, Egypt, and Asia. Do you see anything similar about their architecture?"

"Naturlich! They have all settled on using a pyramid-like structure. Can that have happened independently?"

"No one knows. I believe there was some type of communication."

The next day they flew to what Don considered the Shangri-La. The Thais called it Ching Mai. Mae soon realized why Don believed Ching Mai was Shangri-La on Earth. "The men all bow, smile and offer Swaddee. The ladies, in gorgeous, full-length Thai silk gowns, nod under their parasols and smile. Everyone seems to be nibbling hot tidbits purchased from street venders. Everything, the houses and public buildings are all made from Thai silk and teak."

Don did not want to cause a dampener on Mae's enthusiasm for what she beheld in this dreamtown, but he felt he should warn her. "Remember this time well, my dear. Ching Mai has been discovered by the outside world, especially by we Americans.

Unfortunately, wherever we go the local people seem to latch on to our worst features. I have already gotten my first glimpse of Ching Mai's demise!"

As their taxi handed them over to the concierge at the Rincom Hotel, Don laughed. "I have a real surprise for you, my dear! The Rincom Hotel has just opened. It is the first luxury hotel in Ching Mai. I was able to get advanced booking. We will be its first honored guests!"

Mae could hardly believe this news but when she saw her room she exclaimed, "Paisan, I'm a believer. Each trip we take, I believe is more magnificent than the last and I am sure I will never see anything to surpass it. However, it seems, that is never the case!"

That first night, the Thai Air Force lieutenant in charge of the small Thai detachment at NKP joined them for pre-dinner cocktails and also as a guest for dinner. This young officer was not a happy man. "Colonel, see how the Thai waitresses avoid even looking at me. They know I could never even consider a drink for them in this salon because of the mismatch between the cost of a drink and my salary."

Mae could understand that the demise Don had mentioned had already begun. Don had never been able to construct a suitable answer to this complaint although it had happened in many countries. So he did not reply.

Mae was more diplomatic. She laughed and then so did both officers. She simply had that effect on people. "Lieutenant, you are so handsome I'm sure the girls are not looking for just a cocktail!" and of course the tension was broken.

Don had hired John, whom he knew from previous visits to be a reliable driver. John remained on duty twenty-four hours a day. Mae could hardly believe she was not dreaming. Each day she experienced unbelievable experiences that exceeded her previous joy while watching *The King and I*. "They went to see the elephants haul the huge teak logs from deep in the forest. The mahout allowed Mae to sit on his elephant's trunk. It was clear that the mahout considered that more of an honor for himself than a gift to Mae—even the elephant seemed to enjoy the occasion.

"Each little village," explained Don, "has its own specialty from which its citizens make their living."

The first stop was at the umbrella village. "They're the parasol makers. The parasols are constructed totally of wood!"

When Mae saw these beautiful creations, she proclaimed, "I must have several of these," and immediately purchased three. The young woman who sold the parasols to Mae did not want to part from her. It was a sentimental moment.

And so they went from village to village until they got to Pusan. "Mae, Thailand believes they have the world's most beautiful women. It is in Pusan where they are considered special. Pusan is also known for its high quality Thai silk."

When Mae went into a small silk-cloth manufacturing company which used antique looms, the young girls stopped their work and crowded about Mae who was a bit taller than they. "Beautiful, beautiful," the girls exclaimed as they touched Mae's gorgeous blouse made of flowered synthetic material. "Never see such cloth!"

On the way out of this heartwarming shop, Mae told Don in unmistakable language, "Those girls are truly the most beautiful I've ever seen. And I could not believe it. They are whiter skinned than I am!" And on her departure she gave each girl a pin made to look like a United States flag.

Don shrugged. "Of course, the Thai government has prohibited the practice, but one can still purchase nearly anyone of those gorgeous creatures for a relatively small amount of money. Illegally, of course!"

Don turned his attention to his excited wife. "Mae, I know you are enjoying Thailand. I know you earnestly desired to savor the relationship you saw in *The King and I*. Our next stop is your chance! Now I'm going to give you the closest interface with the queen and king of Thailand that you will perhaps ever have!"

"How can that be? Must I dress properly for it?"

"No. You are perfect, my love!"

John drove his chartered auto out from Ching Mai and stopped it at the foot of an unbelievable stairway, which seemed to stretch up endlessly into the sky. "Don, look, it has an extended dragon running down each handrail and it has open-jawed, scary heads here at the bottom that look right at you. Are we to climb this stairway?"

"Yes, my dear, and the queen and king's summer palace is at its top!"

Mae could hardly catch her breath. She could not believe that such wealth existed anywhere on earth. The building itself, its rooms, its furniture all spoke of countless wealth. Mae did not want to leave this place. She felt she was born to live here. But Don diplomatically edged her on their way.

"And now," said Don, "we'll examine the other side of the coin. John began a tortuous drive up the mountain. It was an hour's drive in low gear and over dangerous roadways. When Mae saw the village she pronounced, "Don, this is simply a page from ancient history. The people are dressed in medieval-age costumes. Their homes are more like wooden baskets. Their shops are small and poor."

Don clicked, "Now you have the crux of it."

But Mae knew being poor did not describe a people. And so it was there. It seemed all the village crowded about the tall, richly dressed Americans. And they were thankful for the several purchases these wealthy people made.

On the way down the mountain Don saw a tribe of perhaps thirty Montagnards attempting to walk across the road. "Stop, John. Those are Montagnards. Mae would you like to get a picture?"

"No," shouted John, "these Montagnards are armed and hostile!"

Nevertheless, Mae got out. She approached the old lady who seemed to be in charge with her arms raised high and her hands open. "Hello," greeted the country girl, from Ohio.

The old lady was overcome by viewing this beautiful woman, dressed as a goddess. She raised her own hands and hugged Mae. Mae gave each of the thirty tribespeople one of her United States stars and stripes flag pins. They were all jubilant and shouted something in chorus that Mae could not understand. She took their picture.

When Mae and Don returned to their auto, John turned and looked at them. "Colonel, I have never seen such a thing. Our Thai government officials are terrified of these people!"

Unfortunately, an end came to the dream. It was time for Mae to depart and for Don to go back and fight a war. Mae's mind was always at work. She said to herself, "God, protect this wonderful country boy who has been so good to me!" And Don, enjoying looking at his beautiful wife, hugged her and prayed, "God save me so that I can return to my wonderful family!"

But the highlight of their Rest and Recuperation had not yet arrived, SEATO, the Southeast Asia Treaty Organization, was to meet in Chang Mai. Colonel Tom Owens, as NKP base commander, was invited. He knew that Mae and Don were both in Ching Mai and he invited both of them to attend.

Mae was the only female present. Of course, the round-eyed, gorgeous female's presence was not lost on the Asian men. Everyone wore casual civilian clothing. Don whispered to Mae. "The clothing is so no one can be easily identified."

Don sat on the floor on one side of Mae and a tall, handsome Thai man sat cross-legged on her other side. A hundred important people sat in the circle, prepared to eat. It was apparent that the gentleman next to Mae found her more interesting than a casual dinner partner. He must certainly have been surprised because Mae just returned from Europe, Asia, and Africa, and was totally current on world affairs. The two of them had a lively conversation. Don was left silent!

When the food was served, the gentleman waved the waiter away. "Mae, that rice is no good." Try this," he commanded, holding up a huge bag that looked like a bowling bag made of raw leather. He stuck his hand into the bag and pulled out a handful of rice, depositing it on Mae's plate. "That," he grinned, "is good rice. It's northern Thailand 'sticky rice.' There is nothing like it!"

The host announced, "And now we are ready to hear the honored SEATO general, everyone's friend, give us the featured speech!"

Mae turned to Don, her face ashen, "My goodness, I wonder what I said to him?

The general smiled. "Gentlemen, before I begin my speech, I would like to thank Mae Kipfer for some very interesting information about Europe and the Mideast that I had not been in possession of before. Mae, I thank you. You are welcome in Thailand whenever you wish to visit us. And now, gentleman on to our SEATO concerns."

But this time nothing occurred to interrupt their parting. Both Mae and Don went their ways, hating their parting more than when Don was required to leave for West Point. The second half of Don's tour went much as the first except for one incident which he never reported to Mae. Colonel Falcon, deputy wing commander worked closely with Don to insure all operational and base activities were coordinated. One noon Don went in to the colonel's office to brief him on the plan for housing an added operational squadron scheduled to arrive at Ching Mai in one week.

"Looks good to me, Don. Any problems?"

"Nope. We'll take care of them."

"Well, I have to run, I'm scheduled for a mission in about an hour."

Don knew that meant another combat mission in an A-1 up north over the Plain de Jars. Just out of curiosity, nothing more, Don stopped at the Combat Control Center that monitored all combat operations. He arrived just in time to hear the lieutenant colonel in charge bellow, "My God, Colonel Falon is down!"

Don ran over where he could hear the conversation. Colonel Falon came on a little muffled: "Those little bastards are firing and coming in after me!"

Standard operating procedure cautioned American officers not to fire back when downed and surrounded. There could be no win. The Vietnamese desperately wanted to capture officers, especially senior ones, for propaganda purposes so your life had a good chance at being spared.

"I'm going to tear some holes in their little butts," came Falon's voice. That was the last communication from Colonel Falon. Don searched the Missing in Action and casualty roles for the next two years but never found his friend's name.

Most Americans have always supported and honored their fighting men. This was so in the American Revolution, the War of 1812, the Civil War, the Spanish American War, the World War I, World War II, and Korea. This was not universally true in the case of Vietnam. In the United States, elected civilian authority governs national policy. The military serving in Vietnam were sent there by their civilian leadership, many against their own desires. Still the military seemed to take the brunt of the criticism from adamant college professors, protesting college draft-dodgers and anti-American rabble-rousers. But unless you saw the picture from both sides it was unbelievable that people who sang, "and shine thy good on brotherhood" could treat their sons in such a dastardly manner.

Don told Mae when he landed in Montgomery, Alabama, "Most of the officers came home by military air, Mae. I provided food, shelter, clothing, law protection, entertainment and hospital care for these young men, some still teenagers. I decided to see how they were disbursed on their return. There were more than two hundred aboard the civilian contract aircraft I was on. I was the only officer aboard. Most of these young men were wounded in some way. Two had lost limbs!

"Conveniently, the authorities scheduled us to arrive in San Francisco at 0200 in the morning. I assumed, I hope incorrectly, that this was so no one would see their embarrassing arrival. It was a free-for-all for each man, regardless of his physical condition, to arrange his onward travel! There were no bands, no ticker tapes, no jubilant citizens!"

Washington, D.C.

"As you know, you were a committee of one to meet me at the airport, lady."

Mae could not comment. She was simply appalled at the appearance of the husband she had sent off as a healthy, well-adjusted officer, who weighed in at 180 pounds. The stranger she saw before her wore a uniform draped with combat ribbons from his chest halfway to his waist that dwarfed his 150-pound body carrying a person she could barely identify. His eyes were sunken, his shoulders sloped, his voice shaky. "Let's go home, lover!"

As Don opened the door to their home on Court Street, his life took an upturn. "You know I've just scheduled three days to get packed and out of here. We'll have to move fast."

The house was beautifully decorated, bright, and clean. On the dining room table was a birthday cake. Around the cake was a dozen boys and girls, friends of David's, but kids Don had helped and supported during their grade school and junior high school years in Montgomery.

It was just like Don had never left. It was just like his absence had been a dream. "Welcome home, Colonel. A belated Happy Birthday," they all shouted from jovial, healthy, shining faces. This homecoming reinforced Don's determination during his tour in Vietnam. Already, life seemed more appealing!

Don whispered to Mae, "I finally believe I'll live. This party has started me on the upturn! Mae knew that was her purpose! David had not been at the birthday party in Montgomery. He was at the University of Miami. Mae and Don went there first. They did not arrive until after lunch. Don took one look into the university's reception hall and almost became nauseated. Boys and girls were lying on the floor in every stage of intoxication and wearing anything or nothing as their mood happened to strike them.

"My lord," gasped Don, "Where are the school authorities? Is this the civilization the fifty thousand dead young men went to Vietnam to protect? I'm leaving!"

Mae grabbed Don's arm and held on for all her might. "Wait a minute, please, Don, Please. David will not be like this!"

Sure enough, in a few minutes, David appeared. Don was pleased to note. "He's healthy, fit, clean, hair trimmed, and can still smile." Don knew his friend Colonel Arnold Tucker, from West Point, head of the Reserve Officers Training Corp was responsible.

David hugged his father. "Pop, we are all so glad to have you back. I'm ready to go fishing. How about you?"

Almost with his rather feeble last gulp, Don managed, "Roger!"

Dave and his parents had a light dinner together and then parted. But David was not kidding about fishing. He called about 9.00 P.M. "Hi, Pop. I'll pick you up about 11 o'clock. I've got rods and bait."

Now, Don was really confused. "You mean in the morning?"

"No, tonight. We're going after the big ones!"

David drove through Miami to the old concrete docks, now abandoned, in central Miami. The two men drove onto the docks and began fishing. Suddenly a chopper flew over them at twenty feet altitude shining a powerful light on them.

"What's that about, David? Aren't we allowed to fish here?"

"It's okay, Pop, Everyone fishes here. It's something else!"

They didn't have to wait long. Out came a Miami Police car, with four policeman aboard. They hopped out with drawn revolvers. David asked, "What's the matter, officers?"

"Well, a black man robbed the liquor store at the dock entrance. He killed one man. We believe he's hiding on the dock. Have you seen him?"

David answered, "We haven't seen anyone. Do we have to leave?"

The policeman seemed unconcerned. "Suit yourselves."

David looked at his father. "What do you think, Pop?"

"I've just got back from a shooting war. This is kid's stuff. I know you keep a gun when you're out fishing at night in isolated spots. Be sure it's loaded and handy!"

Don had hardly finished talking when Dave's reel began screaming out. "Got a big one on, Pop!"

But before David had even turned the fish, it had torn the leader and was gone. He rebaited and was soon rewarded by another run. "I've got him this time, Pop! He's plenty big."

An hour later, they could see the huge shark on its side near the dock. David said, "Pop, hold the rod and I'll put a flying gaff into him."

The gaff didn't help for the shark was too heavy for both the line and the men. "I'll bring my car over and tie the gaff to the rear bumper. I saw a smooth log on the dock. We can put that under the gaff line so the concrete won't cut it."

After the shark was on deck, David reported the length. "Eleven feet. Wow!"

Don could hardly believe it. "A lemon shark. I'll get some pictures!"

Mae, awaiting in her motel laughed. "First, I'm glad you're both back". And when she learned of the encounter with the murderer and the police she realized that waiting for men who think danger is fun, is no fun! "And besides, I know you fishermen. I don't believe you caught an eleven-foot shark!" And, until she saw the pictures, she never conceded that the fishing trip had been so successful.

On the way to Miami, Mae and Don had stopped near Fort Walton Beach where the Kipfer family and often, their guests, had stayed at Mr. Halfacre's motel to be within feet of the Gulf of Mexico's beautiful beaches. Don had shivered there in spite of the warm suit he was wearing. "Mae, I've never been so cold in my life. I hope Miami is warmer!"

Mae hadn't answered. She knew that this scarecrow, accustomed to the sweltering heat of Vietnam, was simply a casualty of that war. But she understood that while many returnees would simply drop out of society, her man would be expected to carry on.

Now they were headed north again. Montgomery and Athens. Don was not the only one who had withheld disturbing news. Mae had explained while they were en route to Miami, "Charlie was determined to go live with his grandmother and work in the steel mills so he could buy a new car. Your mother was encouraging him. I didn't want him to go for obvious reasons. But I couldn't stop him. Everything was going okay until the last week. He was making huge money as a roller. Suddenly the machine he was operating failed, The machine's steel arm caught Charlie across the jaw and knocked him twenty feet. Your sister said the men working with Charlie thought he had been killed. He had four teeth damaged. One additional one had to be crowned. But Republic Steel doesn't want to pay the dentist!"

Don had trouble keeping his cool. "My lord. There goes Charlie's perfect body! But we'll see about Republic's position!"

Athens College was just as they remembered. The huge, beautiful Southern plantation house had not changed. Charlie's dorm and anticipated fraternity house were adequate. Charlie told his folks, "Let me take you for a ride in my new blue, Chevy convertible. We'll take a look at our fishing spots on the Alabama River and the places we hunt. Charlie never mentioned the awful price he paid for his auto and neither did Don. Mae and Don were satisfied with Charlie's progress. Unknown to him, they stopped to see his dentist. "Yes, Charles had quite an accident," agreed his dentist. But the damage has all been repaired. Of course, his teeth are not the original, but he's as good as new. But Colonel, Republic Steel doesn't want to pay."

"Doctor, that's a human reaction. No one wants to pay. But never fear, they will!"

All the reunions were bonny in Newark and Massillon. "Now," smiled Don, at long last, speaking to Mae, "I know why we've devoted so much time and energy to our country's security!"

In Massillon, Don went almost at once to see the president of Massillon's Republic Steel. It was no mistake that Don went to see him in full battle uniform. He wore a command pilot's wings, a command missileer's badge, and eighteen medals and ribbons. Over coffee, the president, in a friendly voice asked Don, "What is it I can do for you, Colonel?"

"Well, my father grew up here and was close friends with Ben Fairless. He eventually became the foreman of the blacksmith and heat treat shop. He and I were lifetime friends of your employment chief, Jack Price. My uncle, Howard Kipfer, was foreman of the riggers. I worked as a machinist for Saddie Criswell."

As the president caught his breath, he admitted, "Quite a résumé. I'm sure you don't want to come back!"

"No, but my son worked here as a roller this past summer while I was flying in Vietnam making our country secure. The machine he was operating failed, striking him in the face. His injuries, considerable, have been repaired but apparently Republic refuses to pay his medical expenses!"

The company president's demeanor turned cautious. "Tell me more!"

"I'm a Massillonian. I don't want to cause our largest employer any embarrassment. We want only to be reimbursed for medical expenses. We are not seeking a huge settlement. Charlie was a five-letter athlete. In Massillon that counts. He knew all the men on his shift. I remember many of them and they remember me. They would all testify that the equipment failure was the cause of Charlie's injuries!"

The steel mill president whistled. "Colonel, I'm glad I don't fight you. Have Charlie's dentist send his bill directly to me. Here is my card. Rest easy. We'll take care of it!"

Their fence-mending complete, Mae and Don motored to Washington. First they drove past Don's new office of assignment in Roslyn to pinpoint where to look for housing.

Mae spotted the Clarendon Motel long before Don as he was trying to navigate the traffic crossing the Georgetown Bridge, passing by the Roslyn office and headed west. "Don, it's close to your office, close to Mark at Georgetown, and has access to good bus routes." They gladly checked in.

Both Mae and Don had noticed the elegantly dressed, middle-aged couple walking down the sidewalk as they checked into their motel. "I've never seen anyone outside of *Vogue* magazine who appeared so obviously wealthy and cultured," commented Mae.

"True," Don had agreed and when they went to their assigned room they noticed that the same couple were entering their room across the hall from their room.

"Nice," commented Mae.

But that night both Mae and Don had one of the surprises of their lives. "Those lovely people's loud voices, screaming and cursing, are really disturbing, Don!"

Don held up his hand for silence. "My gosh, I hear chairs being broken and glass shattering. Now she's screaming. 'Help, he's killing me.'"

Mae whispered to Don, "Should you call the police?"

"Nope. I think perhaps we are being exposed to a case of kinky sex!"

At breakfast both the Kipfers expected their neighbors to be walking wounded with black eyes and broken limbs. Not so. They were smiling and immaculate! And this performance continued every night for the month that Mae and Don stayed at the Clarendon. "We never figured it out!" Mae later told Vada.

During their summer vacation, Mark and David had worked long hours at good salaries for the Beltway Movers. Like Charles, they both wanted a new car. There was good reason for this. Don had told his sons, "When you really want a car and can pay for it, go ahead. I'll pay all the insurance costs!" David bought the very popular General Motor GTO. Mark settled for a more conservative Plymouth Sedan. Charlie had motored in sporting his blue Chevy roadster for Christmas.

Circumstances had dictated that all the Kipfers spend Christmas at Mae's aunt Vada's apartment in Silver Springs. Christmas dinner of roast beef and Yorkshire pudding was wonderful. But by two o'clock one could no longer see through the snow. By four o'clock the Washington police were warning everyone, on penalty of arrest, not to try to drive on the public roads.

Mark and his brothers were livid. One could easily say they were out of control. Mark shouted, "Mom, we're invited to a big party in Georgetown tonight. We have to go."

Charlie added to the clamor, "Yes, Mom, Mark's right!"

Don cautioned his determined sons, "Fellows, you wouldn't get far. The police are arresting anyone on the road!"

Mark, who had noticed his mother's overnight kit in the trunk of their parents Cadillac, carried because of she and Don's uncertain travel arrangements, was orbital. "Mother, you just planned this!" Eventually everyone calmed down and everyone returned to their own routine.

"Mae, I say again, there are supposed to be some perks for we military to reward us for the dangers we face. One of the good ones is an offer by General Motors to provide to anyone in active combat a greatly reduced price on a new car.

"Remember, I knew this and had written to you to fill you in on all the details. I had definitely made all the arrangements and had an ironclad contract with General Motors. That contract allowed me to accept delivery in Washington, D.C."

When Mae and Don went to Capitol Cadillac they had no record of such a transaction. However they agreed. "We'll make copies of the contract and within a week you should have your gold Eldorado!"

Mae totally surprised Don. "I have saved money during your year and a half combat tour in Vietnam to pay for our Eldorado." When they received notice from Capitol Cadillac that their Eldorado had arrived, they hurried to the dealership and Mae put her check down. Mae cheered gleefully, "Don, when the dreamboat pulled out of the dealership and you saw it, I wish you could have seen your face! I thought you were going to pass out!"

"What could you expect, you sports driver, you!? That gold boat is no car. It's a fantasy dream. What lines. It shines like a huge nugget of gold. It has the largest standard automobile engine ever installed in an American car. I'm almost afraid to drive it through Washington traffic."

Mae tucked her arm through Don's and pulled him to her. She smiled up at him and gave him a non-wifely kiss. "Bruno, maybe you're afraid. I'm not!"

Things were happening fast in Don's professional world. "Mae, I'm happy. Colonel Deets changed my assignment from the Pentagon to Roslyn as the chief of plans for the Office of Scientific Research (OSR). He's the deputy commander of OSR. He told me, "Don, OSR puts out the most comprehensive plan for out-year research efforts in the country. Changes are in the air in the Research and Development Organization. This may be the last such research guidance plan OSR issues. Please hurry, I want this one to be good and complete!"

"What on earth does Colonel Deets mean?" probed Mae.

"It certainly sounds like OAR may be disappearing, but how could that be? But with such a time demanding ultimatum, that may leave you as a loner—to find a house suitable for us to buy."

"Thanks!"

Mae spent all day every day house hunting with various real estate agents. Finally she told Don, "It's time for you to look-see. The one I like is one block from two good bus routes downtown. It's a brick rambler with a kitchen, dining room, living room, and three bedrooms. It has a large room downstairs paneled in knotty pine. It's in a nice neighborhood and in good condition as opposed to the many wrecks I've been shown. It's a bargain!"

"Hard to believe." And when Don saw the outside he was not sure about it being a bargain. "I won't enjoy the steep front bank I will have to mow. Neither of us will like the really steep driveway into the garage." But when Don inspected the house's interior he was really thrilled. "Sold," he told Mae. "Good job, sweetie!"

The next week the happy couple closed on the house at 1946 North Woodrow, confident that they were set for a standard Air Force tour. After her monumental task of finding a good home in Arlington, Mae turned her thoughts to Don's situation. "How are things going in the office, my dear?"

"Well, I thought things were finally in my favor, but before I can even get started, I find that Colonel Deets is leaving because of mandatory retirement."

The boss who I knew personally, has been reassigned and a brand-new brigadier is coming in. However, with the help of the two bright lieutenant colonels they assigned me, we have completed the Basic Research Planning Guide. I totally restructured it, drawing heavily on my work in Europe, Asia, and Africa. It leapfrogs the contemporary objectives, which had previously been used. However, the new brigadier is pressing me to cut huge numbers of existing basic research projects from the OAR program. I just have the feeling that he is not really his own man. He is being pushed from above, perhaps by near sighted operational officers. Still, I've had all the project officers in from the field for reviews and am prioritizing the work, in an attempt to keep a viable program.

But near the end of this exercise, the brigadier called Don in. "Don, we've been levied to provide a full colonel for the major's promotion board at Randolph AFB Personnel Center. We want you to go."

Don smelled the trap. Colonel Deets is gone. The knowledgeable commander is gone. And now I'm out of the way. Whatever the maneuver there will be no one to object! What does one ever say to the request of a brigadier? 'Yes, sir.'"

Mae was included. She was happy to go back to where they had spent so many happy years. "San Antonio has grown, Sancho. No more cattle drives in the streets, or knife fights in the river cafés. But Tai Shans and all the other restaurants are still in business. Randolph's beautiful officers quarters were still in place.

Don told Mae the first night when he returned from Randolph's Personnel Promotion Board's briefing. "You'll never believe this. I'm walking down the hallway and who do I see but Colonel White, the wing commander from NKP. To all intents and purposes anyone noticing us would assume we're two full colonels of equal rank and similar decorations. I know why he is here. He's snooping, trying to do anything that might help him be promoted to brigadier general. He has no earthly idea what I'm doing here. He knows I'm not a candidate for, nor a member of, his promotion board. He doesn't have the nerve to ask me why.

"I noticed he turned a shade of gray. Perhaps he was attempting to relate my face with his past. He simply nodded and said only, 'Hi, Kipfer.' I returned his noncommittal greeting, 'Hi, Colonel.'"

Back in Washington, as always, parties were the fashion. The Systems Command, West Point, The European Office of Aerospace Research, the Daedalians, the USAA, the AF Athletic Association, the WP Athletic Association, and many others, each had their affairs. Mae had house cocktail-dinner parties on three successive Saturday nights to accommodate all the officers and their wives in Don's directorate. She and Don, frequently with other couples, or Vada, went to see and hear Jim Nabors at Shady Grove, Beverly Sill at the Wolf Trapp Farm, Dinner Theater at Burn Brae, the Springfield Country Club and Olany Inn, among others.

Then suddenly, almost like a tornado, the orders had come out!

What Don had feared had bushwhacked the most wonderful organization Don had ever been a part of. OAR was to be abandoned! The military portion was going to the Systems Command at Andrews AFB. The civilian portion was to remain as the Office of Scientific Research (OSR). "But further," Don told Mae, "I'm to have a division in the Directorate of Laboratories and will be back in my old haunts doing development work, ten years after my protest to the haughty major general!"

Mae was crushed. She loved her house. "Will we have to move?"

"Let's see how it goes. I'll commute at first."

But the reorganization changed Mae's connections with Andrews Officers Wives Club and Golfing, as much as it did Don's. She became an officer in the director of laboratories Officers Wives Club. She was head hostess for the Base Officers Wives Club and a member of the Base Officers Wives Golf Club. She won trophies for bowling scores and dozens of silver goblets for winning golf tournaments.

All three sons had always excelled at sports, but it was Mark who continued his football career through college at Georgetown. In his freshman year just as his advisor at Georgetown had suggested to him, football and academics were just to much. But as a sophomore, Mark was back. On the day after the opening game of the 1971 season, Mae opened the *Washington Post* to the sports page. "Believe it or not, paisan," Mae screamed to Don. "Your son Mark's photo fills a whole page in the sports section of the *Washington Post*, showing him scoring a touchdown for Georgetown. The paper calls him 'a pleasant surprise!'"

Georgetown, over the next two years played Fordham, Manhattan, Catholic, Juniata, John Hopkins, Dickinson, Susquehanna, St. Peters and others. Mae told Don. "We're not missing a game, my man. We can pick Mark's friend, Anne, up and meet Mark after the game. I love to dance and dine at Fort Ritchie. And we can stay there in the Visiting Officer's Quarters all night."

That year Georgetown qualified for and played in a bowl game. It was the first since they had played for the national championship in the Orange Bowl so many years before. Mark's unyielding competitive character played a significant role in this accomplishment.

The Kipfer family never wasted a vacation period. Christmas of 1971 was no exception. The first half of that vacation was to be a trip down memory lane and the second half an experience that few families would undertake lightly!

Mae and Don, in their new gold Eldorado picked up Mark at Georgetown and Charlie at Athens College. They motored to Montgomery and picked up David, who had flown in on military aircraft from the University of Miami. The sons were now twenty, twenty-one, and twenty-two years old and each owned his own car so that the five drivers could rotate driving positions in the Eldorado.

When the Kipfers reached the mighty Mississippi River they realized they faced a problem. The bridge across was as dangerous as a combat mission. Mae was deeply concerned. "Don, there are train tracks and two very narrow lanes of traffic, both carved from what was normally a single lane. There is barely room for two autos to pass. Do you think we should detour?"

Don covered his concern, "Don't worry, sweetie. We'll make it!"

Don quickly realized that it was Charlie's turn at the wheel. Now, Charlie was an excellent driver, but he drove exactly like he played middle linebacker and halfback at football and soccer. And Charlie was such a good driver he believed all the other drivers were also. So, consequently he trusted them. Don sat in front with Charlie. He closed and covered his eyes. He used the time to pray but didn't open his eyes again until he felt the sound of normal pavement under the Eldorado's tires. He was sure that was the fastest crossing the Mighty Mississippi had ever endured. Don also heard a sigh of relief from the rear seat, and even David exhaled a "wow!"

In Lafayette, Louisiana, they stopped at Don's Seafood House, where Don had enjoyed such a memorial evening fourteen years before. And although Mae and Don had spent only a short time in Shreveport, they stopped at 808 Modica Street to remember. In San Antonio they went to the San Antonio river cafés, Christie's Sea Food restaurant, Tai Shans, and roamed the city's parks.

In San Angelo they visited Mrs. Albro's house at 2314 Waco Avenue, their house on 130 Morris Avenue near the base, and the USAF dispensary where Mark and David were born. Neither man was impressed. They ate at Mr. Volkman's Golden Spur Hotel. Mae concluded, "And so remembrances have been relived by all of us. It had been a tear-jerking time for me."

In San Antonio, they had returned to 1207 Tilden Avenue. Unfortunately Frances had died but Kate was delighted to see them. Mae and Don were flabbergasted to see that their small home in the Findlay's yard was now a national historical site. Mae laughed and said to Kate, "I suppose that's because Don and I lived there!"

"Yes," roared Kate "that's surely a part of it!"

In Eagle Pass they picked up a Sanborne map and a Sanborne book for guidance in driving through Mexico. The boys all laughed when they read the book and studied the map but it was Mae who was aghast. "Look, the map actually shows locations where banditos may attack you. It shows gasoline stations but warns you to watch for trouble there!"

And Charlie added, "The map shows individual houses and spots where donkeys may be on the road!"

Don laughed. "Looks like we'll have a thrilling trip!"

Not one of them was prepared for the splendor of the high mountains in central Mexico. Mae groaned. "How do these people make a living? What do they eat? I have not seen anything but cacti for two hundred miles!"

Don tried to soften Mae's observations. "The map shows a town just ahead."

"True," said Mae, but when she was departing the village, she raged, "Did you see the poverty? Yes, their merchandise was elegant, but their stores had dirt floors!"

Mexico City was different. The Geneve Hotel was first class. The restaurants were fabulous and invariably resounded with Spanish/Mexican music. Don had called the American Embassy. "Hurrah!" he reported. "They say the flan sold so intensively on the streets is safe to eat! Sitting up there on a tray, aboard a señor's shoulder, I could snatch a cup. I'm going to eat all I can hold." After his first bite, Don pronounced it the best flan he had ever tasted!

The family rented a mini bus with driver and spent a whole day viewing and climbing the pyramids of the sun and the moon. Mae was tired but enthralled. "Can you believe this city? It was built more than a thousand years ago. It surpasses anything we have in the modern United States. In many ways it is the grandest city we've seen anywhere."

The last day of their stay in Mexico City, Mae and Don decided to window shop and relax. Not so their sons. Charlie broke the news, "We're going to take a local bus that the ordinary Mexican uses and go back and spend more time at the pyramids. We think we can find some artifacts.

Neither parent was overly thrilled. But their sons were grown men. "Have a good time, fellows," agreed Mae, "but no one wants to be a boarder in a Mexican jail, so be careful!"

When the men returned from their personal sagas, they were wound up. "How did it go?" queried Don. "How did you find the ordinary Mexican?"

Charlie laughed. "We went through villages you would never believe. A fat Mexican sat next to me. He held two live chickens in each hand. One chicken seemed to glare at me. He turned his rear end to me and pooped all over my trousers."

Mark had been offended. "The bus was so noisy you couldn't carry on a conversation. The aisle was packed. One young woman, her hand bumped by the baby she was carrying, dropped her flan on my head!"

David squirmed. Mae quizzed him, "Apparently you escaped unscathed, David. Didn't you have any fun?"

"Don't kid yourself, Mom. One little kid who was held in his fathers arms hit me on the head with a stick!"

The bullfights were real in Mexico. Not like the European ones where the fight was fake. They were bloody and bulls were killed and dragged from the arena by a team of horses. The Kipfers paid the extra charge and sat in the shade. When the fight was over, Charles announced, "Pop, we're going into the ring, just like Madrid, but this time we're going to buy some real pics from real picadors."

Before Mae could object, her sons were gone. She could not look at the ferocious-looking blood-covered pics when her sons returned.

The Kipfers left Mexico City and proceeded directly east, past Lake Texoco, then north along the Gulf of Mexico to Matamoros and Brownsville. Mae was astounded. "Can you believe it, señors? Here in eastern Mexico along the Gulf Coast, in as lush an environment as any I have ever seen. It's tropical. Tropical fruit lies on the ground everywhere. It is so plentiful it lies rotting on the ground. The people are all wealthy looking. Why would anyone live in the desolate highlands?"

Of course, no one knew. Don sighed, "Some people seem to enjoy suffering!"

When they crossed the Rio Grand into Brownsville, Charlie joked, "Hey, Mom, I believe we're home!"

David flew back to Miami. The others remained a day for some successful fishing and then headed north and east. When Don reported into System Command Headquarters, he felt happy to be back doing what he knew he was meant for. He reported to Mae, "That stubborn two-star general in Air Force personnel who told me my next tour would be back in Research and Development was not there to welcome me!"

Mae joked, "I guess not. That was ten years ago. He's probably happily signing his pension checks. You were a major. Now you're a full colonel. Forget him!"

"It seemed strange to walk down that same old corridor, Mae. Heads popped out of the doors. I recognized most of them. But for some reason they seemed apprehensive! Perhaps it's because I'll be running four laboratories and a few projects in two divisions."

Two weeks later, Don updated Mae. "Now I know what was bothering the staff. I had them brief me on all their projects. Can you believe it? They're still beating to death the same old projects I left here ten years ago!"

Mae was silent. She knew fur would fly.

As time went on, Don briefed Mae, deleting anything that was classified. "Mae, when I went to the Radar Bombing school in Sacramento nearly twenty year ago the radar scope pictures were indiscernible by anyone except intensely trained experts. That was primarily because the only way a radar beam could be narrowed to give a TV-like picture was to lengthen the snow shovel antenna then in use. That was impossible because of the restriction of the plane's fuselage cross-section. You may remember I went to the antenna laboratory on top of the hill at Wright Field. It was empty except for a half-dozen scientists marking time there. I huddled them for a day. I found out they knew how to solve the problem!"

"For goodness sake, What had they been waiting for?"

"They claim they tried but couldn't raise anyone's attention. Now they have. I can assure you, they'll have a priority project before the month is out. And there'll be no more coffee breaks!"

Mae was never passive. She probed, "Is there any other information I can share?"

"Rome Air Development Center has the responsibility for large ground radars, which can search and track airborne targets. They have demonstrated an airborne command and control system, which is simply unbelievable. It would revolutionize battle field search and track capabilities."

"What's the problem with this one?"

"The same old not invented here syndrome. The system people have a competing system. I suspect they do not want to share their accomplishment with the research and development people!"

"How can you solve that?"

"I believe I've already done that. I've directed that the name of our system be changed so that it can be incorporated into the core of the system being pushed by the system people but will be unidentifiable. That will save face for them. We'll see, next week the generals will meet at the electronic systems division to consider the problem."

When Don returned from the high-level meeting, he was all smiles. "Well, how did it go," questioned Mae.

"Well, I'll tell you I've never seen anything like it. It was a large conference room and was filled with more generals than I have ever seen together. They were obviously all there to protect their turf and hopefully to see fur fly! Can you believe it, for awhile I thought I might not get in. I had to carry in my own chair and sit in the rear!"

"So?"

"Well, the briefer presented a glowing picture and a correct one, I believe. He never mentioned the inclusion of the RADC technology that makes the system so super valuable. Very clever of him. Also critical to acceptance."

"And what was the reaction?"

"No controversy. Not a negative murmur! Unanimous approval. It will be one of our country's most valuable tools, should we need it, for places like the middle east throughout my lifetime! You will hear it mentioned many times. It's to be called AWACS!"

Later, Don complained to Mae, "I can't believe to what dastardly lows human beings will stoop. There's a civilian doctor, a scientist, with a cross to bear. He's briefing anyone who will listen in Washington that our military equipment is unreliable."

Don went on. "That's rubbish. Dr. Noble, and a multitude of others knew that it took a bushel of extra tubes to keep a B-52 operational during flight. All these men knew, although it was difficult to convince the operational people, that there were three basic reasons for this. The small interior connections within an electronic tube, could be seen under a microscope to frequently have joints that did not even make a connection. Heat frequently destroyed the solder that connected the parts. All the small internal parts, some of which moved, had to be perfect to prevent failure."

"And?"

"Solid state electronics solve these problems. No moving parts, almost imperceptible power levels, and no connections."

While scientists such as Dr. Shockley with his transistor, Dr. Noble at the Avionic Laboratory, as well as many others, were working the details,

Rome Air Development Laboratory developed a mathematical model for combining individual elements to give unbelievably reliable results. For instance, they believed that a radio could be built that would never fail. I promise, you'll have one of the first to appear. It will not be like the one you won twenty years ago at the party at Randolph, which never worked! They believe and I believe that a personal computer can be built so small and reliable that every housewife could own and use one. A long trip from the monster I used at WPAFB to do my master's thesis on!

"With my bosses' permission, I arranged to have RADC brief a two-star in the systems business who could have this dream come into reality!"

"What did he think?"

"Who knows. It was a repeat of my experience with the two-star personnel general. This one left before the briefing was complete!"

"Is it a dead issue?"

"It can't be. Either our country will lead or someone else will! It's like President Eisenhower's rejection of space operations. Yes, either we'll do it or someone else will! I had some of the RADC scientists give Westinghouse an unclassified briefing. I told the Westinghouse staff it had better attend to reliability concerns in their proposals if they wanted to get government contracts!"

"How did Westinghouse take that?"

"I suppose they reasoned that so long as the rest of American industry did not respond, they were safe. Still, this current year I understand they will offer the USAF an insurance policy on any hardware they produce along with their proposals."

"Will that make a difference?" wondered Mae.

"Perhaps not, but eventually this reliability will filter down to all commercial electronics, as well!"

And so things prospered. And of course even full colonels were entitled to leave. Mae was delighted to go back again for an EOAR reunion and visit Paris, Brussels, and London. It was fun for her to go to the Thousand Islands for a week of fishing with son, David and his fianceé, Jamie.

Mae and Don, together with Vada, had gone to Athens College for Charlie's college graduation. Senator John Sparkman who had run for vice president of the United States, was the guest speaker; afterward lingered around the banquet held outside the mansion. He especially seemed to like Mae. Don laughed, "I knew he would fall for you, love!"

Mae poked Don in the ribs. "You men. When the senator found Vada's family name was Gentry, he got excited and abandoned Mae. He told Vada. "There are lots of Gentrys." He wouldn't leave Vada's side.

Later Vada confided in Mae, "Votes, you know, Mae!"

The three visitors rushed from Athens to Georgetown just in time for Mark's graduation from Georgetown.

Although Mae found that there was never a dull moment in her life, she never complained. Her next assignment was to arrange for Charlie's wedding at the Andrews AFB chapel. Then to reserve living accommodations for a hundred friends and relatives. Finally she had to plan and supervise a grand reception for all the guests at the Officers Club.

Charlie went to work as a management trainee at Sears Roebuck and moved into a nice condominium on campus way next to the local community college.

Mark was off to California by auto and would return to helicopter training at Fort Rutgers, Alabama.

Between these exciting activities, Mae had her own agenda. "Yes, my man, as you recall, I'm on the director of laboratories Officer Wives Committee. I'm the chief hostess for the Base Officer's Wives Club, and I'm on the Base Ladies Golf Committee. I play golf twice a week and bowl with you twice a week."

Don knew all this. "When do you find time for all the golf you're playing? I assume you're pretty good since I see all this silverware showing up around the campfire and fellow officers tell me their wives are terrified of you on the Golf Course."

Mae laughed, "You bet your boots, Colonel, and I've signed us up this August 13 with the Doyles for a Scotch foursome. It's time you began having some fun." And so began Don's commendable golf career.

President Nixon of course was president at the time. Andrews AFB was the perfect landing place for a president returning from an important trip. It was secure. The whole military population could be turned out if desired to provide an audience.

So it was when President Nixon returned from China on 29 February 1972 with one of the world's great diplomatic accomplishments under his belt. He, his wife and daughters shook hands with the Kipfers during a gala reception in one of the hangars. Both Mae and Don felt the whole family was very impressive.

As the president's party passed by the Kipfers to greet others a *Washington Post* reporter stopped to interview who? No one else but Edna Mae Kipfer. The next morning the *Washington Post* gave Mae's opinion of the president's visit to China: "I think what President Nixon has done was a good idea. I'd rather have the Chinese with us than against us!"

It was about this time that Don was being forced to make a decision that would promote or end his military career. He felt compelled to discuss the matter with his better half: "Mae, I have to make a decision that could help my career or essentially end it. You're a vital part of that. I want you to have a say."

Mae had never seen Don so serious. "Talk on."

"Well, several years ago the office of director of Defense Research and Development realized they should replace all the old radios in all our Air Force aircraft, antiques that had roughly 2.5 hours meantime to failure, with new technology that would insure 1,000 hours meantime to failure. They tasked my office to research and develop such a radio. For once our development community applauded these men who we believed were to far removed from practical problems to understand them!"

Mae relaxed, "Sounds like a routine program to me."

"Not exactly. We wanted to nail this one to the backhouse door! The Avionic Laboratory selected two of the country's most outstanding contractors to undertake this job. They contracted with the Battell Institute in Columbus, Ohio, to put each of these radios in locked cases, under guard, to check their reliability. You know the president's pilot of Air Force One lives just down the street from us. We put one of these radios in Air Force One for a trial. The crew loved it!"

"Really exciting. What's the problem?"

"My sleuth found out the system people are going to bring in a proposal that would replace all the Air Force's radios with the same old hardware they have right now! This would be a program that would keep our pilots from having the tremendous added operational capability available and waste billions of taxpayers money!"

"Wow! Why can't you go to your boss?"

"Therein lies my problem. He's a two star, counting on three. He's only temporarily in the director of laboratories chair and has a system orientation. If I brief him and he says, 'Cool it, Don,' the whole game is lost without ever having been really examined. Can I take that chance? No, it's up to me. What say you, oh wise one?"

"You and I have always played everything straight. Your mother told me on her last visit, after realizing the social and business stress we were under. 'I think Don has enough stress. He doesn't need more!' You are the only one, my dear, who must look into your mirror each day. No matter what happens, I'm with you!"

So, the proposal came in by presentation to the headquarters. All middle management knew what was going to happen. Only the general staff sat, relaxed, believing they were to hear a rather boring, routine presentation.

When the system people completed their pitch, Dave Anderson, Don's staff civilian in charge of the radio development, stood up and asked permission to speak.

"Mae, the crux of his counter presentation was that the Avionics Laboratory, through competent contractors, had developed and tested a specification-busting radio that exceeded 1,000 hours mean time to failure!"

"What on earth happened?"

"Our three- and four-star generals didn't get their stars because they were foolish. They simply thanked the system pitchman and dismissed the group!"

"How could they do that?"

"Easy. It was a brilliant move on their part. What they had heard was only a proposal. They will reject it and in will come another proposal that will incorporate the reliable technology. They'll be heroes. They may even again be promoted!"

"Don, you're the one who should get a medal!"

"Mae, you must be kidding. The system people have the senior officers. They are not happy travelers. You know very well that whistle-blowers are dead meat. Anyway, my dear it is time for a new assignment. My work is completed here. Again, it's time for you and I to have some fun!"

"Sure. Ben Partin, you remember from Cape Cod days, has called from the Pentagon. He knows what I did through MIT and Avionics Laboratory to jump start the laser program now headed solely by a brigadier who nominally reports through me to the Air Force chief of staff."

Mae interrupted, "I remember you took his call here at home, but what did you tell him?"

"You know colonels run errands, arrange conference rooms and clean ash trays in the Pentagon. I told him I believed I had shaken the research and development tree enough. I planned to head west, where every young man should go!"

"You didn't!"

"I did. Now let's start having that fun and begin planning to shake up California!"

But as a preliminary to a new assignment and a treat for Mae, in January 1974, on a tour arranged by the Department of Defense, Mae and Don went to Charlotte Amalie, St. Thomas, in the Virgin Islands. "What a wonderful place to rest and recuperate. You research fiend! Wonderful weather, friendly people, and good shopping for me!"

"I agree," laughed Don, "with all those findings!"

There had been only one hiccup in their whole vacation. Their hotel was obligated to transport its guests to and from the beach each day. The first morning, their driver, a young black man, sitting next to Mae and Don on the front seat of their minibus, announced, after pretending to fidget with the bus' controls. "Sorry folks, but the bus won't start. No beach today!"

Mae had uncovered and corrected many serious scams in her life, but this really insignificant one was transparent and blatant. She suspected that this incompetent had other, more personal plans for his morning, than to transport customers who were paying for his livelihood! She patted the driver on the arm. "You sure you've tried everything? We've paid you and your boss good currency to get to the beach."

The pious one was serious. "Oh, yes, ma'am. I can't think of anything I haven't tried."

Mae gave the driver a look he would never forget. "Try looking at the gas gauge, my man. I've noticed it reads zero."

Don storied this incident. He treated it like the Irishman who when he heard a good joke, shouted, "That's a good one. Write it down." Don repeated it many times. How could anyone who depended upon the United States for food, shelter and clothing be so self-destructive? Thankfully, that young man was not representative of all the wonderful people they met in the Virgin Islands!"

Back at Andrews AFB. Christmas in 1993 was at the Kipfer quarters. Vada, Glenna, Suzanne, Charles and Dorthea, Mark and David were present. Mark had his own program arranged for his brothers. David took them all again to Tridelphia Reservoir where, years before, he had caught the largest Northern pike ever caught there, and Charlie had caught one that weighed in just ounces less. And, again, they all caught plenty of fish.

Covertly, Don surprised Mae. She laughed and shook her head. "*You* mean you're already planning to have some fun, don't you?" realizing she would have to cancel dozens of committee appointments, social commitments and golf tournaments."

"Amen. We've been all over North America, Europe, Africa, Asia and Central America. But we've neglected South America. We're going to be in Rio de Janiero from 2–10 April 1974! Meantime I understand we're going to Vance AFB in Enid, Oklahoma, for a very important affair!"

Mae pretended to be upset. "Don, you know very well David and Jamie are getting married. It certainly should be a gay time!"

Charlie went with Mae and Don. They met David and Jamie and had a good steak dinner as the prenuptial celebration. Dave's squadron mates and their wives were all at the wedding and at the reception afterward. Don was thunderstruck. "Mae, that Jamie surely cleans up well. Her wedding gown was beautiful. Except for you, I've never seen a female with such a striking, upswept coiffure. She's just beautiful. But I can't believe she couldn't even wait until after the reception to downgrade. Down went the beautiful coiffure into memory land!"

Mae nodded her head. "She and David have everything going for them!"

Mae's life was just one exciting extravaganza. David and Jamie were married on Saturday, 16 March 1974. When Mae and Don arrived back at their quarters at Andrews AFB they had hardly entered their quarters at Andrews AFB when the phone rang. "Hello, Pop, this is Mark. I've been trying to reach you and Mom."

Don tried to forestall any bad news, "We've just helped your brother, David get married at Vance AFB. What's stirring at Fort Rucker?"

"Hi, Mark," added Mae, who was listening on the second phone.

"Well, I got married, too, on the 16th at Fort Rucker!" Silence . . . silence . . . silence!

"Mark," asked Don after he had recovered his composure, never suspecting that Mark even planned to marry, "who's the lucky girl?"

Mark's voice seemed to jump. "Carole King!"

Again silence. Don knew Georgetown was a bastion for antigovernment activity and anti-war sentiment. He expected anything! Don and Mae's family lived on South Court Street during Martin Luther King's demonstrations. Don wondered if there was a daughter in the King family? Could Mark have found her? Whatever, it was none of his business. Still, because he couldn't help himself, half in jest, and perhaps because of his disappointment in not even getting an invitation to his son's wedding, he asked. "Mark, is Carole black or white?"

Now the voice from Alabama was not so jumpy. Perhaps now Mark realized how uninformed his parents were. "Pop, she's white!"

Mae was more stable. "Mark, you have our congratulations. We hope you will both be very happy! We are certainly looking forward to meeting Carole!"

After such earth-shaking matrimonials, on 2 April it was time to depart for Rio de Janeiro, the romantic city on the sea with its fabled girl of Ipanema! Getting a relaxing start, that first afternoon, Mae and Don went to the beach just in front of their hotel. "Whoa," cautioned Don, "here comes *the* girl!"

Sure enough, there, clad in what looked like an Indian sari, was one of nature's most beautiful female creatures. She was perfect in proportions, almond-colored, dark brown eyes, shining black hair, and a smile that would melt any man's heart. She was the girl from Ipenema!

"May I take your picture, young lady?" pleaded Mae.

"Of course, ma'am,"

So Don and the girl from Ipanema had their picture taken for posterity. But before the two North Americans had progressed more than a few feet onto the beach, Mae was totally shocked. "Don, there are human feces all-over the sand!"

Don covered, "You can put on your shoes."

"No," exclaimed Mae, "there's a better solution. I can stay off this otherwise beautiful beach!"

Don went on, "I don't want to be critical of another country, but can you see how high all the buildings are? I've been told that because of Ipanema's popularity, and tourist business, these buildings were set right on the beach!"

"That seems to make sense, economically speaking," agreed Mae.

"Yes, but the buildings were so tall that they cut off the sunshine that the tourists came to enjoy!"

"Impossible! There seems to be plenty of sunshine now, countered the sunshine aficionado.

"Yes, my dear, you are exactly correct. They simply extended the beach!"

On the top of Rio's Sugar Loaf mountain, they visited the huge, beautiful Cahaelaria Church. In its vestibule, in a corner on the floor sat a young woman in her very early twenties. Mae almost lost control. She whispered to Don, "That girl has a baby, golden hair and blue eyes, in one arm, and an infant, black as ebony with black curly hair, squeezed in her other arm!"

Don hadn't missed this. "Well, you remember when the Brazilian officer students at the Air University told us that contrary to what they found in Montgomery, Brazil had no racial prejudice. Now you can believe them."

"I should like to, paisan. But I noticed that there were no black Brazilian officers who attended our Military University. And I dare anyone to find a young mother sitting on the floor in the vestibule of a church begging for food in the United States!"

Because Don had been told that Brazil had emeralds in great abundance, believing in the theory of supply and demand, he believed emeralds would be inexpensive there. Apparently the Brazilians had learned from the diamond dealers of Amsterdam. Their emeralds in Rio were little cheaper than in the United States! "Don, you shouldn't spend so much on a single green stone," halfheartedly, but hopefully, cautioned Mae.

"My dear, I came here to buy a large emerald for you because you deserve one, and a large emerald its going to be!"

Returning to Andrews AFB, it was now time to go to McClellan AFB in Sacramento. Mae knew it was breaking Don's heart. He had been ripped from an operational career to help provide a super technological base for the

United States Air Force. He had fought for money to support a strong research and development program. He had traveled North America, Europe, Asia and Africa seeking brilliant men who could perform technical miracles. Leaving this quest was a tough choice for him.

Don was philosophical. "Mae, don't stress yourself. I've done all I can do. Besides, in going to the logistics command for my final tour, I'll finally be back working with operational people!"

Don's service at Andrews was honored by a grand dinner and ball at the Andrews Air Force Base's Officers Club. Six other officers from his staff were also leaving and with their wives sat with Mae and Don at the head table.

Don welcomed everyone. He then commended the officers at the head table and briefly described their contributions to their country's security. He explained what the directorate of laboratories responsibilities were. After a general briefing of the many fields that DOL supported, he became more specific about several areas. "Ladies and gentlemen, I will just touch on a very few details. We development people have been criticized because our electronics are not reliable. I can tell you that we now have technology that is so reliable any of you may purchase a radio and have faith that it will never fail!

"The computer which I completed my master's thesis on in 1952 that filled a large room and had to be air conditioned has now shrunk to handheld size. And you ladies out there, don't snicker. You will be able to have a fine, reliable computer, held in your hand to do your grocery shopping with!

"And to counter the criticism that some civilians direct at our spending their money on research and development, tell them this story. The obscure emergence of the laser at Woods Hole in 1957 is now an Air Force program headed by a brigadier general and has necessitated the building of the largest all wooden structure in the world. But that significance is almost a side issue. Everyone of you knows people whose life or capability has been protected by this remarkable technology. Surgeons use it to repair eyes, hearts, brains, and many other problems. It is used to directly etch large scale integrated circuits directly from a design computer. Its value to the civilian population would pay their total income taxes for many years!"

Sensing that no one was really bored, nevertheless Don quipped, "I have been talking too long. But please, never forget that being in advance of the rest of the is your insurance for health, happiness, and prosperity!" And Don sat down to a loud applause, but Mae was sure also to the reaction of many incorrect skeptics.

Mae had wondered who was scheduled to sit in two of the empty chairs at one of the tables during dinner. Now, almost too late to be served dinner, in came Dr. and Mrs. Knausenberger. Mae knew the doctor had been responsible for providing Adolph Hitler's government with the technology to launch a missiles from underwater. She knew Don had worked with him in Germany and traveled the North Countries with him. She knew they remained good friends after the doctor, had been brought to the United States. At a party one night he had told her, "Mae, they asked me to write a history of OAR. I've found many policy letters that Don wrote and I'm including them."

Don caught Mae's glance. "Oh, my gosh, the Knausenbergers love to dance and I've noticed the band director looking at his watch."

Don stood up preparatory to leaving the table. Mae grabbed his blouse, "Where to, mister?"

"I'm going to pay the band leader to stay on another hour!" And so the band played on!

Mae and Don went to where life is sane and easy going; Newark and Massillon. First the Camp Meeting at Academia, Ohio where the Adventists meet to rejuvenate their faith. Mae was aware that her ancestors had been at this very spot for meetings. Mae, now a world traveler and famous among this crowd was engaged in continuous conversations. She was also invited to say a few words at one of the meetings.

In Massillon, Mae played in the Ladies Day Golf Tournament at the Elms Country Club and naturally won second place. Mae suggested taking Don's sister, Mary Helen, and her husband, Louis, to the Bali Hai Restaurant to celebrate their wedding anniversary.

The Kipfers were invited to Mother Kipfer's neighbors, the Browns, for a sweet corn cookout. "It takes us back to basics," allowed Mae. "But isn't the corn wonderful! Thank you Phyllis and Hattie!"

In Newark, all Mae's family were well and happy and there were again all the family reunions.

Now Mark and Carole were off to Fort Campbell, Kentucky. David and Jamie were off to Vance AFB, Oklahoma. And Mae and Don were again on the move, this time west.

First they stopped in Fort Campbell, Kentucky to see Mark and get an up close look at their new daughter-in-law. Mark had been appointed by the base commander as Don's official escort and had placed an impressive sign in the lawn in front of the senior Kipfer's quarters. COLONEL DON KIPFER. Mae could hardly wait to meet Carole. Both families ate and did sightseeing together. On their way, after leaving Fort Campbell, Mae gave her fixed opinion. "Carole is a healthy, intelligent, beautiful girl. I can understand why Mark wanted to marry her. They should be very happy!"

Then they motored on to see Jamie and David at Vance AFB, where things were humming nicely. Dave liked the flying and Jamie was already working for the colonel's wife, who was president of the Officer's Wife's Club.

But now all the domestic ties were to be broken and more serious thoughts were about to be taken up. They stopped in New Mexico long enough for Mae to purchase Navaho and Zuni squash blossom necklaces directly from the Indian craftsmen who fashioned them. The Indian proprietor suggested, "Buy two of each, ma'am, sell one of them on the West Coast and get your own free!"

"Is he correct?" asked Mae.

"Who knows?" replied Don.

In Arizona they took beaucoups time inspecting the Petrified Forest. "Could it spare a souvenir?" suggested Don.

"No," Mae said emphatically. "They have legal ones for sale at the entrance."

The Grand Canyon was unbelievable. But Mae and Don had time to only walk halfway to the bottom and return.

Mae knew Don had been an engineer all his life. So when they started up U.S. Route 93 toward Las Vegas she knew they must pass Lake Meade and the world-famous Hoover Dam. She wondered, *Can Don bypass it?*

Nope. After a careful inspection Don turned to Mae. "I'm an electronic, avionics, and automatic control engineer, my dear. But anyone can see what a civil engineering marvel the Hoover Dam represents."

They stopped and found Las Vegas as glamorous as ever. Then up the eastern side of the mountains to Reno, Nevada. There they crossed over and motored down the west side of the Sierra Nevada mountains.

Sacramento, California

They deliberately bypassed McClellan AFB, passed south of Sacramento, and went directly to the Nut Tree Restaurant. Mae knew Don had been anxiously awaiting a meal there. The Nut Tree really does have an exciting history. But Don wasn't remembering that. He remembered with extreme pleasure their supremely wonderful fruit plate. Mae laughed, "Now, my gourmet companion, I guess you'll live!"

A satisfied Air Force officer agreed, "You said it, world traveler!"

"Yes," said the lady at the McClellan AFB housing office. "As you requested, you have been assigned one of the eight on base quarters. However, there will be nearly a month's wait until they're vacated. Meantime, we've assigned you an apartment in the VIP's section of the Visiting Officers Quarters."

When Don relayed this information to Mae she replied, "Same old story, magic worker. There I sit while you are busy. No luggage, no furniture, no food to prepare, in a hostile environment where I don't know a single person!"

Don pretended to sympathize, "I know you, mate. You'll be in control here in no time."

Nighttime's were no problem unless Don was out of town. Every evening they tried a new restaurant. Mae sat the schedule. "Let's try Nagato Sukiyaki; Colony Kitchen; Carrows BBQ; Senior Pepe; China Camp; Fuji Sukiyaki; Hamburger Factory; Carnation Icecream Factory; Tiki Village; Di Ciccos; The Refactory Lamb; Old Sacramento (Fulton Prime Ribs); Rams Restaurant; Loves BBQ; Imperial Restaurant; On Stage Restaurant; Eppies; Mexican Cafeteria; Gallion; Music Circus; Zekes, and Buffies Buffer!"

Meantime, Mae had become a member of the base tennis team, base bowling team #10, and Lawrence Links Golf Team. "She had also become a member of the McClellan Officers Wives Club and a member of its staff. On the 28 of August 1978 the Colonel Kipfers finally moved into Quarters 108!

Mae was more than ready. "Now, boy, it's time for some home cooking!"

Mae could hardly believe her quarters. "Don, these quarters are just marvelous. Living room, dining room, kitchen, and maid's quarters with bathroom on the first floor. Three large bedrooms on the second floor. And wonder of wonders, our quarters are attached to the Officers Club. We're living. What a way to live during our final assignment!"

"Yes, dear, You have wonderful taste. These quarters are special. They were built by the men of the Works Progress Administration. They are formed by solid, poured concrete, perhaps the only homes so constructed in the United States. And I can tell you, we have earned such quarters. They are long overdue!"

Mae and Don both loved the outdoors. One officer had told Don on a trip from Washington to Sacramento. "The Sacramento River is full of big stripped bass. They're even taken commercially." Another raved about the steelhead in the American River, which joined the Sacramento River right at Sacramento. Mae and Don soon found that this hype was a little strong. Still, they were catching more than they could eat. They also toured all of California's wonderful national parks! Tahoe, Calaveras Big Trees, Yosemite, Sequoia, Big Basin Redwoods, Lake Shasta, Humbolt Redwoods, Sutter's Fort and many others.

And then Mae suddenly went humming about her house. She had tricked Don into playing in the Mather AFB mixed foursome golf tournament with

David and Gail Arnold, their next-door neighbors!

Meantime all the social activities continued. The RCAF relied upon McClellan AFB for a portion of their logistic support and so they had a contingent of officers there. On 30 November, Mae and Don attended a very formal cocktail dinner party at Wing Commander Shenfield's home. On 21 December they were entertained at General McLaughlin's quarters. And so the social whirl continued.

But beyond any doubt, their most memorable social affair was the dinner dance given in honor of Governor Ronald Reagan on 12 December 1974. Mae and Don went to the head table after the formal dinner and shook hands with the governor. Mae not only adored this man as a movie star, but respected him for his professional conduct as her governor. She smiled and told him, "Governor, you should run for president of the United States. We desperately need you. You have my vote!"

Governor Regan had known the most beautiful women in the world, but none more striking than Mae. That fact was not lost on the governor as he took Mae's hand and squeezed it. "Why, thank you, Mae. Your endorsement is important to me!"

At each place setting, on the extended table, was a fancy, pint-sized glass container filled with red and white Jelly Bellies, often called jelly beans by the proletariat. After dinner and dessert, Don made a move to try one. "I believe I'll try one."

But Mae quickly grabbed his sleeve. "*No*, my dear man, Governor Reagan is going to be our president. His Jelly Bellies will be famous!"

The military is not totally all hard work. There are some perks. For the Kipfers, that was not only the privilege of living in glorious California, but being close to Hawaii. Also, as a full colonel, Mae knew Don could get space available transportation right out of Travis AFB! She petitioned Don, "Well, amigo, when are we going?"

Don sidestepped. "What do you mean, cozy one?"

But Mae had read the tea leaves. "When are we going to the magic Sandwich Islands?"

Don was mystified. "Who squealed? How did you know? We're leaving from Travis on 2 February and we'll be back on the 15th!"

"Goodness!"

"No wonder those calloused, uneducated, immoral, brutal sailors from New England believed they had died and gone to heaven when they leaped onto the Hawaiian shore. They had!" exclaimed Don.

"How can such things happen? God must be preparing us for the hereafter! Our room in the Hilton Hotel overlooking Kanapale Beach is beyond anything glorious I can describe," agreed Mae.

"The clear blue skies with their puffs of white cumulus and their sparkling swimming pools are breathtaking!"

"Wait till you go to Ohana night, Pua'a, and a real luaua! And, my dear wife, when you are standing among the huge poinciana blooms, I am struck helpless!"

Each night they reviewed their day so that they would never forget. Mae recalled, "It was unbelievable to set in the Tree House on Maui's coast and watch the whales playing! And I could not forget the geological implications when we visited and walked across and singed our rubber tennis shoes on the floor of Haleakala Crater!"

Don was more practical. "I'll never forget the Baldwin House, I'm sure the Baldwins would have been relatives of my mother, Laura Jane Baldwin. The New England Baldwins, of course, were missionaries, and their home is the oldest existing structure on Maui. They were probably friends of the Phil Whitney's ancestors!"

Don rented a car. He and Mae traveled every road and sometimes the pathways on Maui. When they turned the auto in to the attendant, he exclaimed, after reading the astronomical mileage on the speedometer. "Impossible, sir. I cannot charge you for this. We do not have that many roads on Maui!"

Mae and Don had visited Hawaiian families up in the hills who still raised taro, pigs, sugar cane, pineapple, and lots of kids!

They visited the statue of Kamehameha, and the old Hawaiian capital buildings. Mae remarked, "What a huge, handsome man; well-built, also, I notice!"

They visited the Polynesian Culture Center where the people, their customs, and customs of the South Pacific inhabitants were shown by live people, in moving panoramas. Don proposed to Mae, "Let's have some fun. There's a headhunter chief in full native dress. Stand next to him and I'll take your picture." Mae did but uncharacteristically, perhaps high on Hawaii, she was even more daring. She went inside the chief's large hut and relaxed on his Polynesian bed. "That's the most fantastic view I've seen in all the Islands," joked Don.

Don could not believe this woman was his wife. "By gosh, girl, if I were in the chief's shoes, I would never release such a beautiful captive. But Mae did recover her composure and departed with Don.

Still, it would not be accurate to omit much of Hawaii as Mae and Don experienced it on the islands of Hawaii and Oahu. Hold your hats.

They had landed at Hilo Airport, small and neat, graded from volcanic rock. Mae and Don stayed on the Island of Hawaii at the Waiahea Resort Village built on a great Lagoon and lit at night by torches.

They went to the Great Hall (Keysuna) for the Hawaiian gourmet delight, Chicken Dali Dali. Late at night under warm tropical skies they dropped in at the Kip Mai Lounge to dance with the music of Bunny Brown. Suddenly a voice rang out from the rear of the room, "Bunny, why don't you ever play some real Hawaiian Music?"

"Okay, okay, Joe!" Then going to the mike, Bunny told the rest the audience that Joe Keawe is a Hawaiian patriot. He's from Los Angles. He will transport you to a Hawaii that few today know!"

Joe Keawe, tall, huge, handsome, stood at the mike. In the high falsetto, which typified authentic Hawaiian music, Joe sang the tear-jerking strains of "Mother, Dad," and other great Hawaiian favorites.

Mae whispered to Don, "Did you hear the old Hawaiian chiefs and kings? It is as Oloha Nui Loa!"

Breakfast on a platform supported by poles over the lagoon. Don ordered the Nectar of the Gods, papaya with orchards. Mae cooed, "Please bring me pineapple spears with orchids and mahalo!"

"We must try some real Hawaiian food," demanded Mae, And so to Jimmy's Drive-in they went. "Mae named all the dishes: Pail, Taro, Laulau, Pipi Kaula, and Lomi Salmon!"

They visited the Black Sand Beach and the Queen's Bath. They arrived at their hotel on Kona, the new Kamehameha just in time to be a part of its grand opening.

After settling into their scrumptious room at the Kamehameha Mae and Don drove south along the Kailua-Kona coast to the point where Captain Cook landed at Kealakekua. Mae shuddered. "This is where the Hawaiian warriors killed Captain Cook!"

"For your information, hula girl, Kealakekua is also the city in the ukulele song, "Little Grass Shack!"

"Yes," replied Mae, "and Pu' Uhonna is also right here: the City of Refuge!"

"Whew," gasped Mae. "Kamehameha was seven-foot four-inches tall and displayed great physical beauty. He used a 180-pound spherical lava ball for lifting and throwing to his partner for conditioning!"

At the Beechboy in Kauai, their minds were again stretched. But most memorable was their dinner at the Coco Palms. "Here we are, Kameha, sitting at this table burdened with food in the island's oldest coconut grove. Look at those handsome men dressed only in loincloths, running from torch to torch to light the night. Hear the piercing wail of the conch and the eerie beating of the drums!" gasped Mae.

On their last night Don had to philosophize, "We now know that Old Hawaii still lives for those who want to find it. One must go to the country; go to the museums, look in the mountains; look in the valleys; look in the villages and towns."

Mae added, "Also it helps to find an Hawaiian! Look for a face with a smile, the hand of a friend; for Aloha, listen to his story, listen to his song, watch the surfer and the outrigger, eat poi and lomi-lomi salmon, and fresh fruit, enjoy the laughter of the children. Then you will know, you carpetbaggers, despite the hideous modern distractions that old Hawaii still lives!"

All to soon it was time to return to their government's business. But even back with the Air Force there were perks. "David and Jamie are coming to visit and Mark and Carole are following right after."

Mae insisted, "Everyone must have a barbecue in our back yard. They must see the square miles of artichokes in Hollester. They must visit the Monterey Peninsula. How could they miss the Tree House in the giant redwood? And my favorite town is the sawmill town of Scotia where everything is made of wood."

Don interrupted, "The men might also be interested in the high country's Kings Canyon and fishing!"

Military paths cross in unexpected ways. First Lieutenant David and Jamie arrived in Merced at Castle AFB for KC-135 training. Mae shouted, "Wonderful. And so near!"

In the military, the Officer Wives Club is always raising money for various causes. The Kipfers had hardly settled in when Don got the message: "Entrepreneur, we're going to dinner at the Officer Wives Club Art Auction at the Club tonight."

Don told Mae, "Okay, my dear, but I'm not going to bid."

But Mae knew her pushover husband and saw him raising his hand several times.

"Sold," shouted the excited female auctioneer. Don still didn't realize he had paid a considerable amount for a picture he hadn't even seen. He turned to Mae. "What in the world have I purchased?"

"The still picture of a beet and a parsnip!" gaily razzed Mae.

Don was attempted to explode. Then he began to laugh. "You must have put them up to this, you schemer. But now I finally realize the significance of the work of art I've purchased!"

"What on earth do you mean?" laughed Mae.

"Look at it, my dear. See the intent. Beat par! Every golfer's dream. And you're the golfer in the family!"

"Yee gads!"

Every weekend the Kipfers explored a different part of California. On 10 May 1975 the were off to Montego, Carmel and the Big Sur. "What country!" commented Don.

"And these redwoods are marvelous," added Mae.

Mae had a difficult time including all the events to which she was invited or obligated. But she told Don. "This is one job I want to include. I'm on the California Golf Rating team. We're rating Lawrence Links on 29 May 1971."

It was just as difficult for Mae and Don to keep track of their sons. Charlie was now an outdoor salesman with Sears Home Improvement Professionals and making enormous money. He had his own fax at his desk at home and arranged the home modifications with his own subcontractors. Mark and Carole were still at Fort Campbell, Kentucky. Jamie and David were just ready to leave Merced AFB for Wichita, Kansas.

David Kipfer, and Jamie, with Mae and Don, had done all of California, but perhaps the most fun had been the day they waded the Merced river and everyone caught his limit of rainbow trout.

Mae may have hit her peak as a golfer while at Sacramento. She had led her Lawrence Links golf team to the top amateur award for the whole State of California. Don asked her, "That state win was amazing, honey, but how are you doing in the base golf tournament?"

"We have two rounds in and I'm ahead. Are you coming to see the finale?" joked Mae, knowing that Don never showed up for fear of disturbing her concentration.

"No, but I've been selected to go to San Bernandino, Norton AFB, to attend an accident investigation qualification school. Sorry, I wanted you to go along, but the school fell during the time of your final golf round."

Mae didn't even miss a beat. "No contest, señor. I'm going with you."

A week before the Colonel Kipfers were to leave for Norton, Don whispered in Mae's ear before she dropped off to sleep, "Now, don't you tell anyone. Promise! Our secret will shake up the golfing community!"

Mae went to sleep smiling, with dreams of sugar plums in her contented brain!

When Mae and Don got to Norton there was a low cloud cover in every direction. "I thought you told me," demanded Mae, "that there were tall mountains as a backdrop for the base."

"Believe me," joked Don, "when we came over those mountains in T-6s in 1949 we were happy to see Norton AFB. I guess the darn things have just disappeared!"

But the next morning when Mae awoke and looked out her window toward the east she shouted in triumph. "Mon Dieu. Of all the wonderful sights I have seen this view of the mountains with the sun in the east and their shadows seeming to reach us here at the base is among the most beautiful!"

When Don was free, the two visitors toured the many Indian reservations in the area, marveled at the Salton, visited Tijuana and the fantastic Coranado Restaurant. One weekend they stayed overnight in the motel on the cliff of the Pacific at Santa Monico where Don used to stay when he visited Hughes Aircraft Company so many years before. That night they visited the Buckhorn Restaurant and Cafe where ad lib vaudeville-like acts came right off the street and performed.

But the greatest thrill of all was yet to occur. It was time to surface their secret: Don took Mae to the Ontario Airport. "Now, my beautiful champion, is the chance to be so well known that no one will ever forget you. I've called ahead. Gail will pick you up!"

Two days later Don picked Mae up at the Ontario Airport. He was apprehensive. "How did the tournament go, sweetie?"

Mae was only human, after all. She could not restrain her joy. "I won. I won! No one expected me to show. I suspect they had hoped to have a chance at the championship without my being their obstacle!"

"Did they offer congratulations?"

"Of course, you saboteur. They are all ladies and sports women. The base commander presented the trophy and there was newspaper coverage. The colonel knew what we had done but he never referred to it. He only commented, 'How is the Accident Investigation Board School going, Mae?'"

While the Kipfers were down south they stopped to see the Eberles, their long-ago friends from the Command and Staff College days in Montgomery, Alabama. The Eberles were happy and settled in Woodland Hills.

Don had kept in touch with E. B. Kipfer, his great uncle, over the years and he and Mae had visited him once in Atherton. Now Don said, "Let's stop by and see E. B. in his new home."

"OK," agreed Mae.

E. B.'s new house looked like the White House to Mae and Don. It was simply too beautiful to describe. But, Mae said, "Don, there's something the matter. This place doesn't look lived in and there's not a sign of life here!" Since they were unable to get a response, they moved on.

Back in Sacramento Mae was really busy. She bowled in two leagues, one as a single and one with Don. She golfed every week with the ladies and on weekends with David Arnolds, not only at Mather AFB but at courses such as Hagin Oaks, Diamond Oaks, and Riverbend. She played tennis twice every week and was on the base ladder. She held key positions in the various Officer Wives Clubs. And believe it or not, when Don's boss's wife went off to New England for six months, Mae acted as official hostess for all official organizational affairs. She really should have had a share of the boss's next promotion!

Mae's father Tracy was a died-in-the-wool patriotic American. When he was exposed to a different ethnic lifestyle it upset him not because he harbored racist thoughts, but because it seemed to threaten his own security. Mae had used all the pressure she could apply to get her father and mother to visit them in Europe. They would not agree to come. Now, Mae was determined to have them visit California. She told Don, "I'm sending them the tickets. They can't refuse!"

When the tickets arrived on Dayton Road, in Newark, Ohio, Tracy asked Mae's sister, Margarette, "What am I going to do now?"

Margarette smiled and told her father, "Be thankful. You're going!"

When Tracy, Anna, and sister Carolyn got off the plane in Sacramento, Mae asked her father how his trip went.

"Hi, Mae! It was the finest trip I ever took. The hostesses gave me anything I asked for!"

They went to see the statue of Mark Twain's famous Calaveras County jumping frog. "Just like our bull frogs in Ohio," agreed Tracy. They went to see the Calaveras big trees. Again Mae told the famous story about the one huge tree that had been felled by the loggers a hundred years earlier just to prove that they could fell it. One could plainly see its unimaginable trunk. It was large enough so that at various times it had held a church, a store, and a dance floor. Tracy grimaced and reluctantly admitted, "We don't have any trees like these back in Ohio!" Always interested in government, Tracy summed up his visit to Sacramento's Capitol. "It is more beautiful than any building I have ever seen, including the United States Capitol Building in Washington."

After examining Sutter's old fort, Tracy gave his own viewpoint: "We all know about the gold strike out here. We've all heard of Sutter. But I never expected to stand here in the center of his fort where the Gold Rush really began!"

When Mae served huge artichokes, unknown to her Ohioan guests, she asked Tracy how he liked them. He tried stripping another leaf from the cantankerous vegetable before he answered, "Well, Mae, you know anything would taste good, dipped in sweet butter!"

Best of all Tracy liked the maid's quarters in Mae and Don's home where he explained, "I can do my own thing and not bother anyone!"

When everyone went to the American River and stood watching it, Tracy had to swallow twice before he spoke to Mae, "Well, Mae, I have to admit. They've got us beat with their river. This one is fast, clear, and cold, ours are not!" Don ran through his own thoughts, knowing there was no one to share these private thoughts with. How proud Tracy and Anna must be of this astonishing, absolutely beautiful woman, totally sure of herself, so kind that no one would dislike her, sitting at the head of their table in a stupendous house, offering them the best foods that God could provide.

Back in Washington, D.C., eons ago, Glenna and Vada had befriended a young college student at Washington Missionary College and provided him supplementary food at a time when Clark Nary really needed it. Now he was a dentist in North Highlands, just outside McClellan AFB. This relationship from the past was now to give Tracy the opportunity of his life. Tracy had always sung professionally, and when he, Anna, Carolyn, Vada, Mae and Don attended service at the largest Adventist Church in the country, where Clark was the congregation's publicity chairman. Mae had clued Clark that Tracy was a professional vocalist. So Clark arranged for Tracy to sing with the church's huge choir. Mae turned to Vada, "I'll bet Dad never expected to sing in a nationally famous, one hundred and twenty person choir!" Vada added, "Nor did he anticipate singing those few bars as a soloist and being introduced to the congregation by the choir director as the visiting soloist."

And when Tracy disrobed and joined the others after Sabbath School, Mae asked him, "Dad, how does it feel to be famous?"

Tracy was never at a loss for words. "Well, it felt good. Do you think that for my good work, maybe Saint Peter will let me past the golden gate?"

David and Jamie loved the Isabel National forest, growing bravely at a 10,000-foot altitude near Buena Vista, Colorado. They fished there often for rainbow trout in Cottonwoood Lake and Cottonwood Creek. They were so attached to it that they had been looking for property near it to purchase. They were absolutely astonished when on a visit there they saw a FOR SALE sign on the very campsite they always used. They went immediately to Buena Vista, determined the name of the seller and made their down payment. David called Mae, "Believe it or not, Mom, Jamie and I own twelve acres in Isabel National Forest at the very site we always camped on!"

Mae was just as dubious as anyone that a person could purchase property in a national forest. "How can that be, David. It's a national forest."

David could hardly contain himself. "It seems that once the mining interests were powerful enough so that when the National Park was established the federal government exempted from condemnation any property that had an active mine! Our property is split by Cottonwood Creek and has a gold mine on it."

"David, you are lucky!"

"That's what the local people claimed when the newspaper carried the news. No one in Buena Vista could believe it."

Now, in mid-June 1976, Don and Mae were bound for David's property to sleep on a three-foot wide by six-foot long bunk in David's fold-up trailer. When Don and Mae arrived at the campsite, Don jumped from their Eldorado and ran to shake hands with, David. Don almost fell, slipping to one knee. Mae was petrified. "Don," she screamed, "what's the matter!"

Don looked at her sheepishly. "Thin mountain air, woman. I forgot I'm at 10,000 feet. Flatlanders have to move slowly!"

Dave and Jamie's dog, Pooh, was fearless. Mae and Don finally understood how strongly Jamie felt about her nondescript dog when she went into a near spasm. "Dave, Pooh is attacking a skunk behind the trailer!"

Before David could stop her, the skunk had scored a direct hit and the damage was done. The skunk was gone. "God," roared David. "Pooh is a smelly mess. She can't come into the trailer!"

Mae, always prepared for any event, with the contents of her handbag, with information, even surgery, laughed, "Jamie, get out your tomato juice. It neutralizes the skunk spray! You know, we're sleeping in that trailer, also."

More important activities awaited! David and Don tramped Cottonwood Creek every day hoping to catch rainbow trout. The first day when they returned they questioned Mae who was fishing in the creek not fifty feet from their trailer. Expecting a negative answer Don asked "How'd you do, fishing expert?"

Mae held up her catch, with pride and said, "I've limited out. And they're huge. We'll have to eat some of these before we can go fishing again tomorrow."

David, the real fishing expert and guide, was crestfallen, "Egads!"

There was another mystery. Don and David had found a large pond made by the beavers damming up Cottonwood Creek and could see hundreds of large rainbow trout in its clear water. These trout were just treading the waters swift flow. They wouldn't even look at any of their live or artificial bait.

"David, tomorrow we'll have to take your mother along with us. She's good luck!"

It so happened that a late lunch trip to Buena Vista made this confident threesome late for fishing. Working their way along the trout stream they arrived at the beaver dam at 1615.

Then as Don and Mae stood stunned, David raced after a large rainbow trout he had hooked as it jumped across a sandbar from water to water.

Some new factor had entered the contest. Don was certain it was Mae's good luck. "Look, this one has even jumped out of the water onto the beach."

No one ever knew the reason, but each day at precisely 1615 Mae, Don and David filled their limit at the beaver dam.

There were unexpected perks from being in California. Mae and Don's nephew, Gary Soldatis, was on the golf team at Valdosta College in Georgia. When he graduated he was depressed because he could not find a job he liked. He wrote to Mae: "I'd like to come to California if you could house me until I can get settled."

Mae was a soft touch. She was never slow when she could be helpful. She wrote back: "Come ahead!"

Now, on 30 September 1976, Gary arrived. He liked living in colonel's quarters next to the Officers Club, across the street from the tennis courts and almost in walking distance to Lawrence Links Golf Course.

Don commented to Mae: "Things keep happening. Mark and Carole were with Charlie and Jane in Bowie and are now on their way to Europe. They were there to help Charlie and Jane get married!"

Don laughed. "Mae, when you think about your travels, I'm sure you'll remember fondly the large flea market at Roseville."

"That's true. What a marvelous assortment of interesting heirlooms those salesmen have collected. I'll never forget the perfect, three-legged tortilla board and molded roller made from volcano stone you bought from that Indian couple on 8 January 1977."

"Nor will I, antique appraiser! They said their family was tired having it around and that no one used it anymore. They claimed it had been in the family for generations. There was nothing like it, even in the National Museum in Mexico City."

Mae grinned. "Remember, Mark and Carole were with us. He almost went atomic when you tried to negotiate that Indian man down from fifteen dollars to ten dollars. I suppose it was a side of you your son had never seen."

"Air Force wives have the toughest job in the world," Don told Mae. "All work and no play was not the reason we came to California," Don admonished Mae. "Pack your duds, fraulein, you're invited to go with me to Australia and New Zealand. We'll be gone 5 February 1977 until 24 February 1977."

"Hey, Romeo," Mae answered poking Don in the ribs, "I like honeymoon surprises like this. Will we have to wait for the space 'A' flight at Travis?"

"I hope not."

When they arrived at Travis AFB the base commander whom Don had know many years, greeted him and then announced, "We're scheduled to have a transport with high-value items aboard depart for Australia in the morning. Don, you and Mae are manifested!"

After the base commander departed, Mae looked around and whispered. "Don, these people in civilian clothes are retiree Air Force officers. They told me they've been waiting here for space available for a week. They are really, really, thankful you showed up."

Mae was ecstatic. "Don, we keep one upping ourselves. Who do you know from Massillon or Newark who ever made it in their own private aircraft, free, to Australia and New Zealand!"

"Only half true, my love. We have both paid for our fare many times over. Still, I have never heard of an Air Force full colonel who was privileged to travel in the belly of a C-130 with the most beautiful woman in the world."

Don was not just polishing the apple. Mae's beautiful baby smooth face, surrounded by thick, shiny black hair, and all mounted on a body that excited men, while looking at Mae, to run mindless head on into trees, attracted personal attention wherever she went.

Their stop in Hawaii was almost incidental. But in American Samoa; the arrival of a plane meant to the local people beaucoups money, and all the shops opened even in the middle of the night when tourists arrived. When Mae glanced around the terminal she could barely hold her mouth closed from sheer amazement. "My gosh, Don, look at the size of these Samoans. The women are all over six feet in height and must weigh over two hundred and fifty pounds. And the men dwarf them! In Thailand I was a giant. Here, I'm a midget!"

And carefully making closer observations, Mae continued, "And what beautiful people. What a heavenly place to live. Since we were the only two people aboard, we'll have to purchase quite a few things!"

"That's the first time I've ever heard that logic," grinned Don.

Then more water and finally landfall. Australia was magic for the Kipfers. They loved the English dialect. They valued the beautiful parks. "Don," suggested Mae, "That shop says 'Gentrys.' Let's go up. And there that work of art, Flinders Gate, right next to the Kaiser Hotel."

Of course the different style shops were enticing but now it was time to visit the wonderful Australian officers who had been stationed in Sacramento to assist in the logistic support of the F-111 aircraft at McClellan AFB with whom Mae and Don had socialized so often. First they went to a grand reunion with a dozen of them in Australia's capital, Canberra. It was a bonny party. Mae asked her closest friend how her golf game was coming. Mae, such a fair-minded person, was shocked at the answer. "Mae, we wives don't play golf here!"

When Mae mentioned this to Don, he knew. Mae only wished she had time for more than just passing through. She would see if such an attitude couldn't be modified! Perhaps she could be as fortunate as she had been in Canada!

Then on to Melbourne where Squadron Leader Ian Sneeberger and Anne lived. Their Australian friends expected Mae and Don to take the grand, improved road for this trip. They could not understand the Kipfers who, instead, chose the rather rough, gravel road that passed through the Australian National Forest. "Stop! Stop!" Mae had demanded. I just saw a head and some eyes starring from behind a tree!"

When Don got stopped, up popped a head and out jumped a kangaroo! And so their whole trip was a rich interchange with nature. Eucalyptus trees were filled so they looked like bouquets of huge white parrots, topped with golden plums!

Their host, Ian, was the huge man who always had sung "Waltzing Matilda" at their McClellan AFB parties. He and his equally large countryman also threw one of the beautiful dark-haired Australian wives back and forth like a medicine ball. "Remember, Mae, what Ian told us when he was served a large chef salad back in California? 'Come to Australia and I guarantee you we won't serve you rabbit food!' Now, we will see," joked Don.

"Betcha," added Mae.

Mae and Don had a wonderful evening with the Sneebergers. Their roast beef and Yorkshire pudding were fabulous, to which Don later paid the ultimate compliment: "Hardly better than my mother's, and of course, your's, my dear. But the kiwi and whipped cream is pretty much new for us except for California. It was supreme."

After Mae and Don departed the Sneebergers home, Mae conceded, "No rabbit food!"

Mae and Don both loved the breakfasts at their Australian hotels. "Lamb chops instead of bacon with your eggs," noted Mae. "Boy, that's living!" And of course they attended a symphony at Sidney's famous Town Hall before they left the Continent Down Under.

When their C-130 had landed in Australia, Mae and Don were surprised to find a small USAF detachment at the airport. When the major in charge met them, he asked Don, "What can I do for you, Colonel?"

Almost too doubtful of success to ask for such a favor, Don replied, "Well, my wife and I are here to visit a number of Australian Air Force officers who served at McClellan AFB with us. But in addition, we would sure like to get a lift to New Zealand."

"When would that be," the major had asked.

"Well, we'll be here ten days. If there's any chance of getting a lift, we can adjust. Here's our hotel phone number."

"No trouble, Colonel, I'll set the date. You be here at noon."

Now, no one understood the value of punctuality better than Mae and Don. They had arrived at 1000 hours and were in the air in another C-130 by 1200 hours, headed for New Zealand. Within an hour of landing Mae pecked Don's cheek and confided to him. "Christchurch is my kind of town, my dear. I love our hotel. I love the flower garden parks, their flower-sculpted clock. Their modern art designed Town Hall is spectacular. "If I'm ever forced to leave the United States, please, please, make reservations for me here!"

"And," Don added, "look at all the trout in Christchurch's small river!"

Mae and Don rented a British compact auto to drive around South Island. They were no more than several miles south of Christchurch when Don stopped the car and stepped out, as though he were witnessing a world-shaking event. "Mae, get your camera! We've got to get a picture of the thousands of sheep that fill this field!"

Obedient to her master's voice, Mae obeyed. "What a special thing!" Little did either Yankee know but they soon found out. "For the next ten days," Mae later recalled, "all we saw were fields full of sheep!"

They saw amazing high falls, beautiful beaches, and across Arahura River a bridge, which carried both rail and auto traffic. But their first night they attempted to stay in Dunedin. "The motel manager told me," said Don, "they are having a fireman's convention here and like they told Jesus' father, the inns are full. However, they're calling a family who sometimes takes in overnighters."

The Healeys were just marvelous. "They must be the pattern for New Zealanders," Mae concluded. "I love them! They have a nice home and a nice car. They both work at a secure job in the woolen mills and they're thoroughly English!"

Frances Healy prepared a wonderful dinner and breakfast—both meals based upon lamb chops. Mr. Healy kept Mae and Don up most of the night. "We've never had Yanks as guests before," he announced. "Please tell us about America. We love Yanks. If it weren't for you, Yanks, we New Zealanders would be speaking Japanese!"

Both Mae and Don loved the huge trout in the clear water of Queenstown's lake and the Maitai trees. They went into histrionics when they saw the first roadside sign featuring a hopping kangaroo, which said CAREFUL-NEXT 13

MILES! When they arrived at the small town of Hokitika on New Zealand's West Coast and checked into their motel, Don proposed, "Mae, it's only a hundred yards to the Pacific Ocean. Let's walk over."

It was a foggy, cloudy day that felt like rain. The visibility was one hundred feet. "Do you want to go in such weather? Are you sure?"

The beach was something out of prehistoric life. "I would never have missed this," commented Don. "There are thousands of trees and logs, some four or five feet in diameter, washed up by the Pacific Ocean. It's spooky!"

"Not an encouraging sight," admitted Mae. "Not a building nor soul anywhere to be seen."

"It's like a prehistoric scene, for sure," admitted Don.

Then as they started to move on, Mae stopped and pointed, "Don, you've been looking for koa wood to carve. That looks like koa to me," she said, pointing. "No, by George, my word, Don, it's a two-foot-tall Tiki god. The god of the Maoris!"

Don picked up the piece of driftwood. "It's heavy as lead and reddish brown like koa. And like a miracle, though no man has ever touched it, its really in a perfect likeness of the Maoris' Tiki god. There are even sockets for the eyes. Now, my dear, you've bought plenty of jade, but I'm going to purchase a jade warclub for this Tiki god and put green stone eyes in its head's sockets!"

"Hurrah," shouted Mae into the westerly Pacific wind, her voice torn away by its velocity. "We'll have a souvenir of New Zealand that no other living person has!"

And so the Kipfers' marvelous tour of New Zealand and Australia was complete. A lift took them to Australia from Christchurch. Then on they flew to American Samoa, Hawaii, and back to California.

Back at Travis AFB Don reminded Mae, "I wrote to E. B. Kipfer and told him we would stop and see him when we returned. We're not staying. Just a hello."

When Don knocked at E. B.,'s door be was surprised to find a nurse in uniform opening the door. "Oh, yes, Colonel Kipfer, we received your letter. I'm terribly sorry to tell you, but Mr. Kipfer died and was buried while you were gone down under. You should go to see his solicitor."

Mae sympathized. "What are you going to do?"

"It may be one of my great mistakes. E. B. was very rich. So far as I know he has no living relatives. But we have enough money. I don't intend to profit from a man like E. B.'s death!"

David and Gail Arnold, the Kipfers' next door neighbors and Sunday golf partners since 1974, as logistics comptroller, was the host for their two-star bosses departure from service. The men were to play golf in the afternoon followed by a gala party that night. The two stars, the guest of honor, and three of his general officer friends, made up one foursome. There were ten foursomes total. The assistant comptroller, Major Paul Edrington, a good friend of Don's and two other officers made up Don's golf foursome team. When the cards were totaled, Don's team had each won the tournament and each were awarded a huge silver punch bowl, all engraved, which Don was sure had been intended for the general's retirement. When Don had arrived at McClellan AFB, the then two-star boss had told him, "Don, you deserve to be promoted. I just don't have enough time left to arrange it!" When the new two-star appeared his first words to Don were: "I noticed you are a West Pointer. When I was up for promotion to full colonel, a West Pointer stood in the way."

Don had told Mae, "I told you, I really didn't have a chance, but that man has just nailed the lid down. Of course he has the authority to say yes or no even though he had never heard of me until he arrived at McClellan. Now Don whispered to Mae, "Of course the golf trophy is little retribution, but it'll have to do!"

On 11 May 1977, Mark and Carole, Mark having resigned his captain's commission as a helicopter pilot in the U.S. Army, and having stayed a month with Jacquelin and Ron in San Jacinto, arrived to live with Mae and Don until they could accommodate to civilian life. Mark and Don were both aware of the fine art of redwood burl tables. "Let's get some burls, Pop." And so they did and finished them professionally.

In the course of time, Mae and Don purchased two-for-one dinner tickets for both families. They then took Mark and Carole to all the spots on the old 49ers trail, Tahoe, Reno, the American River, the theater in the round, and all the other places they had found so glorious.

Don had spoken to Mae many times about Bob Heckert, son of Heckert's Jeweler's owner, in Massillon, Ohio, and his high school classmate. "Mae, even looking back at Bob's capability I'm impressed. He was working at Sandia on the atomic bomb program when he was only nineteen years old and just out of high school. He's just brilliant. He now works for Hughes Aircraft Company!"

"Why hasn't the country heard of him, great oracle?"

"Well, Bob just tends to exasperate people. He simply can't help it. From a technical knowledge viewpoint, he should be running Hughes Aircraft Company and yet he's only a senior engineer without even his own secretary! Now, as you know, the Heckerts are to be here tomorrow, 1 July."

"What will we do with them, oh oracle?"

"Eat out, my dear. And show them Sacramento. Old Sacramento is worth anyone's time for a week!"

Bob and Honeybear arrived at the Kipfer quarters about 1400. When Don got home he hugged them both and went upstairs to change. "Mae, they look terrible. Didn't you assign them their room and let them get cleaned up?"

"Yes, master, but they've been up in the mountains for a week. Probably living in their truck. They've had a rough vacation. They spent a couple hours cleaning up."

"Well, I'm taking them to the Officers Club for dinner tonight no matter what," added Don.

Don prepared cocktails and things settled down. By and by, Bob told Don, "You know, and I know that if a nuclear weapon explodes over our country nothing much will be left!"

"Yes, Bob, that's what I'm attempting to prevent!"

"Well, I can't do much about that. But Honeybear and I have a plot of land hidden in the mountains. We have a garden, chickens, a sow and plenty of canned food. We're going to make it!"

Mae was terrified. She didn't want the visit to get off on the wrong foot. She interrupted, "Men, it's time to go to the club."

Don couldn't help himself: "Bob, you've got a good plan. However, if there are survivors and they learn you have food that isn't contaminated, they'll tramp you into fertilizer meal. Better include some armament among your supplies!"

The Heckerts had barely cleared the base when Colonel Deets called, "Hi, Don, can I speak to Mark?"

Mae was dying of curiosity, Don could tell.

When Mark hung up he smiled, then frowned, then smiled. He announced for everyone to hear: "Colonel Deets offered me a job. He's the director for Sortex, an automatic sorting and packing company. He needs someone to go represent them down in the valley tomorrow!"

"My lord," chimed in Don. "How are you going to get up to speed?

"Jack said he knows I'm a fast reader. I'm to go over to his place right now and he'll check me out."

No one knew it then, but that call changed Mark's life. The Mexican workmen had gone on strike when the tomatoes and other field produce was due for harvesting. The planters were looking at a catastrophe. One of Sortex' machines could replace a tractor, trailing platform, fifteen laborers, and a collective wagon. The Sortex machine rooted out the whole tomato plant, accepted the tomato plant and tomatoes, shook them, discarded the plants, sorted and threw out green tomatoes, dirt and stones. Out the rear came a river of red, ripe tomatoes! A new era was born and the strike was essentially passé!"

On 27 September, Don received the message he hoped never to receive. His beloved mother who had given all her energy to make him successful, had died.

Don and Mae went to Massillon for the funeral at Gordon Shaidnagle's funeral home and the post-funeral reception at his sister Mary Helen Soldatis's afterward. Don told Mae, "You saw the pictures of her when she was young. An auburn-haired girl, beautiful, and with a perfect figure. She was good in school and had memorized many of Longfellow's and Hawthorn's books. She was a force in the community. When she saw anything that needed correcting she was a formidable foe. As she said, when you're past ninety, all your friends are gone. And so, of course they were not able to attend the funeral! Of course, all the relatives were there and all of her friends who remained. Thirty years earlier, it would have been standing room only!"

Back in Sacramento life had to go on. Suzanne, Glenna's daughter and her husband Derald Richard, lived in Hangtown at the foot of the mountain heading west on Route 50, so that he could catch all the accidents that routinely happened on the rush down the mountain. On 31 December the Richards invited Mae and Don to come to Hangtown and go with them to their favorite restaurant. When Mae and Don arrived, Suzanne told them, "Derald called. He has a patient that had an accident coming down Route 50. The patient is wavering between life and death but he says he can leave him if we can't wait!"

Mae spoke for all: "Tell him we can wait!"

By and by Derald arrived and they departed for the restaurant. As they examined the menu, Suzanne suggested, "Their plank sirloin is huge. Derald and I can only eat a quarter of a one apiece. If you agree, one should do the four of us. Medium rare?"

Mae answered again, "Perfect, and that's the way we like our beef."

When the sirloin came, Derald, as the host, became the carver. Don could hardly hold back his laughter when he saw this surgeon, scalpel in hand, making such delicate, precise, damageless strokes to divide the meat. Later Don told Mae, "That boy is no butcher!"

Just as their entree was being served, in walked three of the most unusual couples the Kipfers had ever seen. "My gosh," whispered Don to Mae. "Those women are six feet and three hundred pounds. The men are even larger. We'll never see anyone their like again. Not even in Samoa!"

Mae came right back, "True, but they sure didn't dress to eat out. And I wonder how they got so dirty? Their faces look like a Welch minor at the end of his shift!"

"I wonder what they will order?" grinned Don."

The Kipfers and Rochets were halfway through their dinner when the six giants were served. "My goodness," whispered Mae, "they've each ordered a plank of sirloin!"

Don could hardly stand his curiosity. He told Mae, "I'm going over and ask them where they're from and what they do for a living?"

Mae had watched as the six seemed to hold their heads straight forward and their eyes continually searched side to side. As Don started to get up, she grabbed his belt and pulled him back down. She whispered, "Sure and do you want to live for your retirement?"

Mae had always been interested in Don's work, especially since she knew it was all directed toward the defense of *her* country. So when they arrived at Sacramento Air Logistics Center she probed Don for answers: "What in the world does a logistics center do, lord of secrets?"

Don nodded his head, "Well, the concept is pretty simple."

"Yes, I know. Just like always. But doing it is pretty tough!"

"Right. Now imagine you are a house owner. In the case of the Air Force that would be one of the operating commands such as the Strategic Air Command or the Tactical Air Command. They own the aircraft such as the F-111."

"Gotcha."

"The homeowner does his own small maintenance jobs. He fills his mower with gasoline and goes to the hardware to replace worn parts. The Operating Command must also have replacement parts, except the local, friendly hardware does not carry the parts it needs. The logistic center must provide them."

"Gotcha!"

"If the homeowner wants an updated kitchen, an add on porch, or a new roof he must go to a structural engineer and builder. The operating command must go to the logistic center. Sometimes the modification to the aircraft is so extensive the aircraft must be brought into the center for modification."

"Gotcha. Clear but nasty!"

Don reminisced as he told Mae: "You remember my tour with the CF-105 and my work with the update of the Distant Early Warning system?"

"Yes."

"Well, my division, among many other programs, is responsible for its logistic support. I'm going to Ottawa 24 June to make sure NDHQ is happy. I'll be staying at the Lord Elgin Hotel."

Don's feet had hardly gotten inside Quarters 108 when he announced:

"Well, Mae, another trip. This time our two-star is going along. We have all kind of search and track equipment looking from Nome, Alaska into Russia. Some of the radar antennas are as large as a football field. We've had some hints that our logistic support could be better."

On the snowmen's return Mae asked for a debriefing report. "You're more demanding than the boss, beloved one. No point in buying Alaskan seafood up in Nome. It's cheaper here. When we landed and went to the various stations where the men were housed, we had to climb ladders into their quarters and from the ground there was ice fog not a dozen feet above our heads. Contrary to rumor, everyone in the field seemed happy with their logistics support. I suppose such terrible weather really added to their woes."

"Mae, you know that we were just in San Bernardino so that I could become an accident board investigator."

"Yes."

"Well, we've just had a tragedy in the shops. A young man, a tumbler, in fact, was working on the top of a radar van in the shop. The vent he was trying mightily to remove suddenly came loose and he went over the side, landed on his head, was instantly killed."

Several weeks later, Mae asked, "How's the vent accident?"

"My report's gone. Not much to add to what I told you. Everyone has ideas about how to prevent such an accident again, but I believe the prime solution is better training."

By March of '76, Don had determined he needed to go to Vandenberg AFB to see the stored Saturn Missiles from which he sometimes got requests for small amounts of support. Also it was not clear what role they might play in the Space Shuttle program that was scheduled to transition to Sacramento ALC.

As it turned out Major General Hepfer, Don's friend from Baltimore and Andrews AFB, was in charge of the Saturns. "John, do you need any help?"

"Everything here is fine, Don. We have everything we need."

Don told Mae, "I'm suspicious. I was assigned to the acquisition division because Air Force intended to have NASA hand over the Shuttle to them for operation, as has always been done for an operational system and McClellan would be the supporting logistic center.

Mae shook her head. "I know that. What now?"

"Well, I told you I learned as a lieutenant that as soon as I got a program worth a million dollars a year, or more, I began having calls from Washington."

"All too true. And I suppose those exalted administrators haven't been calling you."

"Nary a single call. Here at McClellan we have plotted out the land we will need to condemn. We have identified the parts necessary for support and their costs. We have selected our best logisticians and sent them to the anticipated operational command. But I haven't received a single call from responsible military or civilian people in Washington. It smells rancid!"

"My West Point roommate, whom you know well, is the two-star contact at the Pentagon for the Space Shuttle. I'm going to see him!"

At the Pentagon, Don's roommate's secretary told him, "The general has a visitor right now. He'll meet you in the coffee shop down the hall in a few minutes."

Immediately Don knew he was correct. Down the hall, off the record. His buddy didn't want anyone to see Don in his own office. After a half cup of coffee and reminiscences Don popped the sixty-four dollar question: "General, has the Air Force lost interest in the Space Shuttle?"

Don knew this man better than his own parents did. He had lived and slept with him for two years. He saw the general's eyes shift left and right. Finally the anticipated spoken word: "Don, I suspect I should have given more attention to the shuttle. Of course, we are still very interested in the Shuttle. But it's just like that expensive watch I bought while we were plebes at West Point." And Don got no further information. To anyone else there had been no transfer of policy direction. To Don the news had been earthshaking.

Back at McClellan Mae wondered if she and Don had guessed correctly. "How was your old buddy? What did he say?"

"I didn't even get into his office. The man you knew and fed so many times during his trials at Randolph when he was a bachelor lonesome and hungry, didn't want any evidence of my visit!"

"What did he say?"

"Nothing that anyone except him and I would understand. When he was a plebe at West Point, he saw an extremely expensive watch in the Post Exchange, which he was determined to have. Unfortunately he nor his parents, could pay for that unnecessary luxury. He had to realize that the Post Exchange would remain its owner."

"I don't understand. What has the ownership of the watch to do with the operational control of the Shuttle?"

"My dear, he's telling me that the Air Force cannot afford the Shuttle. Let NASA finance it!"

"Won't that change things?"

"You can bet your life savings. The military has specific defense missions. They demand financial support. NASA, on the other hand, has primarily scientific missions, with practically no vital national defense mission. The shuttle will undoubtedly be reduced to gathering scientific data, a mission most Americans have very little sympathy for. It's always a very difficult sell."

"But on to other programs. BG Jay Brill, our friend of yesteryears, runs the system project office for the A-10. He is good. And as you recall, he heard my reliability pitch during the Good-bye Ball at Andrews AFB when I left. The A-10 has been started through the gates of transition from development to operations at the Tactical Air Command on Myrtle Beach Air Force Base. We at McClellan AFB have our logisticians and engineers in place. The A-10 has passed its Sustained Wartime Stress Test with flying colors. The Tactical Air Command has had to establish new standards for its unbelievable readiness to fly. If the Tactical Air Command cannot get its other aircraft into the air and protect its fuel quotas, the A-10 can do it for them. Its Gatling gun can cut through six inches of armor plate steel and blow a tank's engine out of its mounts!"

Mae understood most of this. "My, my! To be responsible for the support of such an aircraft is a super way to leave our wonderful Air Force."

"Mae, that's enough logistics information. You know I've just hit the high spots. But I'm sure you're to busy to listen to my everyday debriefing."

Mae and Don both knew that thirty-five years of fun, pain, and hard work were about to end. And so did everyone else in Sacramento.

The military was very good at celebrating one's entrance into service, one's death, and especially one's retirement. So Mae faithfully recorded their major good-bye events:

11–28 February 1978, Maui with David and Gail Arnold

8 March 1978, Australian Officers Dinner, 1830

14 April 1978, Dawn and David Francis, Australian Dinner, 1830

4 June 1978, Close Friend Dinner, Hurrahs Lake Tahoe, 1800

15 June 1978, Dinner, Capistrano, Jacquelyn and Ron, Mexican, 1800

4 July 1978, Dinner, Betty and Gary Soldatis, Mark and Carole Folsom, 1800

15 July 1978, Dinner at Herm and Charlotte Stewart's (Don's Deputy), 1820

19 July 1978, Luncheon, MMA Carmichael Elks Innumerable gifts ,1200

21 July 1978, Don's Senior Officers Hail and Farewell Rockers, 1800

22 July 1978, Dinner, Dawn and David Francis, 2000

24 July 1978, Dinner, Colonel and Mrs. Jack Deets, 1800

25 July 1978, Lunch, Friends at Stubbs: Dinner Smiths, 1800

26 July 1978, Cocktails, MMA Officers Club 1630

28 July 1978, Dinner, Spencers 2030

29 July 1978, Dinner, Colonel David and Gail Arnold 1800

In addition to these rather large, formal good-byes, their were many small couple with couple dinners; Captain Marty and Marilyn Burke, RCAF; Major Tom and Mieko Imais, (JAF); Major Jacque and Pat Gelinas, (RCAF); Major John and Trish Spencer; AAF. Major and Trish Power, AAF; Captain and Gwen Little, RAF.

Finally, thirty-five years, two months, and ten days after Don had left Mae in Newark and his home in Massillon, he turned to his indescribably beautiful traveling partner and admitted to her, "Well, Mae, today's the day!"

"I know, sweetie. Keep a stiff upper lip."

The senior NCOs and most of the center's officers were lined up in formation at the flagpole in front of the Sacramento/McClellan Logistic Center's Headquarters. Military music sounded. The officers in charge of the retirement ceremony called the multitude to attention. Don was sent front and center to stand before the podium where the two-star general stood to send Don on his way. Mae lamented, "Of course, Don always wanted to be operational. So, of course there was no flyby as there might have been if he were a full colonel, operational wing commander. Still, this was not bad and of course, it will have to do!"

The general, over a loudspeaker, gave a detailed and rather glowing synopsis of Don's military career including the award of command pilot wings, command missilier wings, two Legion of Merits, the Bronze Star and fifteen other medals. He then read the citation for the latest Legion of Merit and fastened it to Don's blouse. Finally, he read the retirement order. That put a period on everything military!

The band struck up and played "The Star Spangled Banner." At its conclusion, the commander of troops commanded: "Dismissed!"

Everyone relaxed until 31 July 1978 when one of the base's spectacular dinners was held at 1800 in the McClellan Officer's Club for the departure of Colonel Don Kipfer. When Mae and Don arrived home and were retiring, Don hugged Mae and told her, "Sweetie, I believe all these parties and the splendid formal tonight was because all these people regretted losing you, not me!"

Mae kissed Don and purred, "Hush yo' mouth, you civilian, you! And come to bed!"

At 0600, 2 August 1978, year of our Lord, Mae and Don rose to leave Quarters 108 at McClellan AFB forever. Over breakfast finger food, Mae laughed, "Former sir, the trailer people suggested you drive the El Dorado and Comfort Travel Trailer around the parking lot a few times to get used to pulling the trailer and parking the rig before we hit the trail. Do you think you'll be okay?"

"How tough can it be," laughed Don "Everybody does it."

And when they went out to depart, Don had to get out of the El Dorado and make several adjustments in the hitch to keep it from dragging the street! All this with several neighbors closely observing. By then, Mae pointed, "You can see everyone's lined up on the street watching this operation. Okay, what now, tour director?"

"Well, I believe we'll just go up to Ashland, Oregon, the first day. We'll look for a drive-through park. Hey, lover, I forgot to sign out!" Don bellowed!

"You've got to be kidding," retaliated his traveling partner.

"Yup! Ain't it great?"

"Ashland! That's barely out of California," Mae groaned.

The Kipfers had covertly decided to leave early so no one could see their shaky departure. But that wasn't to be. "My God," whispered Don, now realizing what Mae had already seen.

"What would you expect? They knew our inexperience. Everyone in the housing area are either in their front yards or the women are poking their heads out the front door. No one wanted to miss the fun. Mae waved bravely to each friend as the Travel Trailer passed very slowly by, out the front gate of McClellan AFB, the ten-wheeled monster slithered!

Mae's remorse had caught up with her and she was almost in tears. "I hate to leave all these wonderful people. Especially Gail and David Arnold. David really liked you, birdman. Remember the night before we left their home, at their dinner party, he even gave you his father's, general of the Air Force, Hap Arnold's West Point dress hard hat! What act of friendship could be more meaningful?"

"My dear, you're right as always. David understands I feel exactly the same way about him. But now we're beginning the real part of our lives, the part that we are totally free to use as we please. I know you've traveled over most of the world, but a promise is a promise. Now I'm going to show you the rest of the United States that you haven't seen. Hold on!"

Mae rocked back and forth violently. "Step on the gas, Knute, I'm all ears and eyes!"

It did not take long before Mae was covering new territory. "Oregon," Mae concluded, "is certainly beautiful, with the Pacific off to the west, mountains to the East. Then there's Mount Shasta, Crater Lake and finally the green pastures around Portland."

Passing northward, Don broke their pattern. Vancouver, in British Columbia was a joy to both Kipfers, having known England so well. "My gosh," exclaimed Mae, "the Empress Hotel is so solid looking and with all its pendants waving reminiscent of pictures we saw of medieval England. And look, they have double-decker buses, Winston. I'm sure you can get shepherd's pie and steak and kidney pie at this fine inn."

Don was quick to realize one difference between New and Old World English. "The people here speak the Queen's English more faithfully than they do in London!"

Next the Kipfers were programmed to visit Vietona, and Port Angeles. But in the meantime they visited the Makah Indian Reservation and drove to the top of Mount Olympus.

Many years before, one of Vada's favorite bosses, as head of the Review and Herald Publishing Company, was Mr. Nowland. Now he lived in Port Angeles. The Nowlands invited Mae and Don for dinner. Mae and Don knew Mr. Nowland from meetings in Silver Springs. The sight of Mae then, and now, brought a sparkle to the eyes and a remembrance to the mind of this former CEO. He virtually bubbled at the remembrance and of the Kipfers' visit to his home.

The next morning, Don drove nonstop until they parked overnight at Moses Lake, Missoula. Missoula was a pleasant place and both Mae and Don were ready for a good rest. Not to be! "My gosh," shouted Mae. "Our trailer is rocking, moving up and down. The wind must be gale force."

Don attempted to go outside to inspect the trailers tie downs but reclosed the door. "Mae, I can't go out there. It's impossible to stand. If the wind doesn't slow down immediately, we'll have to get into our car. This trailer may fly away!"

Mae was terribly upset. "Is there nothing else we can do?" But before Don could reply the wind began to slow and within an hour it was normal.

Gardiner, on the border of Yellowstone National Park, was their next stop. It was the Kipfers' routine while traveling and driving long distances each day for Mae to relieve Don. She normally drove for a little over an hour and usually covered about seventy miles. After her turn driving through Wyoming, Don asked her, "What did you see while I was sleeping?" Mae giggled. "I didn't see a single house, a living person, or even a cow," observed Mae, "but I did see two pronghorn antelope snoozing along a fencerow. This beautiful country is surely underutilized."

"I don't know why we didn't allow the American Indian to stay on this land instead of transplanting him to worthless areas where not even a genius could make a living," mourned Don.

But Mae and Don kept looking and moving. Soon they entered the ancestral home of the Sheep Eating Indians, now known as Yellowstone National Park. "Let's have lunch in the main Yellowstone guest house, Don? Okay?" coaxed Mae.

"Naturally. Do we have a choice?"

The Kipfers stood and watched the natural geyser, Old Faithful, through numerous eruptions. Don, timing its outburst, agreed. "Right on time!" They roamed the mountain trails, washed their hands in the warm water, marveled at the deep ravines, and saw innumerable animals.

"A national treasure, for certain," summarized Mae.

Don being a West Pointer and now ex-military, had studied in detail all of the United States military encounters. One of the most fascinating was Custer's Last Stand. "Mae, there can be little doubt of General Custer's bravery and success in the Civil War. So how could such an able officer be as easily outmaneuvered as he was at the Little Big Horn?"

As they approached Hardin, Montana, and the site of the famous battle, Mae commented, "Perhaps, now we'll find out."

As Mae and Don stood on the gently rising hill at the top of the battlefield, Don spoke out, "Of course, Colonel Custer set up correctly for battle on the highest point but that gave him little more advantage than a level meadow would have. As a Caucasian American I'm torn by the results of the battle. Americans had stolen all of the Eastern United States from its aboriginal owners. Now Colonel Custer intended to finish that job. Our treatment of the American Indian is a shabby part of our American history."

Mae, looking over the tombstones on the battlefield and toward the Little Bighorn exhaled in pity. "Solomon, there must have been a kinder way!"

"Almost any alternative would have been better. The newly formed American Nation killed all of our buffalo and all of our carrier pigeons. We treated the Indians no better. One brilliant chief from Coshocton, Ohio, petitioned the Continental Congress to create an Indian state from the tribes in that area. Such ideas were not allowed to see the light of day."

As Mae and Don motored south, Mae shouted and pointed, "There's an Indian restaurant on the Crow Indian Reservation. Let's stop."

"Okay. It's surely not busy. Certainly there's plenty of room to park."

Inside, only a solitary Indian girl was present to wait on them. However, they noticed a tall, well-dressed Indian man and a beautiful girl just taking their seats at a table to eat. Mae whispered, "He's the tallest man I've ever seen! I thought all Indians were short. Are you brave enough to ask them to be our guests for lunch?" suggested Mae.

"Of course, princess." Shortly the three came back to sit with Mae. Lunch was good. Something similar to Mexican food Mae guessed.

"We're not Native Americans, obviously, as you can see. But we're tour-ing the United States. We both have great empathy for the poor treatment our native people have endured from the white settlers."

The giant Crow introduced himself and his wife. "What happened can-not be undone. But my wife and I would like to tell you something of our people." And so most of the afternoon was spent broadening these white people's education."

The chief's wife had carried a large part of the Crow argument: "First, none of the native peoples are 'Indians.' We were incorrectly labeled when the white man incorrectly believed he had reached India when he had reached the New World. 'America' is an artificial name given to our lands because it was the name of a geographer. We are Crows!

"The white immigrants like to refer to themselves as English, French, Italian, German, African, etc. We are no different. We are Crows. All of the native people lived in very rudimentary conditions a century ago. Advances in technology have changed the environment for all of them. We Crows have the same aspirations. We want our children to enjoy these same benefits. Our men have fought in the United States wars to save this country. We want to be a valued and accepted part of the government of *our* land!"

When the Kipfers were under way again, Don spoke. "I'm glad you suggested our stopping, patootie. That was one of the most educational times one could spend in just a few hours."

"Mae, I do believe, according to our map, that we are in the center of the greatest collection of national parks and forests in our nation. Every Ameri-can reveres Mount Rushmore and the gargantuan stone carvings of Presi-dents Washington, Jefferson, Lincoln, and Teddy Roosevelt."

So, when Mae arrived in Keystone, South Dakota, she was prepared: "Don, I've read everything about this sculpture, including how it was carved. I thought I was prepared to accept it. But even from this distance, so many miles away, there is simply only one word to describe it. Awesome!"

On and on, in Mae's favorite country, they motored. "Mae, we've ar-rived at Colorado Springs. You know, of course, that I entered the old Air Corps as a Flying Cadet in 1943. In 1944, West Point 1st Classman Jim Ruth braced me in his room, sweating my shadow on his wall for suggesting that the Air Corps would soon be a service, separate from the Army. I'm sure he's forgotten such stupidity.

"You have been as much a part of our Air Force as I have been. You were the official hostess for General Falois, the first commander in chief of the old Army Air Corp. You were the official hostess for the first astronauts wives in Washington, D.C. You supported your pilot husband through three wars.

Few, living people, if any, know as much about our Air Force as you do. Now you are about to see the source of a large portion of the Air Force's contemporary officer's corp. But that can wait until tomorrow. This afternoon let's motor up Pikes Peak and have dinner at the Stage Coach Inn!"

"Don, you told me that Lieutenant General Ken Tallman was superintendent at the Air Force Academy. His name sounds familiar."

"It should, my dear. It was he and his wife who lived in our house at 3449 South Court Street before we arrived in Montgomery. I arranged to rent that home while I went to Command and Staff School. It was he whom you predicted would be a general because of his shrewdness in selecting a house. He was also my D-2 Company upperclassman and an Army football player from my D-2 Company at West Point. He was one of the few upperclassman who had any compassion whatsoever for fourth classmen!"

"What a small world," commented a dreamy-eyed Mae. "But we're here, not only to see the academy, but we have a date with Brigadier General Bill Woodyard, and my favorite wife, Ruth. "He's dean of faculty here. And I'd love to see Ruth again and relieve our trip to the Middle East."

Just then an Air Force staff car came to their door and a young major hopped out. "Colonel Kipfer?"

Mae was petrified. An emergency in their family? She had been terrified enough by such messages!"

"Sir, I know you had a dinner date with the General Woodyards tonight. I'm sorry to say that General Woodyard suddenly *retired* yesterday. Things at their quarters are pandemonium as you might guess. They will see you for a few minutes at 1800. Please don't make reference to my visit or why the general has retired!"

"Sure, Major, we can do that," replied Don.

When the staff car had left Mae and Don stood, staring at each other. "My lord!" squeaked Don.

"What could have happened," added Mae. 'There goes our reminiscence."

"I suppose no one on the outside will ever know what happened," moaned Don. "Bill is impeccable. Ken Tallman is a fair man. But you can be sure they did not hit it off. But you know when a three-star and a one-star disagree, who must hit the dust!"

Bill and Ruth looked just as they had in Brussels. No one would have guessed that a monumental event had taken place in their lives. They were cordial but naturally no one mentioned dinner."

"Perhaps everyone is aware of the Air Force Academy's trademark building, its ultra-modern, serrated, triangular-shaped chapel," guessed Mae, "but it is much larger and much more impressive when you're standing here in front of it."

After a complete tour of the grounds and conversations with several cadets, Don proclaimed, "Sure, now, its exceedingly modern when compared with West Point. That's as it should be. But the marching and academic standards don't seem so different." Mae could hardly believe one country would hold such diverse places.

Now on to one of their most important visits; Isabel National Park at Buena Vista, Colorado, where David and Jamie now owned eight acres. This time, the four Kipfers were to live in style. Their commodious Comfort trailer contained all the comforts of home.

As soon as the reunion with their son and his wife was completed, David brought out an article from the local paper showing his campsite and now his property with a Mountain Realty FOR SALE sign that had been attached be one tree.

The Kipfers did a double take when they saw the real estate sign posted on a campground on the way up to Cottonwood Lake. At first they assumed some prankster had swiped and posted the sign. Nope, the Kelly's assures them that it was real; eight acres up on middle Cottonwood Creek!

Again they caught all the trout they could eat. They also caught cutthroat trout in the nearby Arkansas River just north of Salida where the Arkansas River International White Water Boat Race is held each year. "Mae," Don cautioned his athletic mate, "You caught larger cutthroat trout than David. He's a little bit down, you know!"

Fun, fun, fun, but finally it was time to start south. None of the Kipfers realized that it would be their last visit to Cottonwood Creek as exigencies led to the property leaving the David Kipfer ownership.

Now the El Dorado with the Comfort trailer attached began its southeasterly trip to the Gulf of Mexico. It passed Dalhart, and Amarillo, where Mae's uncle Cleatus had lived. Then past Lubbock, Big Springs, and past Webb AFB where Don reflexed out of San Angelo. Next came San Angelo, all the old memories, the Little Mexican Café, and on to Lackland AFB where son, David, had quarters on the base.

Don pulled the El Dorado and Comfort trailer into the base's parking lot and Jamie, David, Mae and Don were off to Aransas Pass in David's van, pulling his twenty-foot Mako speedboat.

Don reminded everyone, "We've all been to Aransas Pass, Port Aransas, and Corpus Christi before. It was always a fisherman's paradise."

Nothing had changed. For four heavenly days, Mae relaxed, fishing, dodging waterspouts, oil tankers, and flying fish. Then this revelry was interrupted. On that fateful day when the foursome returned to their motel, the motel owner announced: "You folks probably don't know it, but our telephone link with the mainland is by radio. Sorry to report this message, but we had an emergency call from a Colonel Bebout. He wants you to call him back as soon as possible." Here the owner seemed very reluctant to say anything more, but then he went on, "He says Mrs. Kipfer's father has died!"

The room was paralyzed as if by an electrical charge. Each one of the foursome felt they had been hit by a bolt of electricity. Jamie gulped, "My father has been very sick, It may be him."

Mae asked Don, "Let's call Ron at once. He would hardly be the one to call if it was Jamie's father!"

Don made the connection. Mae took the line, "Mae, this is Ron. I'm sure glad we located you. It took the State Police to do it!"

"Ron, what has happened?"

"I hate to tell you Mae, but Tracy has died. We're delaying the funeral until you can get here."

As all the Kipfers watched, they realized that something terrible had happened by the way Mae seemed to wilt. "My god, Ron, what happened? I didn't even know he was sick. We were planning to have a long visit with him in Newark."

"On the 29th of August he had all the signs of a heart attack. Anna, you well know, is a nurse. She took him to their doctor. He said, 'Pleurisy.' A lie. Tracy even went to a cookout and sang. Next afternoon he was in the hospital with a pacemaker installed. On the 31st he died!"

Mae was trembling. She handed the phone to Don. "Ron, we'll return to San Antonio immediately. Saturday, 2 September or before, we'll fly to Columbus, Ohio. Hopefully before noon, Sunday we'll arrive. Will someone meet us?"

"Yes," agreed Ron.

The return trip to San Antonio and on to Columbus, Ohio, was the saddest, quietest one Don had ever made with Mae. She was simply heartbroken. "Sweetie, I know how much your father meant to you. He was always your number one man. I'm not sure I have ever beat him out. He was a rock. Agree with him or not, Tracy was always constant. You could count on his position in any situation."

The Gentry clan did not subscribe to the joviality of the Irish wake. Still, marriage and deaths were the occasions when everyone of the clan got together and were the ties that strengthened the bindings. Tracy's wife, Anna, his brother Dorsey, his sister Vada, Mae and Don, their sons Charles and Mark, Tracy's daughter Margurette, her husband Ron, their three children, Kevin, Barbara and husband Jerry Childress, Bob White with sons Chad and. Marc, Tracy's daughter Carolyn, his son Tracy Jr. and wife Arlene and kids, Kevin Bebout and wife, Grace and children, Tim Gentry and all the others were present.

It was a time not so much of death as of reunion and strengthening. Stories of Tracy's life were well remembered. When all the sorrow was aired, then submerged, everyone returned to their own lives. Mae and Don returned to San Antonio.

Jamie, David, Mae and Don again visited all the famous places in Cow Town. The Alamo, Lackland AFB Officers Club, Casa Rio, the Teepee, Mi Terra, and the Mexican Market. Again David conned Mae and Don into fishing Medina Lake at Helotes from 10 P.M. until 0800.

They went to visit Bill and Joanne Terrill who were with Don and Mae in Brussels and Bill with Don crossing the Pacific. Bill had always wanted to build his own house. With the help of his two young daughters and two years of time the main structure of huge timbers was complete. But Joanne told Mae and Don in very fiery language, "I don't believe this house will ever be complete. I still haven't a kitchen to cook in!"

Bill and Marge Green lived just outside the gate at Randolph AFB. Bill had been EOAR's flight operations chief in Brussels. The Greens invited Jamie, David, Mae and Don for dinner. Their house was special as was their Texas meal with mesquite-flavored steak. Bill had two bits of news after Don told him, "My last assignment was to provide logistic support for all the Air Force Electronics World Wide, for the space shuttle, and I brought the A-10 into the inventory at Myrtle Beach AFB."

Bill's first news was "Don, after two years of hunting and fishing, my brain was going to sleep. I went back to school and got a degree in horticulture. I have a crew and am now in charge of the grounds at the Alamo! And it was great you were in charge of the support for the A-10. Son Jim flew them in the Gulf War. He blew up thirty-six Iraqi tanks in one day. TAC has just promoted him to full colonel!"

"Tell Jim for me, congratulations. And as an afterthought, he owes me part of a paycheck for putting the A-10, the 'Tank Killer' in the inventory!"

"Reuniting with dear friends," philosophized Mae, "is one of life's great pleasures."

"Next, we're going with Jamie and David to see Kate Findley to do just that. It makes my spine shiver," admitted Mae. "It's been almost thirty years since we lived in that little house in her yard. I wonder if it's still a national monument and still there!"

"Tilden Avenue is still unpaved," joked Don, "and, as I recall, it only is one-block long!"

When Mae rang the bell she was not certain what she would see. But Kate, unlike many people who are unrecognizable, as they grow older, looked just the same, except a little more frail.

"Come in," Kate invited. "Mae, you look wonderful! And I'm so glad to see you both!"

Mrs. Findley and Francis had died, of course. Kate was retired. She asked, "And what about the adorable blond-haired baby you left here with?"

"Charlie's full grown, been over most of the world with us and is married to a nice woman with two boys."

By this time Kate had set the table for tea and cake. "Of course you remember that your cute little house is a National Historic Site."

"You remember that Francis and I were patrons of the art and history here in San Antonio. I suppose that has something to do with it but San Antonio has placed our house, and of course your house, on the list of National Historic Sites! You and Don being Air Force and Don becoming a full colonel of course, has helped!"

Mae nearly screamed, "Well, what a pleasant surprise. We may become as famous as the Alamo!" Of course Mae did not tell Kate Finley that she and Don had seen the notice on the wee house several years earlier.

Then the race for Ohio was on. Mt. Pleasant, Texas, Lake Lana, Tennessee, South Louisville, Kentucky, then Newark Ohio. "Park the trailer next to the garage, Don, I feel like some home cooking. I'm having Mother and Carolyn here tomorrow night for dinner!"

Son Charlie, Jane, John, and Richard arrived a day later. "We'll give them their own 'home away from home.' We'll stay in with mother and Carolyn," decided Mae. Then everyone repeated all the past visit experiences for the benefit of the next generation.

Again it was a reunion cook out at Mound Builders Park, fishing at Rocky Fork Creek, Burning the huge brushpile in the back yard for a winner and marshmallow roast, meeting all the new babies, watching Tamie's cheerleaders perform, repairing the septic tank, and finally the reluctant departure.

Mae could never get past Zelinople if she were any place near. She'd say, "Let's stop and see Uncle Dorsey and Aunt Florence."

Don knew Dorsey had helped Westinghouse with their air conditioning patents and had been rewarded by receiving the use of a company-owned house for life. Her aunt Florence had begun oil painting late in life and had won many awards.

When the Dorsey Gentrys opened their door, Dorsey, tall and handsome as ever, was standing there, his arms stretched high to hug Mae. "Mae, Mae, it's so good to see you," and Don then knew this wonderful man had loved

Mae since she was a baby.

"Aunt Florence, you shouldn't have gone to so much trouble to prepare dinner for us. We were planning to take you out."

Mae's Aunt Florence smiled and hugged Mae. "I'm fixing my best meal, spaghetti and meatballs." Then showing Mae a winsome smile, she added, "Mae, it may be the last time I ever prepare a dinner for you."

Mae asked her Uncle Dorsey, who was unable to drive an automobile, "Is there anything Don and I can do for you while we're here?"

Dorsey looked up, happily, "Yes, Mae, there is. I would like one more time to cruise around Zelinople."

So Don and Mae helped him into the gold El Dorado and toured all the old spots Dorsey remembered. "Mae, I'll point out all the important places to you. And no one will ever believe that I made the trip in a gold El Dorado Cadillac. What a way to meet Saint Peter!"

It really was the last formal dinner meal Mae's Aunt Florence ever prepared. It was the last time Dorsey saw the important sites in Zelinople that described his life. But Dorsey was not quite ready to end his tour that recorded a great deal of his life. Like many an Ohio man raised during the Great Depression, he smiled and requested. "Mae, Mae, let's go to the top of the hill and each get a soft ice cream cone!"

Off again to Bowie, Maryland, where the Comfort trailer was parked in the street in front of Charlie's home. Don and Charles fished the trout streams and the South River. Everyone went to the Sir Walter Raleigh Restaurant, to the Washington Zoo, and to church. Don scraped and painted 1946 N. Woodrow, Arlington, Virginia, where, Captain USN and Mrs. Maggard were their tenants.

Then on to Nagshead for both Kipfer families. Everyone cruised the beautiful beaches and fished in the surf. They visited Wilbur and Orville Wright's memorial and walked the path of the first-heavier than air flight.

Then southward toward their new home. They stopped in South Carolina long enough to inspect a restored turpentine operation. Then on to Punta Gorda, Florida. By phone they learned that Mark and Carole had bought a home and moved to Pony Express Road in Sacramento.

Mae and Don were Euphoric as they moved south through the beautiful tropical marine countryside. But as they rolled south from Arcadia on Route 17, closer to Punta Gorda, Don frowned. "Mae, are we sure we're going to the right place? This road keeps getting more like a buffalo trail the further we go! First a fair, paved road. Now it's barely safe to travel with a trailer. Mae laughed, "The public officials here must know a lot of us carpetbaggers are coming south pulling our trailers. Look at that road sign! VEHICLES TOW-

ING, PROCEED SLOWLY!' Maybe we have made a mistake."

Still, Mae never really panicked. "We did our homework, Colonel. Let's wait and see!"

As soon as they arrived and drove around, they realized that Punta Gorda was beautiful. It's on the pristine Charlotte Harbor with two-hundred square miles of fish-infested waters. Fishing fleets until recently had operated from the center of town and brought their catches to Punta Gorda docks where folks in Southwest Florida came to buy fish, crabs, scallops and shrimp.

"Okay, that is true. There is only one restaurant called Rose City," admitted Mae. She also agreed, "There are only two established trailer parks in town. One is KOA. It's filled. We've been directed to one called Alligator Park!"

"It's not to late to run, patootie!" suggested Don.

"Don't be silly, big boy. I like it here."

Alligator Park was just opening. Ralph and Carolyn Beardsley were the owners. "Would one hundred and twenty-five dollars a month be too much," questioned Ralph. "That includes water, electricity, and sewage."

Don looked at Mae. He recognized her pleasure. "Sold, Ralph; we're your new neighbors!" Later, Don told Mae. "That one hundred twenty-five dollars was our electricity bill where we came from. The time spent here while our house is being built may make us wealthy! Hallelujah!"

4

1970–2000: The Creative Years
Life's Great Rewards

Punta Gorda, Florida—1978

Monday morning, map in hand, Mae and Don went to the Burnt Store Marina to look at the lot they owned. "My God," reacted an astonished Don. Nothing has happened here since we were here twenty years ago; no real marina; not a single house; no golf course; no stores or fire station. And by gosh, it's nearly twenty miles to Punta Gorda!"

Mae wasn't excited, she had not only done her homework, but had memorized her contract. "Don't panic, commander. Remember Al John's contract gives us the right to trade for any available lot, even up in Punta Gorda Isles. Let's see what kind of a man Al really is!"

Don wasn't as sure. "Do you believe everything someone promises you, mad woman?" So Mae and Don met their salesman, Charlie Austin the next morning. While Charlie was in the main office consulting, Mae told Don, "Much more uplifting, eh?"

"Charlie is young, smart and cooperative. He's shown us the exact lot we want and it's an even trade for the one at the marina!"

"Correct, as always, my sweet companion, But I still don't believe it. And Charlie's a real salesman. We already had a modest house plan picked out that we knew would be within our budget. Now we're going to live in a house ten times what I had ever expected. And as son David insisted, being in Florida, we'll need to have a grand pool with a cage."

Mae roared. Things were going her way. "The first time I saw a pool and cage at Arnold Tucker's home, I knew we had to have one. And, my dear, you'll have a dock twenty five feet from your backdoor and access to Earth's total waterways!"

"It sounds to me like you are gung-ho for water cruising. But I don't think I'll ever use all the seas and oceans."

The next day they discussed the plans Charlie Austin had given them with Ron Debock, the PGI building supervisor. Mae was first. She said, "I will settle for nothing less than a separate bathroom. We have here a sketch, which shows how two can be accommodated in the space you have allocated for one. We do not want the dead space you have located for a patio outside the family room. We would be playing footsie with our neighbors."

Then Don tagged on. He had to get his concerns satisfied also: "Ron, I'm retired. I want no exterior maintenance. No wood on the outside. Here is a sketch, which shows how you can fake the exposed beams on our Spanish-style house. Otherwise we are satisfied."

Ron examined the suggested changes. "Can do. No additional cost."

On 19 November 1978, Mae and Don went especially early for their dinner date at the Cramers in order to visit beforehand with Franklin and Helen Southard and Letha and Walter Ritter. They both spent most of their year, winters included, in Venice at their Via Corsa homes. Mae and Don again reviewed these two couples' backgrounds. Helen had been Don's cousin; Mae served as her nanny, caring for her son, Jack, in Newark, Ohio. Franklin had been a lawyer there. Sister Letha's husband had been a chief executive officer for Enterprise Aluminum, then superintendent for the Enterprise Division in Eaton, Georgia. Now, of course, they were retired. "We are so happy" bubbled Helen, "Mae and Don, to have you so near."

Letha, Don's cousin and mother of Terry and Jane, whom Don had tried unsuccessfully to interest in his West Point roommate so many years ago in Dayton, Ohio, was just as warmhearted. "Perhaps now we can see more of you two world travelers."

Reminiscences were recalled, handshakes and sweet kisses were exchanged. Then on to the Cramers for dinner.

After thirty-five years in the military, Don kept encountering people who had previously worked with him. Doctor Lee and Bea Long were examples. Lee was an optical expert who was Don's and the USAF's representative on the international The Optical Measurements Program (TOM). Since he had retired, he had been rung out by one of the legal but rather shady developers in Southwest Florida. When Don and Mae met them at their new home in Osprey, they were beaming.

Bea said with excitement, "Mae and Don, we've been waiting so long for you to get here. We even went to see your property down at Burnt Store Marina. Now we're going to have a pleasant dinner and talk about all the things you've been doing."

Doctor Lee was just as enthusiastic. "Don, you remember I'm an amateur radio buff. After dinner you and I and Mae can talk to some of my radio friends. I have radio contacts in almost every industrialized country on Earth!"

After an information exchange at dinner that brought everyone up to date, Mae and Don were really impressed by talking with some of Lee's contacts. "Remarkable, Lee. You're doing something you love and you'll never be lonely."

The Cramers, who had known Mae for so long, covertly adopted the newly arrived Kipfers. So, as planned, Mae and Don departed Alligator Park for Cramers and Thanksgiving dinner. Mae confirmed the arrangements. "We seem to almost be living with the Cramers. Do you think they've adopted us?"

"Could be. They have no children and Fay has known you since you were in college."

It was then that Don seemed to realize something he had always known, was thankful for, but had come to accept. "Mae, I want a picture of you right here and now." He stopped the car, both got out and he posed his beautiful wife against a palm tree and snapped. But the real picture of Mae was stored in his own memory.

Don had seen the most beautiful women from allover the world; Ingrid Bergman, Ava Gardiner, and Marilyn Monroe were among the best. But his wife, Edna Mae Gentry Kipfer, eclipsed them all. Mae never appeared outside her boudoir unless she was at her best. Don had never seen her vexed in even the most harrowing situation. Here she stood. After thirty years of the most intolerable stressing life, in a beautiful Hawaiian ensemble, her gorgeous hair upswept, her figure perfect, able to pass as the twenty-three-old who had been his bride. How could any man be so fortunate?

It was on that 23 November 1978 that Thanksgiving was at the Cramers. Dr. Emmord and Kay Pyles were also dinner guests. It was a wonderful day. Afterwards Mae told Don, "Can you believe Emmord is a surgeon and blind in one eye? And his nurse/wife seems to think that's perfectly normal. You know that missing one eye ruins your depth perception. He might get your pancreas instead of your gall bladder!"

"But Mae, that's not as bad as the relationship between the Bob and Ceil Henrys and the Cramers. And, believe it, they just met casually on the front of North Port's Golf Club. Ceil was a GS-15 in the federal government. Bob was a highly paid horticulturist. They came down to North Port to look for a lot near a Golf Course but didn't find anything they liked. Just by chance as they explained to us, they happened to meet the Cramers at the club house. Lou agreed to look for a lot they could build on. Lou found one he thought they would like and the Henrys bought it sight unseen. It was a typical Florida land purchase."

"Remarkable," agreed Mae, "Unbelievable. Still, meeting Bob was good fortune. He told you in just three sentences how to take care of your lawn so it would always be green and beautiful!"

"True. And to use Lou's famous prayer, I also say, 'appreciate!'"

On 12 December Don and Mae went again for dinner at the Cramers to celebrate the Kipfer's "Notice of Commencement" on 825 Via Formia. Three days later they made the first draw as downpayment on their home and celebrated ground breaking later at the Sarasota Yacht Club where the manager was another one of the Cramers' adopted sons.

Of course, time was flying by. They were to spend a rather strange Christmas at Doctor and Mrs. Emmord Pyle's home in Sebring. After a gargantuan meal, Lou informed Mae, by Jiminie, "Mae, we're going to build a complete concrete patio today for Emmord's house." Don whispered to Mae. "It's certainly a different way for me to celebrate Christmas!"

Mae laughed. "My dear, everyone here is an Adventist. We believe that the seventh day, Saturday, is the holy day. Christmas is not so big for us as for you!"

"Oh," gasped Don.

Burnt Store Country Club

Home again in Punta Gorda, even though the Don Kipfers seemed to be settled in Alligator Park forever, life was assuming a civilian flavor. "Mae, you're the professional golfer in the family. You know I have no ambition in that direction. However, without Don's knowledge, Mae signed him up for the BSCC men's Friday golf tournament. "But Don, you have to play, coaxed Mae. You're already signed up!"

After that first tournament Mae asked very apprehensively, "Well, Snead, how did it go?"

"Not bad. I played with three nice guys. I was given a handicap by Al Kousie even though I had a card from our pro in Sacramento certifying I was a twenty-four!"

"Who's Al Kousie?" "He's Al John's starter. He and his wife ran the course from a houseboat on Alligator Creek behind the eighth hole until a few months ago when the course went from nine to eighteen holes."

And so began Don's, Mae's and their combined records at BSCC for the remainder of the century. Mae was confident that Don would be a great golfer. It made no difference to her that his career was starting in his mid-fifties. She rejected the famous golfer, Greg Norman's thesis that he was a nearly forgotten golfer because he had reached the ripe old age of forty-seven.

Ladies Golf

Almost upon her arrival Mae was contacted by Eiko Visvary, who was to be the club champion at Burnt Store Country Club, Kingsway Country Club, and after it was constructed, at Saint Andrew Country Club. "Mae, this is Eiko Visvary. I know you are a low handicapper and are from California. I know you really know the USGA rules of golf. We want you to be with BSCC Ladies golf team."

"How's the team doing?" Mae asked Eiko.

"I hate to tell you, Mae. We're last!"

"Okay, Eiko. I'll play. But I don't play on losing teams. That has got to change!"

It took three years. Meantime Mae became BSCC tournament chairmen, handicap chairman, birdie chairman, BSCC Ladies Golf president, team cocaptain, captain, and president of the SW Florida's Ladies Golf Association. Finally, with Mae insisting they would settle for nothing less, BSCC Ladies finally won first place in SouthWest Florida's annual golf ten team round robin!

Eva Merrick, one of Mae's favorite cousins, and her husband, Roy, lived in Naples, Florida. Mae announced, "Don, I'd like to go down and see Eva. I know she's been sick. Perhaps I can help. You remember her best, I'm sure from our fishing trips with her at Sugar Island, in Lake George."

Roy declined to go with them, but Don, Mae and Eva went to the Pirates Cove, the nicest restaurant in downtown Naples and had a slow, pleasant reunion. Eva and the Kipfers relived again the times Mae, Don, and their sons fished at Eva's fathers, Fritz Glaunsinger's cottage off Sugar Island in Lake George. Mae was secretly terrified when Eva announced in a rather offhanded way, "Mae, Mae, I want you to know I have cancer. I'm dying!"

It took a bit of time for Mae to collect her composure. "But Eva, you're an Adventist. You've never smoked nor inhaled secondary smoke. You've never drank. You've lived on a diet of fruit and vegetables. How could such a thing happen?"

"Mae, no one knows. For some reason it is God's will." Naturally Mae could not shake her abhorrence of someone as sweet and young as Eva being terminated!

But back in Punta Gorda, things kept moving. In a flurry, Warren Wefler, with Ruth Ann, visited; Bud, Arlene, and Tammy visited for a week; Lorraine Douglas of 1948 San Antonio vintage stopped in; Don and Carole Powell came as houseguests.

Then, on Sunday, 29 April 1979, the year of our Lord, in a BSCC Golf Tournament, Don Kipfer, Mae's non-golfing husband broke 80 with a 79!

After the shocking news Mae had received in Naples, she wanted to spend Thanksgiving in Naples with her ailing cousin, Eva.

Mae and Don entered the Staywell Program run by the Adventist Medical Center Hospital of Punta Gorda. "It's the most wonderful program we've ever seen!" said Don.

Don was so impressed that when President Bill Clinton asked for suggestions to improve the nation's health, he sent a complete, detailed explanation of the system. Unfortunately, nothing ever came of it. Perhaps, politicians sometimes don't really want answers to the questions they pose.

Mae, from her nurse's training, told one of her close BSCC friends, "In the Staywell program, they take specimens and give tests on every organ and process in the human body. They print out your record and compare it with the normal for each function. Then they have medical doctors come in and tell you how to change each of your results to match the norm!"

Don silently applauded. "Staywell says I have lowered my psychological age by five years! The price is nominal." Again he repeated, "The U.S. government should use this program for all our citizens. The cost initially would be high but in the long run the cost for medical support would diminish and the country's health would improve astronomically."

Mae shook her head. "Socrates, you work on that!"

Some so called disadvantaged people might be resentful because of the smooth lifestyle enjoyed by Mae and Don or because they believed they were a part of the wealthy class. "No one," emphatically defending their success, said Mae, "would ever understand the frightful economic level at which your family and mine struggled during the Great Depression. The myriad government support programs available today to any destitute person who troubles to use them, make our disadvantaged persons today, far better off than we, at one time, ever hoped to be!"

"Enough on that subject," yawned Don. "Christmas is almost here. A little bird told me, girl, you've never owned a two-wheeled bicycle. That's going to change!" And so, long since a grandmother, Mae became the proud owner of a new, handsome, two-wheeled bicycle!"

Al Johns, the developer of communities from Saint Petersberg to Fort Myers and from east of I-75 to the Gulf of Mexico, was a man of rare talent and compassion. As a part of his repertoire, each Christmas he sponsored the PGI Ball, held at the Community Center in Punta Gorda, free of charge for hundreds of PGI couples. Mae coaxed Don, "This is the social event of the year here in Punta Gorda. If you'll help me, I'm going to organize everyone here in our neighborhood to go." And long before the Neighborhood Watch Organization, Mae knew, "It'll solidify our neighborhood!"

"Great idea," agreed Don. "It will also improve our already fabulous security. Our cooperation might really be called a Neighborhood Watch."

Few people who flowed into Florida after the 1950s knew what being a "cracker" meant. Those were men who went into the swamps and bush with long whips, snapping them so they cracked, bringing out wild cattle for sale in Cuba. Those crackers, who were here first when our government didn't know what to do with the swamps of Florida, often bought land for ten cents an acre. Now Doris and Chuck King's father was such a land baron. He owned land from Punta Gorda to Tampa. But time had changed all that. Doris, their neighbor, never referred to those times but in her eyes Mae and Don could see her hurt when she wished she could say, "If you carpetbaggers, if you snowbirds, if you geese, only knew!"

"My dear, already my clothes are Hawaiian. We have a boat and we're on access water to all the Earth's water supply. Our landscaping plan calls for pineapple, star fruit, avocados, papaya, oranges, grapefruit, bananas, and macadamia nuts. What else can you want?"

"Somethings missing, Kamehameha, What is it?"

"I agree, Lelane. I think it's the Hawaiian Tiki gods you see every where in the islands. I'm going to carve a male and female for us!"

"Good, But I've never seen a female Tiki god. "

"Nor have I. But I'm going to create her and she'll hula with Kona."

Don could not miss the truck and fifth-wheel that pulled in beside their Comfort trailer several months after the Kipfers arrived. When he saw the couple outside their rig he waved, "I'm Don Kipfer. This is my wife, Mae, and as you know, we're neighbors."

"This is my wife, Verna. I'm Ivan Wine. We're building a house south of here."

"I was wondering, Ivan," joked Don, "if you ever hauled anything useful in your truck?"

Having just met Don, Ivan hardly knew what to say. "What do you mean?"

"Well, I need to get two logs about six and one half feet long and thirty inches in diameter from a sawmill about fifteen miles up I-75. I was wondering if I could pay you to do the job?"

"Pay, heck," came back the answer. "I don't have anything to do. Let's go!" And thus began a foursome friendship of dinner parties, fishing, golf, and load hauling."

The sculpting of Kona and Lelone became a gathering place of twenty to thirty people from Alligator Park each morning. One lady seemed worried and Don heard her ask Mae, "I can see Kona's arms and legs but how is he going to give him teeth?"

When the sculpting was complete, Don told Mae, "Even I'm satisfied."

And Mae agreed, "Now our backyard will truly be Hawaiian."

Nearly everyone had their picture snapped with the Hawaiian gods. Mae and Don, Marylou and Bill Blouser, Margarette and Ron Bebout, and their children, Tracy and the Gentry children, Jamie and her sister, David Kipfer, Carole and Don Powell, Anna and Carolyn Gentry, Don Jr. and Jane Kipfer and their family, Faye and Lou Cramer, and a multitude of others. Don could not know that years later, people who did not remember his name, remembered the tiki gods that were carved at Alligator Park!

Don had been forced as a matter of protocol to play in a few golf tournaments that he couldn't avoid during his Air Force days. After Mae had arbitrarily signed him up for men's day tournament she waited. "See, dear," Mae consoled her reluctant husband, "your handicap has gone down to 15!

"Now you're going big time. Sam. You're going to be in your first mixed-doubles tournament here at BSCC. Husband and wife are not permitted to play together."

When Don saw that his fifteen handicap made him team captain, he was ready to leave. His team started in the shotgun start from the par five, tenth hole. His drive was especially long but hooked out of bounds! That was a loss of stroke and distance penalty.

Lee Varlie, an especially good female golfer, a dynamo and an especially straight talker, almost screamed, "Damnit, Don, you're our captain. If you don't straighten up, we're not going to win this tournament!"

When Don told Mae about this later, she went into a spasm of laughter. "That's Lee. What did you do?"

"I straightened up. You know Lee."

Mae could barely contain herself. "You must have, You came in third out of twenty-five teams!"

The Kipfers were really settling in. Golf four times a week. Mae had already been tournament chairman and president of the BSCC Ladies Golf Association. She had rocked the association considerably. She insured that the best-qualified lady golfers played on their ladies golf team; no fraternalism. She, with Majel Anderson, originated and implemented the first constitution for the BSCC Ladies Golf Association. Mae personally met all the new BSCC female members. She made them feel welcome and encouraged them to play golf in the nine or eighteen hole tournaments. Burnt Store Golf Club began to take on the form of the Country Club it was to become!

Bridge and Such

Don and Mae played party bridge both privately and at BSCC and duplicate with one group. Mae and Don, with sometimes a visitor, caught enough trout, sheepshead, snapper, snook, cobia, tripletail, and shark to supply the neighborhood with fish. Mae assisted Don as he wrote and published a novel *Punta Gorda* and while he painted oils for and published two thousand calendars of Punta Gorda, featuring its fabulous scenes. The Kipfers had settled in!

Punta Gorda at that time may have been one of the most invigorating small towns in the nation. At that time there were four couples in Mae's weekly party bridge club. The Colonel Kipfers, the Jim Berrys, the largest importer of Cinzano wine in the United States; the U.S. Navy's Al and Jan Towers and the British diplomats, Tim and Joy Stride.

"These folks are certainly typical of the arriving citizens of Punta Gorda," concluded Mae. "Joy has told me all about their exciting experiences as first secretary for the British Empire in Indonesia."

"And Tim has pitched right in to our county affairs. He's especially important in our home security programs."

But it was not long before Mae came very disturbed to Don: "You know the Strides own that big home. They own a large yacht. They pay taxes. And Tim has been an important man in running our county government. Now someone has found out they have overstayed their visa and are threatening to deport them!"

"For haggin's sake. Has our government lost its collective minds? When an illegal immigrant hits our shore there are bleeding hearts waiting to provide him with money, medical care, housing, food, and a job. He may never pay a dollar in taxes. I'll talk to Tim!"

Don went the very next evening to see Tim. "I've learned about the threat to deport you, Tim."

"Seems both myself and Joy are undesirable types."

"Hardly. A *faux pas*. Tim, keep this whole thing low key. I know several senators and representatives. You two are a national treasure. They can slip an amendment to correct your documentation on some popular bill and this misunderstanding will disappear."

"But it seems that people who are up to no good have the most energy," Don explained to Mae. "Tim's problem has hit the newspapers. Now no political figure will touch it. Fairness is no longer a part of the equation!"

"How sad," said Mae.

Christmas in 1982 was a grand affair at 825 Via Formia. Lunch was at the Hatch Cover with the Langstons. David's Christmas greeting from the 509th Air Refueling Squadron, Pease AFB, New Hampshire, showed forty-two officers in flying uniforms. David was second in command. "Quite an honor, eh, Mae?"

"Of course, *mon signor*. We can both be proud!"

Could anyone expect the Kipfers to settle for long? The wanderlust was creeping into the Kipfers' lives again. Mae and Don had always attempted to stay in touch with events in the old hometowns. Don found out there was a large colony of Washington High School classmates living in Southern California. As Don and Mae were returning to Sacramento again to visit Mark and Carole, Don seized his opportunity. He wrote to Elane Barth and suggested the colony have a mini reunion he could attend.

Back came the reply, "*Ole!*"

Mae questioned Don. I believe I know but why do you believe so many of your most able classmates have left Massillon?"

Don sort of looked up at the sky: "Nothing's black and white, my dear. You left Academia and Newark without blinking. I know you'll swear it was for me. But if I had never came along you would still have had too much education, to much ambition, to much talent for the community to have held you.

"In the days of the Erie Barge Canal, Massillon was a power. When Paul Brown coached at Massillon Washington High School, they were National Football champions six years in a row. But then America's heavy industry went overseas. Massillon's leaders realized the consequences of this to them, but too late. Men like Bob Heckert, Dr. Jack Oliver, Melvin Milligan, and myself, left. The women, too, like Elaine Barth, and Dorthy Green, also bailed out. When a city loses its most competent citizens, it loses everything," said Don.

The great reunion in Southern California was a blowout Bob Heckert and his wife, Joe Cicchinelli and his wife, Elaine Barth, Dorothy Green and all the others were eager to attend. Mae and Don and a dozen others were all in a party and talking mood after forty years of separation. "My," said Mae, later, "some of your classmates' stories were hard to believe."

On 22 January 1982 a new irresistible impulse slipped into Mae and Don's life. Don told her, "Mae, we've had thirty-five years of complete twenty-four-hour-a-day concentration on duty to country. Now we're going to do something totally different!"

"What do you mean, paisan? Our schedule is overloaded already."

Don had said, "We need something more personnel. I watched the organist at the Punta Gorda Civic Association before Christmas at the carol singing. We can play a modern, electronic organ!"

So Mae and Don pressured the Dick Andersons to embark on the same project and they both purchased an electronic organ. With the purchase came free lessons. Thus began a weekly ritual with the Andersons of organ lessons with Rick in Fort Myers and dinner thereafter over all of Southwest Florida. Over time, Mae and Don became proficient enough to read and play any music score satisfactorily.

From 13 May to 2 June, Mae and Don visited Sacramento again to see Mark and Carole and play golf on all the old golf courses.

On 8 July 1982 Mae and Don played golf with David Proctor, Burnt Store Country Club's professional, and his wife, Joan. On 23 August they played golf with David Proctor's brother, Ernie, and his wife, Marge. "Those two brothers," declared Don, "are worthy of starring in a best-seller all by themselves!"

I know," agreed Mae, "they were both born and raised in Rhodesia. They loved their country. David was amateur golf champion of the British Empire. Ernie was just as good."

"True, and how ironical life is."

"We know they are a part of contemporary history. They are intelligent men. When destitute blacks began slaughtering whites in Rhodesia, the Proctors departed for South Africa. When life became uncertain for them in South Africa, they came to the United States. I'm sure they have no intention of moving again."

"Roger. It is our gain. They'll never look back."

On 26 November, Mae assisted the Women's USGA representative Mrs. Mudd rate BSCC's golf course. Mrs. Mudd talked to Mae when they had completed their rating. "Mae, you are overqualified. How would you like to join our rating team?"

Mae was flattered but as usual her normal, sane self: "But I would be traveling all the time. I wouldn't want to leave my husband alone so much."

Mrs. Mudd laughed as though husbands were incidental and said, "Bring him along, Mae. We'll pay his expenses!"

Mae was perhaps one of the most experienced persons of her generation. "Mrs. Mudd, I don't believe Don would enjoy following we female experts all over Florida!"

Christmas at Don's home when he was small had been an opportunity for children to peek into fantasy world. When Mae and Don flew into Punta Gorda from Tampa during pre-Christmas festivities, Mae had been as delighted as a child on Christmas morning. "Don, I've never seen anything decorated like Punta Gorda. Yes, Mexico City was fabulous, but Punta Gorda looks like one huge, glorious flower!"

"Yes, Punta Gorda certainly looks Christmasy on the ground, but from the air it is spectacular. The lighting of all the canals does have its effect."

Thus Mae plotted an action, which would continue for many decades, that she called her "Trim the Tree Party." It was to be a part of her Christmas for the rest of her life. "Don, some day my party will be large. But for this first run I'm only inviting Margurette and Ron, Joan and David Proctor, and Marge and Ernie Proctor. I'll serve cocktails and a full dinner. I'll have the tree in place with its lights strung. While we ladies are placing the ornaments you, Van Cliborne, can play Christmas carols on the organ."

Afterwards Don admitted, "Mae, your food was delicious and the ambiance was perfect. I'm sure it was one of the best Christmases everyone had ever experienced. Lighting the tree in a midnight-dark room was genius. You are commended!"

In those early days, when Punta Gorda Isles was just coming into existence, the community was close-knit and everyone was supportive of each other. For its New Year's Eve celebration the neighborhood had an unusual party. Mae had evaluated their plan. "Don, this night the party begins at the Hick's home. They have an outdoor pool and everyone is expected to swim. I'm planning to go in formal attire and with an upswept hairdo. You can believe I'm not going swimming."

From the Hick's home they went to the Prescotts' for hors d'oeuvres and cocktails. By midnight the whole shebang were back at the Kipfers for a late dinner and fireworks. "My everlasting soul," complained Don. "Some of these folks are staying for an early breakfast!"

Mae laughed, "I expected it, Napoleon. Remember I served military duty and entertained military officers in Canada!" Mae had talked Don into showing some of his work at the PGICA Arts Show on 30 January. "You have some very good stuff, Michael. Oil paintings, calendars, several novels, and beautiful wood carvings."

"Are you sure, Mae? I made my bones years ago at a totally different trade. I don't care to tarnish that record by doing something foolish."

"Try it, *mon ami*, you'll like it."

Don's work was admired by many patrons, especially for their original ideas. It turned out that Don did like the show. And so began his interest in writing, painting and sculpting.

Along with all the other activities, Mae's expertise in golf kept improving and on 26 January 1983 Mae bested Carlson, 3-2 for the Burnt Store Country Club's Ladies Golf Championship.

From 15 through 25 February, Don's aunt Glenda, of European tour fame, visited Mae and Don. She told Don, "I really didn't know if I should impose on you and Mae or not, but I did want to come. Dick said, 'GO' and so here I am."

For Don it was a memorable time. Nearly all his close relatives were gone. "Mae, Uncle Melvin and Aunt Annie, my father and mother, my uncle Howard are all gone on the Kipfer side of my family. Only Aunt Glenda remains. It will be a trip down sunshine lane for me. And it was. He and his aunt toured the sights and cruised the canals while Mae played golf. All three hit the best restaurants in Charlotte County at night. Mae really made Don feel good. She announced, "Aunt Glenda is a good houseguest. She's full of fun."

Don sat silently, meditating over desert at the Kipfers' dinner table. Mae wondered what important action he was about to divulge, "Mae, Punta Gorda has been everything, it seems that we hoped for. What do you think?"

"What you say is true. It's a place of magic. Our daily schedules are bursting with fun things to do. Why do you bring this up?"

"For a very good reason. Before we were married, I promised to show you the world. You have seen North America, Europe, parts of South America, Asia, and Africa, New Zealand and Austrailia. Now we're going to add to your journey!"

"Oh? Goody! Where?"

"Our first experiment will be to the Yucatan Peninsula. I'll need your expert help in planning our campaign."

While awaiting their departure south, Mae and Don went north to see Leroy Flounders and his wife, Evie, in Lewiston, Maine. Lee had been Don's business partner when Don was just in junior high school. And although Mae hadn't realized it, she was to get a real test of her French-speaking ability. The French Canadians were a majority where Leroy lived. In those old days in Massillon, Don could never get Leroy to a dance. Now he and Evie went dancing at their club several times a week. From what Mae could determine, "Don, these people are all French. And Lee says they are lumbermen. They make the rafters shake when they dance! And they deafen your ears when they talk and sing."

"True. I can only wonder at the metamorphosis that Lee and I have undergone in forty years! He's a terrific dancer!"

"Now you understand, Caesar. Love can work greater wonders on a man than any other emotion," contributed Mae.

On their way back south, Don couldn't help an evaluation. "Lee surely lives where history was once made. I really enjoyed rubbing elbows with the French Canadians and visiting the Coast Guard Light Station at Portland Head and Fort Georges."

Back in Punta Gorda, Mae and Don caught a fifty-pound cobia and a twenty-two pound triple tail. Mae was preparing to pick another huge bunch of bananas. "Don, I love to eat these 'silky figs' as our Caribbean black friends refer to our small, plump bananas."

The Bebouts, Crammers and Whites all dropped in for dinner. With great pride Mae showed them an eight-inch sea horse she had unbelievably caught that morning on a shrimp baited hook in Charlotte Harbor!

Believe it or not! After four years of domestic tranquility, Mae was about to enter the international jet set again. It was time to be off to Merida, the capitol of the former empire of the Mayan now centered in the Yukatan. "The Mayans, we learned," said Mae, "are proud that Merida had never been captured by the Spanish."

Don explained, "Why not! But they had powerful help. The Yucatan, and Merida, was separated from the rest of Mexico and especially from Mexico City, by nearly impassible mountains. It was the collecting point for all the gold and silver from the Pacific coast of South America. These treasures were transported overland and then by sea to Spain."

"I just love the outside markets," gushed Mae. "I'm sure they are just like they were in Columbus' time."

"And dig these people's clothing. No fake. They're the same people who built the great pyramids and temples," added Don.

Young and full of vim and vigor, up and down the pyramids topped by temples, went Mae and Don. Mae sat on the lap of Quetzalcóatl's stone statue. "I wonder if Quetzalcóatl will be angry with me or bring me good luck?"

"Even Quetzalcóatl would want to bring you good luck, my dear. What art! I've asked everyone including our guide, to see the tools the Mayans used to work these millions of stone blocks, some of them weighing dozens of tons, or the means of moving them. All of our guides have ignored me."

"That, my dear Watson, is because they don't know."

Up and into the interior of the pyramids through low-ceilinged passageways to the burial chamber they went. Mae almost exploded, "My man, have you noticed that the Mayans built and carved just like the Egyptians, only better? Have you noticed the color of these people's skin and their long, narrow heads with sharp pointed noses? I care not what some stuffy professor setting in his university says. These people and their culture are at the very least first cousins to the Egyptians. These people look and think in no way like the Eskimo nor our own North American Indians."

"I'm on your side, fellow explorer. I believe you, great oracle," smiled Don, pleased that he had at least one adherent.

The Mayans tall, circular planetarium was simply mind-boggling to a man like Don who had so much to do with America's space program. "Mae, these people, nearly two thousand years ago, could tell time more accurately than we were able to do until the laser was invented!"

In Chichén Itzá, where anthropologists and modern civil engineers had restored many of the ancient buildings, the scenes were simply mind boggling. At the night show of lights Mae huddled near Don and said, "This show makes my spine shiver. It's spooky!"

Next, Mae and Don were to see the bureaucrats at work. The travel agency apparently wanted us to see a Mexican Government sponsored luxury seashore town. "But Cozumel is grand," laughed Mae.

"The Mexican government is either a bit inept at business relations or attempting to make sure their facilities are one hundred percent occupied," concluded Mae, when their thirty-person group found out from the tour director when they arrived in Cozumel that no one was expecting them and that no one had reserved a room for them to stay in.

After a wait, however, taxis came to take them to the hotel where they mistakenly believed they had been booked. The tour director announced, "Things are nearly back on track. First, everyone is going to a private dining room upstairs. Pick any meal you want from the menu. No charge. Drinks are on the house!"

Mae pretended to complain, "But, señor, I don't drink!" It turned out there were only half enough rooms. Don told Mae, "We're to stay the night with the Moellas, dear. The room has two double beds. We must be quiet as mice."

"That'll be the day, Romeo," moaned Mae.

So it had been with humor and a little sarcasm that the whole group accepted the new arrangements and moved on.

But Don had another project in mind: "Mae, you remember the Mayans never discovered the arch that is essential to our buildings. They used ciracote wood over all their huge, heavy doorways. That wood has been in place for two centuries and it is in the same condition it was in when they first set it in place. I must have some ciracote for a carving!"

Mae smiled, "Well, it took Michaelangelo years to find a huge block of white marble he felt was suitable for his masterpiece, David. What makes you believe you can find a ciracote log here in Cozumel?"

"Mae and Don ducked into the restaurant in downtown Cozumel where the six couples from their tour group planned to eat a Mexican dinner that night. "Well?" quoth Mae.

"The manager told me there's a sawmill just out of town. It's easy walking distance. They'll have it!"

The owner of the sawmill was tall and handsome and could easily have been mistaken for Caesar Romero. "Mae, he doesn't speak a word of English. What can I do?"

"Just get out of my way, boy," joked Mae. "Remember I'm somewhat of an expert in the French and Spanish languages."

Mae spoke the word *ciracote* several times, pointing from an eight-foot-long log about ten inches in diameter. She formed her hands into a ten-inch diameter circle and then held them twenty inches apart."

"Will it work, do you think?" asked Don.

"It's worked in world trade circles for centuries, guru, but no need to wonder," chuckled Mae as the handsome man picked up his chain saw. Within seconds, a log to Mae's specifications was bound with a rope so Don could carry it over his shoulder..

"Diez pesos, amigo," determined the hombre and Don happily paid.

"Mae, your Spanish was wonderful!"

Back to the restaurant they went and got permission from the manager to store the ciracote log until dinner time. In route to the restaurant, almost every Mexican man they passed laughed and pointing, shouted, *"Mas grande!"*

"Must be a real treasure, DaVinci. *Mas grande?*" speculated Mae.

It was not the end of the saga of the ciracote log. After it dinner the Kipfers carefully transported it by taxi to their hotel. Next day they took the same care in transporting it to the airport.

"My heavens, Quetzalcóatl, that's twice you put that tagged and addressed ciracote log in the baggage loading line and twice the custom porters removed it and stacked it along the wall!"

"Never mind, my dear, their Mayan treasure is going to the United States with me!" Mae laughed as Don removed the ciracote log from the luggage roundel at the Miami airport. "Well, Mayan expert, you did it!"

Don wasn't so sure as he wrestled the log out the exit door and set it next to the luggage compartment of the bus their tour group was taking to Punta Gorda. When he returned to the bus with their luggage, he screamed like a banshee. "Damn, Mae, the log is gone!"

A search turned up nothing. The bus driver was getting nervous. Suddenly one of Don's buddies whispered, "I believe I saw that log over behind the check-in desk."

Everyone roared. Mae did not. "I'm afraid Don doesn't see the humor." That night in Cozumel at dinner with a total of six couples from the tour group, at their sumptuous Mexican meal when someone asked Don, "Do you know Dom Moella's wife?"

Don stood up, as though in respect for this gracious lady. Mae was aghast for no one could guess what Don might say. "Everyone, I've just been asked if I know Dom Moella's wife. I should. I slept with her last night!"

The Moellas slumped in their chairs. Everyone else was stricken mute. Then the truth registered, and everyone howled. The Moellas relaxed. The two couples were close friends for rest of their lives.

On the group's last day they were scheduled for a picnic on the beach. They all waited on the puny dock near the hotel. "By Blackbeard's oath," shouted Mae, "here comes a two-masted pirates' ship and its the captain, I suppose, who's yelling at the top of his voice."

"The captain is yelling at us, dear. He's shouting *¡Vamos, hombres! ¡Vamos!*"

"I believe that means, 'Let's get going,'" agreed Mae. On board their pirate ship, they could see a burly, pirate crew. These pirates were sitting on the deck. Mae was awestricken for she suspected what was going on. "Don, they've dumped those two huge buckets of fish on the deck and they're pouring warm sea water over them from buckets full they've hauled up from the ocean."

Before Don could answer, one of their uninformed but positive fellow travelers told Mae, "That's bait for us to fish."

Don didn't want trouble. He told Mae in confidence, "My dear, that's not fish bait. It's our picnic!"

"*Hombre*, I hope you're wrong," sneered Mae.

Their boat anchored off one of the most beautiful beaches Mae had ever seen. "Don, have you ever seen such beautiful, clear water? I can see Imperial Crown shells covering the bottom. We must have some of those."

So, after landing, Mae and Don waded out to collect several of the magnificent, huge, colorful shells. After Don retrieved the first, he agonized, "Mae, robbers have destroyed everyone of these shells. They are all worthless. That's the reason they are here. Each shell had been crushed and the creature removed to serve as dinners for we tourists!"

"Oh, my—"

Once more home in Punta Gorda the travelers found the parade of houseguests continued. Golfing, bridge, writing, painting and fishing filled the gaps. It was a grand summer for Mae and Don on Charlotte Harbor. Mae summarized: "Imagine, a sixty-five pound cobia and a twenty-four-pound triple tail. We're pros, captain. I mean pros. When you have to put an oar through a fish's mouth and out his gill so that it can be placed on each of our shoulders to lift him, that's memorable!"

When you have served together so many years in the military, your friends always wonder what has become of you when you become a civilian. So Mae was not surprised when she received a letter from a Canadian friend from the past who asked, "Mae, are you still so active as you were here in

Canada?"

Mae wrote back: "Eunice, here is one of our typical months when we are not on a cruise.

11 December 1983 Church AM; 1230 golf with Wilsons

12 December 1983 Day-long fishing

13 December 1983 Mae beauty Parlor, Don Golf practice, Sears deliv ery

14 December 1983 Mae golf, PGI Formal Dinner Dance, 2000-2400

15 December 1983 Mae's Member/Guest golf, Kingsway, Couple Twi light

16 December 1983 1530–1730 Christmas caroling; Christmas Lights up

17 December 1983 Pick bushels of oranges; Heiber 1800 dinner& bridge

25 December 1983 Mae's Trim The Tree Party; 50 for Dinner/cocktails

30 December 1983 Pauline Doneley, Cub Scout leader, 35 years ago

31 December 1983 New Years Eve Neighborhood Party, 2100

No individual month was much different, but the year 1984 was a time of super activity for even Mae and Don. Son, Charlie, had heart surgery for a quadruple bypass on 2 February. Such an event was extremely traumatic. Don, who had a severe case of the flu, was not able to attend.

Every Sunday and Thursday Mae and Don played couples tournament golf with another couple. On 9 February they played with the James as partners. Colonel Ben James, "Smiling Ben," as he was known among Air Force pilots, was an especially good friend of the Kipfers as both couples played golf and bridge together. "Smiling Ben" retired as a full colonel and served during the same years as Don.

Ron Bebout, Mae's sister Margurette's husband, was a neighbor of Mae's when she was a teenager. Don had known him since he and Margarette were married. Ron was now a retired Ohio Army National Guard colonel awaiting his first retired paycheck. The Kipfers and Bebouts exchanged dinners, played golf and bridge at least once a week. One night in mid-March, when the Bebouts were just sitting down to dinner at the Kipfers, Ron grimaced and announced. "Sorry folks, but I'm just to sick to stand it. I can't sit here and eat. I'll have to go lie down."

Needless to say, Mae and Don were shocked. Mae turned to Margarette. "What in the world is wrong? We didn't know Ron was sick."

"Ron's been sick maybe six months," answered Margarette. "He's been to three doctors. They can't find anything."

Late that evening, Don quizzed Ron, "If you feel that bad I wonder if they found anything in your military retirement physical?"

Ron looked sheepish. "Well, I didn't have a military doctor do my physical. I arranged to have my own civilian doctor do it. He said I had a spot on one of my lungs but it was probably just an old tuberculoses scar. Many Ohioans had them."

Don managed to get Mae alone. She told him, "God save Ron. I'm going to get him an appointment with a real doctor." And she did, the very next day.

The result of the physical struck the four people involved like a bolt of lightening. The verdict: lung cancer. Mae and Don both knew what that meant. Now on 16 March and 6 April Ron was taking chemo treatments.

So, having done all she could do, Mae realized that life must go on. On 9 April, Mae was serving on the BSCC nominating committee. On 14 and 18 April she was shooting 83's to win the BSCC Ladies Club championship.

They both recalled that Don's mother had told both Mae and Don as she passed her ninetieth birthday. "It may seem grand to others, but all your friends, all those with whom you could discuss all matter of things from the past, are all gone."

Now, Mae and Don were beginning to fully understand Laura Baldwin Kipfer's caution. Ron Bebout, whom Mae had known all his life and Don had fished, bridged, and socialized with for nearly fifty years lay helpless in the Punta Gorda Medical Center. Ray Bebout, Ron's brother, came from Newark, Ohio, to see Ron. Don attempted to divert Ray's grieving temporarily. He invited Ray for a special cruise. "Ray I know you've never really seen Florida. Tomorrow morning, I want to take you fishing."

Ray was a little reluctant. However, it was Ray who had arranged to get so much black walnut wood for Don to carve and Don was determined to repay Ray in some small measure. As the two entered Charlotte Harbor in Don's Riviera Trihull motor boat, progressing not more than two hundred yards, Don killed the motor. "What's wrong?" asked a shaken Ray Bebout, not accustomed to such an expanse of water.

"Look, just ahead of us, not more than fifty feet on top of that waterway's marker!" Ray could not believe his eyes. "By God, as I live and breath. That's an American bald eagle and it's caught a large fish—a trout, I believe."

In total silence the two mature men sat in wonder. "Don," whispered Ray, "what I've just seen was worth my trip to Florida. I never in my life expected to see a bald eagle, much less a wild one with whom I felt I had shared a meal."

Don restarted the boat engine and slowly passed the huge bird, who seemed to look at them with toleration. Don had given Ray a huge rod and reel and baited its sharp metal hook with a large silver trout.

"What are you expecting, Don," gasped Ray. "The bait is larger than any fish I ever caught in Ohio,"

Almost before Ray could close his mouth his reel began to sing the avid fisherman song and a song that puts chills into the spine of the rod's owner and Ray's line screamed out at an unbelievable twenty miles per hour. "What's happening? What's going on?" shouted Ray, his rod popping and his hand struggling to find a firm grip on the rod.

"You've got a huge tarpon on Ray. Close the bail and jerk the tip of the rod." But all instruction forgotten, Ray was simply paralyzed to inaction.

Now, the tarpon, feeling the steel of Ray's hook, was not. It turned back toward the boat, jumping five feet in the air. Of course Ray had not been able to retrieve any line. On the second jump the tarpon jumped over the fore half of the boat, brushing Don with its tail, just barely missing a direct hit. The monster tore the eighty-pound test line, flying free, and he was gone!

Ray was physically and mentally exhausted. "What happened? What a fifteen-minute trip!" chirped Ray. "I've just seen and done more on the water than I ever expected to do in my lifetime.

"You know, Don, back in Ohio, I'm sort of a joker. How about coming back with me and backing me up when I tell this story?"

Later, numerous people asked Don, when they heard of this real-life adventure, "Why didn't you put your arms around that tarpon and bring him in so we could get a picture?" "Hey, brother, he weighed about one hundred and twenty pounds. He was traveling at twenty miles on hour. The flap of his tail is like the kick of a mustang and the edge of his mouth is like a razor!"

That night Mae said, "Guess Ray had a raucous time!"

"As so did I. Perhaps you are correct. Sometimes a higher power gives you a hand."

Every day was a madhouse. The very next day began with Easter Sunrise service at 0630. Golf with the Andersons at 0900. Lunch at the Yacht Club with the Andersons.

On 23 April Don's cousins, the Isabel and Howard Kaneys, who still lived on Ninth Street in Massillon, Ohio, visited. The day was filled with good fishing and dining.

Mae loved California. She and Don had explored every square foot of that amazing golden country. They had traveled from north to south, west to east. They had prospected, fished, gambled, dinned, played tennis, bowled, golfed and socialized. Now on 9 to 23 May they were returning for a family trip. Mae was ecstatic: "I'll finally get to spend some time with my grandson, Marc Brandon. I wonder if he'll look like Mark?"

"Don't look to me for help," cautioned Don. "You know I can't tell one baby from another before they walk."

But when Don saw Mae hold a baby again and watched the mellow, happy expression on her face, he had to admit, "Yup, that boy is special."

Old Brandon was still a bouncing baby boy but Don supposed what won him over was the logo on Brandon's handsome shirt. "Future USMA Cadet!"

Returning to Punta Gorda, brought Mae and Don back to the more difficult side of life. They both gave serious thoughts of what death really meant.

Miss Digel, Don's high school math, chemistry, and physics teacher, the daughter of a Methodist minister, the best teacher he was ever to have, taught him, and also Mae, many lessons that were not included in the curricula. She said, "Look at your body, students. Now imagine you are dead. Nothing traumatic has happened to your physical body. What is the difference between these two states?"

Of course no one knew. But with Ron a terminal case in the hospital, it was a dichotomy both Mae and Don again pondered.

Miss Digel gave Don's class something to think about. "You're all physicists. The difference between the living body and the dead body is a small charge of electricity!" Right or wrong, Miss Digel gave everyone food for thought!"

Don's favorite nephew, Gary Soldatis, had lived in Sacramento at McClellan AFB with Don and Mae. He was still living in Sacramento but hadn't divulged to anyone his current address. "Mae, I'm not coming three thousand miles to Sacramento without seeing Gary. What can we do?"

"Easy, my dear, Watson. We know where he works. Let's be there when he arrives for work."

When Gary pulled in next to their car, he couldn't miss his Aunt Mae and Uncle Don. He didn't even seem surprised. He jumped out of his car, shook hands and joked, "Uncle Don, I knew you would find me."

They arranged a dinner date at Courtland for Mae, and Don, Carole and Mark and Gary and his girlfriend. It was one of those memorable events, never to be forgotten. Everyone except Mae had to taste the wine Gary had selected. Old stories were recalled. New stories brought everyone up to date. Everyone was as gay as a human can be!

Again Mae and Don were back home in Punta Gorda. Now, on 27 May, Mae and Don were to see Miss Digel's theory about life and death in action. Very early that morning, before the sun was totally up, Margarette received an urgent message from the hospital: "Mrs. Bebout, your husband is having a very lucid moment. He's asked for you to come and wheel him around the hospital grounds."

Margurette could not comprehend such a thing. Ron could barely whisper. He had to be moved by another person even if he needed only a hand or arm in a different position. That evening, Margarette explained this phenomena to Mae and Don. "However, the nurse warned me, this is not necessarily a good sign!" She said, "Remember Mrs. Bebout, that the match burns brightest just before it fails!"

Don had to place his ear physically against Ron's mouth to catch his few words. "Saw flowers and trees. Beautiful." But Mae felt Ron's shoulders and feet. "Don, he's cold as ice. There's no circulation except from his heart to his brain!"

At 1:30 A.M. on Memorial Day, Ronald Lee Bebout left this earth. He was mourned officially by members of the 37th Division in Newark, Ohio, on 7 June 1984.

Nothing had ever been slow in Mae's life. To be with her was to have days filled with action. By 1985 she had established a routine that would try the most energetic soul. Golf, bridge, social activities, fishing and houseguests who changed from month to month. But the activities, themselves vibrant, went merrily on. Look see!

January 1985

2. Mae Golf, called. Mark and Carole .
3. Hair appointment, met Margarette at airport, golf 3 PM
4. DC Golf, Heibers for Bridge
5. Golf with Andersons.1225
6. Golf Smiths 0900, 12th Night, Strides 1730
7. Fishing
8. Music lesson, 1900
9. Mae golf, Margarette's for dinner 1800
10. Hair appointment, Golf 1500
11. DC Golf, Cocktails and Buffet Van Zants 1800–2100 .
12. Bridge at Starks 1930
13. Golf 1230
14. Fishing, Margarette's 1800 dinner and bridge
15. 1400 Eiko Visvary Memorial, Dentist, music lesson 1900
16. Mae golf
17. Hair, golf 1500
18. DC golf
19. Starks, bridge 1930
20. Golf 0900, English's Home Super Bowl, Dinner Margarette's
21. Fishing, Dentist
22. Mae team play 0900, Golf meeting 1500, Music 1900

23. Golf, Doyles dessert and coffee 1900
24. Hair, Couples golf 1500
25. DC golf
26. Bridge with James 1500
27. Golf with Edwards 0900, bridge with Starks 1900
28. Fishing
29. Mae Team Golf play, Music 1900
30. Mae golf, Dog races with Edwards at Bonito Springs with Edwards
31. Hair, Couples golf 1500, Margarette's for bridge and New Year's Eve

It always seemed strange to Mae that Don having flown as a pilot, senior pilot and command pilot, missileer, senior missileer, and command missileer, in World War II, Korea, and Vietnam, was not eligible for even aspirin from the Veterans Administration. She knew he did not resent the considerable help given two of Don's boyhood friends who had served less than a year as privates and were discharged because of back problems. However, to Mae, this seemed like a great difference in treatment. Nevertheless the Air Force, itself, still provided some medical help for retirees provided it was available.

"Thank the Congress of the United States for this perk," Don chuckled. "But I suspect it will not be available much longer. There are fewer and fewer members of Congress who have served in armed combat."

But for now, Mae and Don were off to Homestead AFB for what Don described as a "real physical. All the tests, dental exams, and eye checks!"

And Mae, who had enjoyed every moment of her military life, glowed, "Yes, and we'll have the Base Exchange, Commissary to shop, and the Officers Club for meals."

Back home again, Mae had one more reason to recall Don's mother's complaint about all her lifelong friends dying. Now Mae asked Don, "Moses, you know our very dear friend, Dr. Lee Long is in the Venice Hospital. Bea says he isn't going to make it. You better call!"

Don was silent for a few minutes. "Doctor Long was one of the truly fine gentlemen of his generation. I'm going to do more than just call. We're going up to see him. I'm calling Bea this minute!"

But when Mae and Don arrived at Lee's room in the Venice Hospital, things were worse than Don had imagined. Bea told Don, "Lee's not seeing anyone, not even family, but I'll ask him."

Seconds later, Bea was back. "Lee brightened up when I mentioned you. He'll see you and, especially, Mae."

Mae and Bea sat by the bed as Don and Lee talked. The two men reminisced about old times. Don told Lee, "Lee, we have always been good friends.

You and Bea have always been real class. You two's visit to Brussels and the trips onward with me to Denmark, Norway, and Sweden demonstrated to everyone you spoke with the capability of the United States in optics. Your leadership in The Optical Measurements Program (TOM) made major contributions to the international community. Mae and I and your country are proud of you."

Lee was unable to respond, but everyone noticed tears rolling down his cheeks. The following morning at 0900 Dr. Lee Long left this planet and went into immortality.

Mae had known Helen Southard as well as one person could know another, because Mae had served for many years as a governess for her son, Jack, and as an employee with all the responsibility for many of the household chores. Helen had listened when Don, seventeen, and just out of high school, had told her, "Helen, I'd really like to be a pilot in the Air Corps and serve my country that way in this war."

Helen, so softspoken, but in this case so positive, didn't even hesitate. "Don't sit here hoping, Don. Go sign up!" So in a way Helen had much to do with Don's military career. Now she and Franklin were living in Venice's The Corso. Mae smiled when she recalled those long ago days. One of her very own favorite ambitions was to have a sharp golfing outfit like Helen's and to be able to drive off in her own car and play golf. Now she smiled. "Yes. Now we can see them often!"

But fate is fickle and, in this case, was not kind. Helen, always so helpful to all her friends, was out pulling a few weeds from the neighbors garden while they were on vacation. Inadvertently she stepped backward into an open garbage hole, breaking bones and tearing ligaments. "Now we discover that she's in a rest home!" complained Mae. "What's worse, her vanity won't allow her to see visitors because she's flat in bed!" Mae added.

"For god's sake," hissed Don.

Now, on 20 March 1985, Mae and Don were attending her memorial. "What a waste. She opened one of the first schools for the mentally handicapped in Ohio." But no matter the tragedy, life had to go on.

Few citizens in the United States realize the pain and labor their military personnel endure for the people's security. Among the most giving are the Air Force pilots who risk their lives on operational missions almost every day of their lives. The greatest perk a military pilot can receive is the notice that you're on the promotion list." And so it was most satisfying to Mae and Don when Dave called to say, "I'm now Captain David Kipfer!"

Mae had always been a determined competitor, coach and referee in track, swimming, volleyball, soccer, and golf. Burnt Store Country Club had some of the best amateur golfers in Florida. So it was with great satisfaction that on 10, 17, 24, and 27 of April Mae shot 90, 88, 87, and 86 to win the Burnt Store Country Club Ladies Championship.

Everyone has probably gotten themselves into a situation not of their choice from which they were unable to disengage. So it was with Julia and Starky, Mae and Don's bridge partners. The Starks were determined Christians. They followed all of Christ's rules. Starky raised the funds for and directed the total renovation of the beautiful brick Methodist Church in Punta Gorda and had it listed on the National Monument list. So it was with disbelief that Mae and Don received an official invitation, "Requesting your company at the Starks' home for the purpose of tasting wine."

Mae was totally astonished. "What do you make of this, vinter?"

"They're both getting old, you know!" was all Don could contribute.

And so Mae, who had never tasted a drop of alcoholic beverage, and Don, went to the huge, gala, wine-tasting party at the Starks' home. No one ever explained and neither Mae nor Don inquired concerning this dichotomy.

Mae had gone to college at Washington Missionary College. Her aunt Vada and Glenna both lived in Silver Springs. So it was fun to return and get updated personally on the events there. Son Charlie, Jane, John and Richard lived in Bowie. So it was no surprise that Vada held a birthday party for Mae at her apartment for this family group.

Charlie had, of course, bought five acres of land on Swan's Harbor, a bay off the Chesapeake. He had improved it by putting in a Maryland granite sea wall of huge carved blocks and added a beautiful four bedroom log home.

This visit gave Mae and Don an opportunity to fish, boat, and shoot skeet from Charlie's backyard on Swan's Harbor. Also they explored the primeval island in the Chesapeake that was the model for the home of the leading character in Michener's novel, *Chesapeake*.

Mae and Don's adventures in the military kept rising up to generate new unbelievable excitement. Such was the arrival in Punta Gorda of Bob and Arnella Corrigan. They had been such good friends in Brussels that Don and Mae did everything humanely possible to show them the area and to introduce them to interesting people. "But Don, there is something strange about the Corrigans showing up here. They're city folks. True, Arnella is taking fishing lessons and has joined the bird watchers club, but Bob didn't stay here a week. He's always traveling. What do you think?"

"Former military officers get into all kinds of spook businesses. I'm the only thing here that might interest a man such as Bob. Don't worry, as I told the vice president of Kenya, we're as pure as snow. Bob is wasting his time in Punta Gorda!"

And so the whole episode was forgotten and then closed when the Corrigans moved less than a year later.

The Wines had become the best of friends. Historically, in rural America, when Mae and Don were small, the classical whistler was as much sought after as the best vocalist. "Ivan," Mae announced, "says he's a whistler. Can we hear and see?"

So the next time the Wines came to visit at night, Verna, an excellent pianist, and Don, the first chair clarinetist in George Bird's famous marching band, struck up the band and Ivan whistled.

"My, oh my," gasped Mae, "Ivan, your whistling is beautiful. It brings back wonderful memories. You should be on the radio or television. I haven't heard anything like that in fifty years!"

Don was almost crying, "Ivan, you're a hero in my eyes!"

Europe

But all these local events were being nudged gently aside, and greater events were being planned. Mae, Don, Margarette and Ron had planned for thirty years to travel in Europe together. They might have done so, too, except for Ron's fear of flying. Now that Ron was gone, Mae raised the question with Margarette. "Sis, you know we four were going to Europe together. You know we had finally convinced Ron to go. Now, he's gone. What do you think?"

Margarette hesitated about two seconds. "Mae, it's already in the budget!"

Mae, as usual, had no problem with her buddy, Don. "I'm delighted to tour Europe with two ravishing ladies. EOAR is having a reunion in Brussels. It will be first class. Let's plan to incorporate that."

Waves of humanity from Africa in prehistoric ages, from Manchuria in the medieval age and constant wars had formed a modern Europe that immigrants to the United States from England, Ireland, Scotland, Wales, the Viking Nations, Germany, France, Spain, Italy, and many others remembered fondly as home. Because of the expense few were even able to think about going back for visits until the advent of air transport. Now a return was possible for most anyone with determination. And so it was for Mae, Margarette and Don.

Mae and Don had lived three years in Brussels, Belgium, and had traveled all over Europe. Now it was Margarette's turn to see Europe. In Paris, the three stayed in the Kipfers' favorite hotel, the Princess Carolyn, just two blocks from the Arc de Triumphe. They had their delicious croissants, marmalade, and hot chocolate at their hotel for petit dejuné. The proprietor advised them that they should eat at a restaurant two blocks from the Arc de

Triumphe at dinner time. It turned out to be the most unusual establishment the three Americans would ever experience in Europe. The menu, for its meals, was fixed. Its food was delicious cuisine. Only the number of meals required for the number of guests with reservations were prepared. Generous portions were served at each table and as one finished his meal he was admonished to have seconds. "My word," exclaimed Mae. "I have never seen the French act so generously!"

Their visit to Paris became bedlam. They walked or rode the Metropole, that miracle of transportation, everywhere. "My, the Eiffel Tower dominates all of Paris, doesn't it, Mae?" queried Margarette.

"Yes, Sis, it does. And so that you won't minimize the other spectacular items of Paris, thinking about it, we're going there first."

Walking across the Eiffel Tower's enormous concourse, approaching the tower, Mae reminded even Don, "This structure is huge. Mr. Eiffel thought big!"

Having reached the upper étage where they could view all of Paris through provided telescopes, Don suggested, "Ladies, we're really in Paris. And like the famous poem says, it's time for 'A loaf of bread, a jug of wine, and . . .'" And so, sure as it rains in Belgium, they sat at the rail of the Eiffel Tower and each munched a loaf of warm French bread and a glass of wine. All except Mae.

She said, being a teetotaller, "A loaf of bread, a glass of Coke and pleasant memories!"

No matter one's religion, the church of Notre Dame was beyond description. "It's just like in the movie *The Hunchback of Notre Dame*," said Margarette.

"Don, let's go up to the chimes," added Mae. And up they went.

Next they walked to the Tulleries, passing by the golden statue of Joan of Arc. Along the Seine, they stopped to oversee one of the artist's oil paintings. The climb up the stairs to the Sacre Cour just about did them in and necessitated a stop at a colorful French pub, where a warm croissant and a glass of wine or Coke helped them on their way.

Early the next morning, about 3:00 A.M., the three were settled at a sidewalk café on the Champs Elysees sipping café and tea *au lait*. "No other place on earth," said Mae, "is so exciting just to sit and watch. Here is every nationality, every costume, every skin color every language."

After a practically all-night party in Paris, it was difficult to arise the next morning even for croissants and café au lait. Still, there they were on Place Charles de Gaulle viewing the beautiful flower gardens and the statue of Venus de Milo. Shopping along the Champs Elysees was an experience in itself. Glaring at the hundreds of cloistered book and art stalls on the banks of the Seine took one's full concentration.

There are luxury cruises, river cruises, airplane international flights, but as Mae commented, "The Trans-European Express, that wonderful passenger train, beats them all. You get on in Paris, sit at a luxury-appointed table, and as the train leaves the station on silent, rubber-dampened wheels, your appetizer is served. While you eat, the French and Belgium countryside rolls by."

"See," Mae pointed out, "The picturesque farmhouses and horses and machinery working."

"And I love the flowers growing everywhere," Margarette added, "and just as you are finishing dinner, you roll in to the Gare du Midi. And off to the Canterberg Hotel and a good night's rest."

Mae had planned to arrive early in Brussels before the EOAR reunion so that they could sightsee. First they were off to the most wonderful block of buildings in the world, the Grand Place. Built in the twelfth century, Don told them, "I still believe they are the most beautiful existing block of buildings in the world!" It so happened that as the three arrived, the mummers were having a gathering all dressed in their ghoulish costumes. Two of them their identity kept secret by their masks immediately identified Margarette as an American and each had to hug and kiss her. "Mae, good-natured American that I am, I smiled, but I would have liked to punch them in their noses!"

The Kipfers had been stationed with EOAR in Brussels from 1965 to 1968. Now EOAR had moved to London. Don's first secretary, Michelle Smeets, continued to work at the U.S. Embassy in Brussels. Vera Alexandre, also his secretary, went to London with EOAR. Between them and several USAF officers one of the grandest banquets ever staged took place in this hotel. Mae looked around, really impressed at the amount and beauty of the food and drink. She began to introduce Margarette to the attendees she knew. "This is Joan and Bill Terrell, who flew the EC47 with Don to Vietnam. Here are Frankie and Ed Myers who were stationed here with us and later with us at Andrews AFB. Of course you've heard us mention Don's secretaries Michelle Smeets and Vera Alexandre. This is Bill Woodyard, technical operations here, and dean of faculty at the Air Force Academy. The Woodyards and the Kipfers were neighbors here in Brussels, together with Colonel/Doctor Jane and Bruce Warren. Bruce gave Don the only medicine, he claims, that ever worked. It caused Don to go from spastic to euphoric."

Up early, they set off for the Grand Place and Belgium waffles, those delicious works of art covered with real whipped cream and bright red, sweet strawberries. They were really surprised to have Ed and Frankie Myers drop in just behind them and they had a great reunion over breakfast.

No visit to Brussels would be complete without a visit to the Kipfers' chateau at 13 Hetres Rouge and to the neighbors, the Michael and Helen Hughes. Helen did most of the talking, and of course served sweets and wine. "Michael is now a police inspector. Patrick is an officer in the Coast Guard, Perhaps, Mae, because or the Kipfers' influence. And our lovely daughter is married. We are quite alone. Mae, we often remember your exciting stay here and how you influenced our lives," Helen said.

Of course, they had to visit Chez Leon's restaurant on its small side alley just off the Grand Place. Don was energized by past memories. "I must have a basket of their moules." But neither of the sisters ordered Don's preferred dish!

However, the Grand Place was built deliberately with a huge square surrounded by twelfth-century buildings. Any gathering at that time of any consequence took place here. It just so happened that the Binch Festival was under way. All the actors wore elaborate costumes modeled after those worn by the South American Indians, whom the Spaniards conquered and brought a few back to Europe. It was a festival celebrating the unbelievable wealth exported by the Spanish from South America to Europe. The participants carried huge quantities of oranges, which they threw everywhere at pedestrians, at automobiles, and at buildings. All the buildings were boarded up to prevent damage. Viewers were crammed onto every available balcony.

One of the world's great events that changed the course of human history was Napoleon's defeat at Waterloo. So off the threesome went to that high point of land south of Brussels where with miniaturized terrain and movie narration one could relive the battle lost there by Napoleon because one of his marshals, Ney, failed to obey his orders. "I never thought," cogitated Margarette, "that you and I, Mae, would be eating lunch here where Napoleon met his!"

On to Amsterdam, for wooden shoe measurements and more exquisite flowers. Anne Frank's story was a saga in the United States that no one of World War II-age would ever forget. "Now here you are, Sis, up the stairs and looking into the Frank's house at number 263!"

"If anyone used one word to describe Holland," Mae noted, "it would be flowers. Belgium is startling, but Holland is in its own class. Wherever you go, there are flowers of every color, texture, and configuration!"

Near the end of September 1985, the threesome arrived in the land of double-decker buses, went right to the Columbia Club, once a USAF hotel, across from Hyde Park and moved in. They made their first visit to London Bridge.

From that worldwide familiar structure they walked to the queen's changing of the guards. Mae laughed and asked Margarette, "Good-looking men,
don't you think?"

Before her sister could answer, Don raised the back of his hand in mock
combat, "Steady, ladies, Steady!"

London in all its glory was always a wonder in itself. But Mae and
Margarette. Both members of a radio trio, veterans of many amateur plays,
and aficionados of American theater, had come to London with one violent
mission. They wanted to see live plays. Don knew this and obtained tickets
for every matinee and evening performance that showed while they were in
London. "The plays are just magnificent," stated Mae.

"Can you believe," added Margarette, Tommy Steele in *Singing in the
Rain*? We did that one on the radio, Mae!"

But Don commanded the sisters' attention long enough to eat at his favorite restaurant, Simpsons on the Strand, and to see the London museums
and the underground Silver Depository.

"Don," teased Mae, knowing he was beginning to weary of such strenuous days of sightseeing. "Margarette has to see Windsor Castle!"

"She does?" scowled Don, and then burst out laughing. "You know this
is your last day and Windsor Castle will use it all" he cautioned.

"Yes, father," replied Mae.

So off they went to visit the home of the wealthy royal family. "The flag
is flying, Margarette," shouted Mae. "So the queen is in residence!"

"Mae, you've shown me about everything else in Europe and got us into
everything I wanted to see. Do you suppose we could see the queen?"

"Of course," encouraged Mae, "if she only knew who we were and that
we were coming. But I'm afraid not this time." Nevertheless both women
saw a famous figure in grand attire waving from one of the balconies and
Margarette squealed, "That's her, I'm sure!"

But they arrived back in London in time to be wowed by shopping at the
famous Harrod's store and to buy a snack, which they consumed as a late
lunch in Hyde Park.

That night Don had arranged as he almost always did for a splendid
celebration meal. Off they went to Dublin's Irish Pub. Everything was Irish.
Bills on the wall printed all variety of Irish jokes. The music and talk were
loud and the ragtime piano player was dressed with long-sleeved shirt and
arm garters

"Mae," Margarette coaxed, "What should I order?"

"Be a little adventurous. Try something new, You'll like it."

The waiter joked, "Ere ya hongre, Seer?" Don replied, "I'll try Mrs.

Murphy's Irish chowder."

Both women winced. It came in a crock about ten inches in diameter and seven inches tall with the shank bones of pork chops sticking above the crock.

"Whatever," said Margarette.

"Gross!" added Mae

Don tasted the chowder and pronounced, "Best Murphy's chowder I've ever eaten!" And then, as he often did, he leaned over and whispered in Mae's ear, "Watch this."

Mae was seldom terribly at ease when Don acted like this. When he returned from talking to the piano player in this totally, irrevocably Irish establishment, he said again. "Just watch this!"

The piano player, laughing, arms and hands flailing, looked at Don and began pounding the keys, "Oh, I wish I were in the land of cotton . . . " and incredibly, more than half of the several hundred patrons in the pub for dinner stood and sang along with ear-pounding volume to the rousing strains of "Dixie."

"Imagine that," said Mae, shaking her grand and beautiful head.

All things must end, and as soon as the Colonel Kipfers reached Punta Gorda, their son, Mark, his wife, Carole, and grandson, Brandon, arrived for a visit. Their days were filled with use of the swimming pool, fishing and beach activities. They picked papaya, visited Ponce's statue in Ponce de Leon park, and went on the Anderson's huge luxury yacht for dinner at Salty's Restaurant at Burnt Store Marina. In order to enjoy the most beautiful beaches in the world, they spent a day at Wiggins State Park, picnicking and basking in the sun on the Gulf beach.

Mae had thought their BSCC needed a special annual party. A party to honor the presidents of the now member-owned club seemed like a good idea. She lobbied for it and the first one was held on Don's birthday, 1 November 1985. It was formal and Mae was costumed in a beautiful gold-sequined gown with silver accessories. "My," said Don from inside his formal tuxedo, "you do look ravishing."

On 24 November 1985 the Tracy Gentry Jrs. were houseguests and, besides family renewals, everyone was busy with all the activities available in a seaside town.

Another Christmas and on 6 December 1985 another Trim the Tree party. The dinner, cocktail party had now grown to forty close friends. Mae was expanding.

More year-end activities. The PGI Formal Christmas Dance; a call from Mark in London, England, and a trip with Margarette and Don Hill to the east coast of Florida for a view of Christmas decorations from the cruise ship, the *Jungle Queen IV*.

On 10 February 1986, Mark called to announce the birth of first grand-daughter, Stephanie Brooks.

On 9 March David and Jamie arrived. First stop was EPCOT at Orlando. The two Kipfer families hit all the attractions there; The foreign restaurants, the living seas, Sea World, the seals, the bird show and all the others. After that they took advantage of the beaches and fishing. Then as a special treat the Andersons invited the whole gang for a boat ride on their yacht and dinner at Burnt Store Marina.

On 5 April Don and Mae went to the Charlotte County Auditorium to hear Connie Mack speak. They had an opportunity to speak with him for a few minutes before the program began. As they went to their seats, Mae said, "I predicted Ronald Regan would be president. He was. Here's a man who should be!"

On 26 March through 9 April Mae earned another BSCC Woman's Golf Championship.

Don had not only written and published novels, painted, published and sold Punta Gorda calendars, but had become an acknowledged wood sculptor. Mae took pictures as he presented the Andersons with two bust sculptures of themselves, with crowns on their heads, suitable as bases for table lamps.

On 29 May, Mae and Don left for Bowie, Maryland, to attend grandson John's high school graduation. It was a grand affair and John looked very handsome in his graduation cap and gown. Tucked in on the side were many dinners at the Chesapeake seafood houses and a trip to Charlie's estate on Swan's Harbor, where his new four-bedroom log house was just getting its foundation.

Back in Burnt Store, on 31 July, Colonel John Green, AF Flight Surgeon, Ohio State golf champion, and a close family fried, died. John, a picture of health, succumbed to a totally unexpected aneurysm.

Don had just been commissioned to carve and had just finished the first sign ever to identify BSCC from Monico Avenue. It read BURNT STORE COUNTRY CLUB in huge classical letters, and had carved, burning, blazing burnt stores on each end of the sign. It was large enough that four men, Dick Anderson, Jim Carroll, Jack Ryder, and Don Kipfer were necessary to lift it.

On 28 August Mae and Don departed for Ohio, where they stayed until 10 September. On their way they stopped in Cleveland, Tennessee, to visit Mae's cousin Mary Louise Salyers, who had fished with the Kipfers years earlier off Sugar Island. Mae reminded Don, "You remember Fred Salyers,

Mary Louise's son, was the chief pilot for the Adventist's operation in Indonesia. Now he's the chief pilot for them in Cleveland and flies their company jet."

Joyce's parents were in attendance. Her parents had left Germany during World War II, gone to Argentina, and now were in Cleveland. "What a story they could tell," guessed Mae!

When Don was small, his father listened on the radio to Renfro Valley Program when it was broadcast on the radio. It had been programmed into his brain. So when he saw the sign on the interstate announcing "Renfro Valley," he told Mae, "it's lunch time. I'd just love to have some Renfro Valley food, I just love yams."

At lunch, Don saw a beautiful milk pitcher in the form of an adorable, smiling cow. "I've got to have that milk pitcher,"

Mae laughed, "No, no pilfering. You're in luck. They have them for sale in the souvenir shop. We'll buy one!"

In Newark, Mae's considerable family again gathered for a reunion at Margarette's farm. The day was spent eating gourmet food and attempting to at least say hello to everyone present.

Then Mike and Patsy Gentry came to visit Anna on Dayton Road at sundown. Their son, Justin, had just learned to walk. When Don picked Justin up, Patsy cautioned, "Don, Justin doesn't do to well with strangers."

Mae smiled silently. Patsy doesn't know Don. Don held, walked and talked with Justin for several hours. He explained to him the details about everything in Anna's house and hummed several songs for him. When it was time for Mike and Patsy to leave, Justin refused to leave Don. Mike had to physically separate the two confirmed buddies and Justin went screaming to Mike's automobile! Patsy was shocked and crestfallen.

In Massillon, they went to visit and have dinner with John and Masie Klett and Howard and Martha Klett. There simply wasn't enough time to relive all the ancient events that took place on the Kletts' farm. There were memories of John, an ox of a teenager, hitting a balky horse in the ribs with his fist and putting him down on his forelegs, for example.

Mae knew, she had been told it many times: Massillon Washington High School was national football champions six years in a row while Paul Brown was coach; yes, you were the first chair, solo clarinetist in George 'Red' Bird's marching band that was written up many times in national magazines. "Now I'm finally going to see them play!"

"Absolutely, Mae. Also, listen to the band play their fight songs. Wait 'til you see them do a company front down the field. Look at the stands. Twenty-five thousand paid admissions. More than the population of

Massillon. Massillon is a football town!"

Mae, sitting on the fifty yard line, in the center of the Class of 1941, had to admit, as the score mounted in favor of Massillon, "These are high school boys, Methuselah?" After the game they went with Warren Wefler, Esq. to a motel and to the bar before adjourning to the lower-level dining room. When they attempted to leave the bar area with their drinks, to socialize in the dining room with classmates, a foxy female bartender yelled at Warren, "Hey, you guys can't take drinks out of the bar!"

Warren didn't miss a step. "Watch your language, there, Suzie. If you don't behave, I'll buy this fleabag and *you* won't have a job!"

Mae whispered to Don, "Is Warren serious?"

"Maybe not. But he's worth six to eight million. He could afford to buy the place. That obnoxious barmaid may not know that, but her boss does!"

In the dining room, Dr. Jack Oliver and his wife were the first couple with whom Mae and Don talked. Jack and Don had been best friends in high school and fierce competitors for first in math, physics, and chemistry. Since high school, Jack had mapped the arctic icecap for the United States and run the computer labs for both Columbia and Cornell universities.

As Mae and Don moved on, Don whispered, "Jack's wife has never come with him to Massillon before because we're too rural. Why now? And Jack, uncharacteristically, did not want an extended conversation. Why do I have this strange feeling that Jack has one-uped me?"

Mae was to learn later, through gossip in the ladies' room, that Washington High was beginning a new procedure that would, each year, designate a distinguished citizen. Jack was rumored to be the first candidate. Oh, my!

When Mae told Don, he laughed and said, "And so, Sherlock has been correct again!" It was wonderful for Don, Mae knew, to reunite again with his classmates of 1941. He could look at the tables next to theirs and see Bob Heckert and his wife, Milton Dingler and his wife, Warren, and all the other shining faces.

Don, after so many years in the military where he was responsible for everyone in his organization's food, shelter, clothing, work, and play, could not throw off the mantle. "I must go to Marysville and see that my cousin Dick Kipfer is taking good care of my aunt Glenda."

"Do you have any doubt?" probed Mae.

"No, not really. But one never knows. History is full of examples where great men have made horrendous mistakes."

Dick and Aunt Glenda met them at Dick's front door. Dick was the only other male Kipfer left alive in Don's generation. He looked good and was bubbling. "Come on in Mae and Don. We are really glad to see you!"

They saw Aunt Glenda's luxury apartment upstairs. They laughed about old times, had lunch at a fine restaurant and bid everyone good-bye. No one could have guessed that less than a year later Dick, Don's gigantic, hearty cousin, would have died and Aunt Glenda would be marooned in a retirement home, far away from her beloved Massillon.

Back in Punta Gorda it was time again for the forty some golfers to follow Marlin Reber to Doral Country Club in Miami. By this time, Mae had taught Don all the fine points necessary to win a golf tournament. "A 92 on the Blue Monster is really good, Don!" Mae announced. "Maybe the best in our group."

The three days at Doral were really living, Mae agreed. "Doral takes care of everything; the gourmet food, the luxury rooms, cleaning your clubs, setting up the tournaments." At the summing up of money won in the three days of tournaments Mae was really pleased. "Well, Arnold, we did it. We were the big winners."

Life is made up of ups and downs, joy and sorrow. On the morning of 3 October 1986, Colonel "Smiling" Ben James died. What possible appropriate tribute could his country pay this man? Impossible.

On 21 through 24 October, Mark, Carole, Brandon, and Stephanie arrived in Punta Gorda. Fishing was first on Brandon's mind. Within minutes, from his grandmother and grandfather's dock, he screamed, "I've got one!" And that was true for there he stood, his face nearly bursting with pleasure, and a trout almost to heavy for him to lift, flapping on his line.

Next began Brandon's saga. He smelled the plumeria blossoms, played the drums and ukulele, with Mark on the guitar and Don on the clarinet. He picked papaya, ate gourmet food and frequent snacks, swam in the Kipfer pool, gathered macadamia nuts, boated, played ball, went for a wheelbarrow ride, and practiced riding the large carousel horse Don had carved.

The Kipfers were constantly entertaining houseguests or visitors for the day. So it was when Don Hill's son Wayne and family, Judi and Colin, visited Punta Gorda, that Mae prepared her gourmet meal. When Don asked Wayne, "What business are you in?" he was not prepared for the answer: "I'm the planning officer for a Canadian company that recovers oil from shale and sand."

Don wasn't really satisfied with such an easy answer because the United States had tried that route and had dropped their attempt. "And how is your company doing?"

"We're making so much money we can hardly spend it. We are exploring in Australia and Eastern Europe," countered Wayne.

For Thanksgiving, Mae had Margarette and all her and grandchildren,

Don Hill and all his family, Tracy Gentry all his family for a formal dinner. Afterward, everyone went to Port Charlotte Beach.

On 30 November 1986, Eva Merrick died. Mae was brokenhearted. "It's difficult enough to have close friends depart. It's devastating to part with people who have been like immediate family all one's life," she said.

Mae's Trim-the-Tree -Party on 5 December was almost out of control in size. Cocktails infinitum, green salads, shrimp a la creole, home-baked pastry of every variety, wine and coffee. Nearly fifty folks, all CEOs and their wives, in the holiday mood and clothing had a rambunctious Christmas party.

Christmases were for families, but sometimes the scheduling for families separated by vast distances simply doesn't work out. Thus Mae and Don, Margarette and Don Hill arranged to cruise on the *Britanis* cruise ship from 20 to 27 December. First they visited the captain's station and found his instrumentation and navigation equipment used to control the huge ship to be very interesting.

"Mae, remember our first trip to Panama City to visit Mark and his family? Remember Brandon's favorite restaurant and his favorite waitress?"

"How could anyone forget that. All Brandon could say was, 'Montego Bay, Montego Bay!' Brandon was barely out of diapers but he knew everything about Montego Bay and he was ready to take that huge blond waitress home with him!"

"Well," agreed Don with Mae's evaluation of Brandon, "here we are in the Montego Bay and it really is something super special."

Then on to Aruba with its splendid palms and flowers. "A red and white windmill," pointed out Mae. "Guess what that means?"

"Five meals a day just ruin me for the *Britanis*'s midnight buffet," complained Don.

"Some people around the Earth don't have such problems," countered Mae.

They walked the streets of Cartagena and marveled at the eighteenth-century buildings. "The Panama Canal is just like it seemed to be when we studied it as a military necessity at West Point," agreed Don.

But the luxury line could transport one's imagination to any location just with decorations. That evening for their stupendous sit-down dinner, all four dressed totally Hawaiian, Mae almost screamed, "Don, there's a huge Kona carved of wood standing in the middle of the dining room. Sure, he's magnificent, but still he's not as grand as the one I have in my back yard. And this Kona has no Lalani to keep him company!"

The San Blas Islands were one of the more memorable sights Mae and Don had ever seen. "These Indians escaped the Spanish Conquistadors by coming here. They are fortunate that there is no measurable tide so that their land, only a few feet above the waterline doesn't flood."

Mae purred, "I just love these people. They are so clean and elegantly dressed. And the women only come up to my chin. Here, I'm a giant. Their babies are so small they hardly seem real."

Back aboard the *Britanis*, they threw coins into the clear, saltwater and the San Blas Indian boys, from more than a dozen dugout canoes, dove for them.

It was finally Christmas day aboard the *Britanis*. Mae summed up the dinner for all of them. "We've all had eye-bursting Christmas dinners all our lives, but this one would be, will be, hard to surpass!"

Of course, it was good to be back in Punta Gorda. After a huge brunch for all of Joe and Francis Hodgson's friends on New Year's Day at their home, golf at Sunnybreeze, dinner at Margarette and Don Hill's on 2 January. Mae and Don went on 3 January to Sun City to visit his cousin Lawrence and his wife, Dorothy. They were both a wonderful combination of top class and humility. Don found them to be well adjusted to retirement life and happy. "Mae, I could still see vestiges of my wonderful aunt Isabel in Lawrence's face and eyes, What memories!"

Mae's records of amateur golf tournament wins and runner-ups was astounding. Winning her BSCC Alligator Classic matched play with rounds on 14, 21,28, and 30 January, she added another scalp to her totem.

Life is made interesting by the unexpected pleasant surprises that frequently surface. Back when Don was about twelve years old, a remarkable man named Chamberlain came through Massillon on a fund-raising tour, selling airplane rides in his Ford Trimotor passenger aircraft. "Mae, I had to have a ride. My father knew. He sent me and my sister, Mary Helen, up by ourselves. It was wonderful. I felt like a bird. The gigantic chimneys of Republic's blast furnace didn't look the same from the air as they did from my back yard!"

Mae was almost speechless. "Tell me it isn't so! My dad took me and Margarette for that same ride in Newark, Ohio, but we were sure he stayed on the ground because he was afraid to go up."

Now here the two of them stood in February 1987, on a small grass field near Punta Gorda, inspecting one of the last two operating Ford Trimotors in existence.

"My, it seems small," gasped Mae. "It seems little larger than one of the private four-seater planes one sees."

"It was a miracle in its time and set many records," interrupted Don. "Of course, its gear was not retractable and it cruised at about the same speed as it took off and landed at. Still, it had corrugated metal skin and was a leader of its time."

"Don, look at this," squealed Mae. "This aircraft is owned by a man from Newark, Ohio. Can you believe it? It may have been the very plane Chamberlain took to Newark and Massillon to raise money for his flight around the world."

"I can only believe it because I'm here and I've seen it and touched it!"

On 2 March, Mae answered the expected ring at their front door. Don was tearing himself away from paperwork in his office to rush to join her. The expected guest was one of Don's cousins about whom Don told Mae. "We were raised almost like brother and sister. She was beautiful and was one of the most popular girls in her class. She was known to me as Betty Jo, but her legal name was Joan. When she married Bill Snitzer, an educator, and later director of athletics at the University of Cincinnati, we sort of drifted apart."

When Mae opened the door, Don later told Mae, "I'm glad we knew Joan and Bill were coming. Of course she is a beautiful woman, but I could not recognize one thing, even her eyes, that reminded me of the girl I knew so well."

Covering his surprise, Don laughed and invited them in. Their visit was all to short. Having had their picture taken in Mae's backyard with Kona and Lelani, the four sat on the lanai, watching the Kipfers palm trees wave, and the pool and canal sparkle. It was easy to slip back nearly sixty years and catch up on events. As an add-on, Mae and Don took them to BSCC where they could be photographed behind the BSCC sign Don had carved and to eat dinner in BSCC's beautiful dinning room.

"Mae," Don coaxed, "you know I never get enough time revisiting the unbelievable civilization of the Mayas. How about another visit?"

What could a supportive wife say. "Of course, *Quetzalcóatl*."

So there the party was, in Don's charge, five couples, including the Heibers, Andersons, Bebout, and Hills, checking in to their Merida Hotel. These former CEOs, always skeptical of being one upped, asked Don. "Who's assigning the rooms?"

"Rest easy," replied Don. "This trip is democratic. There are five keys on the reception desk. Each of you pick the one you like best. Mae and I will take the one that's left."

Mae whispered to Don, "Now, that was clever!"

Don told Mae. "I'm slipping out to make arrangements for dinner at that spiffy hotel with the open atrium dining room we liked so much. And I know it's Carolee Heiber's birthday. I'll take care of that!"

The night was warm and the stars were bright. Those who wanted alcoholic drinks were obliged. The meal, served by waiters in formal suits, was one no one present would ever forget. Mae watched as Carolee's birthday cake was presented to her, beautifully decorated in blue and white with green candy leaves and three lighted candles. It was huge and delicious. Mae whispered in Don's ear, "You're a winner, Quetzalcóatl. Look how happy and radiant Carolee is. She may never feel so grand again!"

The group visited what were repeats for Mae and Don; Merida's open markets; Chicken Itza; sisal rope factories; the caves; Quetzalcóatl, the temples; the ball fields, tombs inside the pyramids, the observatory the huge watermelon-sized papaya, the century-old-styled Mayan homes where they sampled on site, toasted tortillas, by a real Mayan housewife, marveling at her old, outside, stone ovens.

Don really got his jollies when their party visited the native homes, one on one, especially the housewife in her kitchen. "Mae, I thought that Mayan lady who baked tortillas for us on half of a fifty-gallon gasoline can would burst with pride when she saw you wearing the identical white dress, embroidered with red, green and yellow flowers, as she was wearing. I'm proud of you. Wherever you have traveled on this Earth you have been the Good American Ambassador. Everyone has loved you wherever we've been. There is no doubt in my mind that you have generated more good will for the United States than any formal ambassador we have ever sent out!"

"Thank you," laughed Mae, "my fan club of one!"

On 21 March Mae and Don traveled to Venice for a mini reunion with the Ninth Street Massillon gang. Isabel and Howard Kaney, Letha and Walter Ritter, Bob and Betty Moyer. "Nice visit," agreed Mae, "but I fear that may be the last one. They are getting a little shaky."

On the 24th to 26th, Fred, Joyce, and Daniel Salyers were houseguests. On the 25th, Mae held a formal dinner for them, with the five Whites, two Bebout Hills, three Salyers and two Kipfers present. "Mae," Don told his beloved wife later, "virtually every day you have some strenuous social activity. I'm not certain how you hold up. Any other woman would have *beaucoup* help and simply play the role of hostess. You do both!"

"Lowell Thomas, it's fun!"

The Dick and Majel Andersons, during the near decade that they were together in Punta Gorda Isles, had played bridge, fished, golfed, dined, traveled, socialized together. Now they were with the Andersons on their yacht for a Blessing of the Fleet at Punta Gorda Isles Yacht Club. "Very impressive," decided Mae, "and I hope prophetic."

"An old and serious custom, my love," pointed out Don. "In sailing days when men were gone for four or five years on working voyages, they needed all the help they could get!"

Just for a little diversion and change of pace, Mae and Don went out to marker #2 in Charlotte Harbor and caught a forty-nine-inch, forty-three-pound cobia. All their neighbors came by the dock to see such a fish.

On 16 June 1987, Mae and Don pulled into Mae's mother Anna's home on Dayton Road in Newark to attend a formal wedding. Tracy, Mae's father was gone. "Mae," sympathized Don," for you I know it will never be the same. Again, you know I agonize with you."

"Don, you know I loved my father. He set standards for me that have never failed. But I have those memories and we'll all just have to move on," said Mae.

And so again began the parties. At the first, in front of the assembled multitude, Tammie, the bride, opened her first present. Her hobby was collecting giraffes. Don had carved her a beautiful, graceful, three-foot-tall giraffe, which, when she opened it, simply broke her and her groom up. Mae spoke out, "We hope you like it, Tammie"

Tammie, her face sporting an angelic smile, her eyes sparkling, gulped, "Wow!"

The primary reason for the reunion in Ohio, of course, was the June wedding of Tammie Gentry and Mark Brownlee. Not only had all the local relatives assembled but Mae and Don's son, Charlie, and his wife, Jane, and sons, John and Richard, had motored over from Bowie, Maryland. John was to enter Annapolis on 30 June. He was excited, as were his proud grandparents. "John," said Don. "You're one of a million young men who want to enter Annapolis. The Naval Academy provides one of the best educations in the world. We are proud of you."

Mae broke the spell. "I dated midshipmen when I attended Washington Missionary College in Takoma Park. And though I married a West Point graduate, I still like the Naval Academy."

The formal church wedding, as with nearly all weddings, was a joyous event. Mae whispered to Don, "All this attention, all this celebration is intended to make the celebrants marriage permanent. I hope it does!"

Tracy Jr. had arranged a reception that had to rank among the most flamboyant ever held in Newark. Barrels of wine, hors d'oeuves, and a stunning dinner. There wasn't an unsmiling face in the hall.

"This is Newark?" asked Mae. "This, by a family that once wasn't certain if there would be a next meal? It's the mark of talent, honesty and hard work, my dear," assured Mae.

And while every minute was occupied with conversation between relatives, Don found time, with Mae and Don Hill's support to paint Anna's house on Dayton Road.

Then as a bonus, Betty Soldatis Hayes came from Columbus to visit. Mae, Don, and Betty took a private lunch in Newark's best restaurant and after Betty had left Don told Mae, "I always wondered what Betty would do with her life. My gosh, she's beautiful, and has her head screwed on rather snugly. She has a family and is a successful businesswoman."

"No doubt," agreed Mae, "she's always known what she wanted and she's gone after it!"

Being military often takes one to places they would not ordinarily volunteer to go. So it was with son David who was re-stationed to fly C-135 tankers at Loring AFB in Northern Maine, Mae and Don arrived there on 8 August, just in time for both David and Mae's birthdays. They found David and Jamie owned a beautiful large cabin right on Long Lake. "Most of our neighbors are Canadians," announced David.

Mae and Don were in for anything and they soon realized they were going to lead the life of Paul Bunyon. "Sheds full of cordwood, trout fishing on the small streams in the bush, ATV races through the hillside forests, land locked salmon fishing in Long Lake, picnics on the grill, picking wild red raspberries in the meadows. "Now that's what I call healthy living!" summarized Mae.

"And I went right to sleep every night," agreed Don.

"I noticed," snickered Mae.

Back in Punta Gorda, Mae and Don were jerked to reality as the Smeets: Guy, Michele, Jessica, and Jerome, arrived as houseguests from Brussels, Belgium. Michele had been Don's secretary there twenty years earlier.

Mae recounted their activities: "It was certainly nice to see Michele again and her daughter looks so much like her. These Belgium frit and steak eaters have bravely faced the breakfasts of papaya, honeydew melons, and pineapple that we raise, and our wonderful muffins."

"Yes, but I believe the wine and braised cobia went better!"

When they all went to the Venice Beach to swim the weather was terribly hot, even for Floridians. Michele, accustomed to cool and rainy weather in Belgium, laughed, "You can't get cool here, even in the Gulf water!"

And, of course, they all had to boat and fish in Charlotte Harbor. Jessica finally spoke as they raced after a porpoise in the boat: "I love this! It's fun."

On 29 August, in perfect form, Mae won the BSCC ladies Swatfest tournament. In September, Mae and Don were back at Doral, winning most couples' money with the BSCC gang lead by Colonel Marlen Reber.

Thanksgiving was with Margarette's daughter Barbara and her family.

Then came the Pink and Silver Ball at BSCC, with the Trim-the-Tree-Party at Mae's home, PGICA Christmas Ball at the Community Center and finally on 31 December, Harold Wyatts' huge, authentic Las Vegas gambling party complete with money, all the commercial games, and attractive hostesses to run them.

It was only fair to say that the Punta Gorda Isles Civic Association Christmas Ball was unusual. Of course there were hundreds of people there, all in formal clothes. The chairman drew numbers and awarded two bushel baskets of the best liquors to two lucky people. Fred Dillon, at the Kipfers' table, received the first bushel. The second, much larger bushel, worth a small fortune, when announced caused the house to ring with applause. The master of ceremonies almost shouted, "And the winner is: Mae Kipfer." Even he had to catch his breath, for nearly everyone present knew Mae was a teetotaler! As she walked up to take possession in her beautiful, burgundy-colored gown, the band counted each step with their drums!

Mae told Margarette, "As you know, Sis, Don has carved many beautiful things. But every grandmother who sees his latest at one of his shows wants to buy it. It's made of thirty cubes, three inches on a side, all of hardwood and each with a complete carving on each of its six sides. It's meant to help Marc and Stephanie with their alphabet and numbers and to visualize the connection between numbers and physical things. If one assembles the blocks correctly, it shows a map of the United States with all its capitals. If assembled another way it reads MARK BR, STEPHANIE B, GRANDMA, GRANDPA, KIPFER. It's elegant."

Margarette was enthusiastic. "Mae, I'm sure it is. The owl Don carved for me is my favorite."

On 20 April, David was reassigned to the University of Missouri as assistant professor of military science (ROTC).Two days later Jamie departed for Missouri by herself.

When Mae heard what Jamie was doing she became angry for the first time in her life. "Jamie has always complained because David was gone from home on official orders two hundred days out of the year. David has risked his military career to get this ROTC assignment so that he can be home a reasonable amount of time. Now that David will be home every day, she's revolting. She always harassed David because she wanted to live in New England. If she's leaving him in Columbia, why doesn't she return to New England? Why is she checking in before David? What tall stories will she tell David's full colonel boss in Columbia? I'm crushed!"

On 26 April, Mark began his family's move from Sacramento to Panama City, Florida, to work for Pitney Bowes.

On 7 May, Karl Koonce and family visited from Ohio. Don explained to Mae, "Karl and I were good friends when I was going through Aviation Cadet Training at Miami Beach and Malden, Missouri, in 1943 and 1944. Karl was married and his wife was a camp follower. When I went off to Cornell's West Point preparatory course, we both lost track!"

"You mean you haven't seen Karl in forty-five years?"

"Right." But when Don met Karl again he realized Karl was one of those remarkable people. He looked just the same as when Don had last seen him. He began their conversation like they had never been separated!

On 23 May 1988, Mae and Don caught their championship cobia; sixty-five pounds, fifty-eight inches. Don, worn out and gasping for breath, asked Mae, grinning, "Do you want to try for another, lechen?"

"No, thank you, I'm exhausted." But when Don submitted a photo of this fish, an oar through its gills and out its mouth supported on Mae and Don's shoulders as a possible public interest item, the paper declined to print it, saying they didn't print fish-catching photos like this, even though they routinely printed photos of people catching small fish not large enough to be used as bait for this monster. *C'est la guerre.*

China

Mae had always wanted to travel in China for two primary reasons. "When I was young, several Adventist missionaries had visited our church in Newark, Ohio, showing slides and giving talks that painted a romantic, exotic picture of China for me. As a result, I read many of Pearl Buck's books about China and became even more fascinated by that country, which every Ohio youngster knew could be reached if you dug a hole deep enough straight down."

Don also had a driving reason to explore China. He learned early at West Point about the unbelievable history of China and about its huge population. "Mae, I knew then that China had to become a great influence in the world. I wanted to spend my career there and be a part of it!"

"What happened, Fu Man Chu?" baited Mae.

"Well, a colonel professor of international relations at West Point, a consultant on the United States president's staff, called our class together and briefed us."

"What in the world did he say," asked Mae.

"He told us that the United States' relationship with China had ended. The Communists under Mao Tse Tung were destroying the Royalists under Chiang Kai-shek and were pushing them out of China

"What about your girl friends, Phoebe Shi and Laurette Sung?"

"Well, being here in the United States they were expected to be safe.

And Chiang and Madame Chiang and all their troops and followers were fleeing to Taiwan."

"So that ended your dream of participating in China. Now you're telling me a trip to China may give you back a part of that dream."

"Correct. Your sister's friend, Don Hill, was a pilot with the two Canadian flying squadrons that flew 'The Hump' from India and Burma into China at the beginning of World War II. They saved China from the Japanese. Now they are a part of a biannual gathering of representatives from the former British Empire who travel to Singapore, Thailand, China, and Burma, to pay their respects at the cemeteries there for the military folks who died in that theater. We've been invited to go along!"

Mae shook with excitement and the most magnetic pressure she could emit. "Naturally, my man, you accepted!"

Don hesitated so long that Mae was reaching a near-fainting stage. Then he laughed. "Naturally, meine liebchen!"

"Since we are going the whole way to Burma, we might just as well touch base with everyone we know on the way," proposed Don.

"Roger," agreed Mae. "And the first folks on our list are son Mark, Carole, Brandon and Stephanie."

"Right on," grinned Don.

And so, just a few miles east of San Francisco Mae and Don met Mark and his family at Don's favorite restaurant, the Nut Tree. After fond hellos, Don told his two grandchildren: "Kids, I've brought you a set of wooden blocks. You can spell words with them, count numbers, make a map of the United States and they have other features. They're unique. Have fun."

And right there on the table at the Nut Tree they did have fun stacking the blocks as high as possible. After lunch and a ride with the grandchildren on the miniature train at the Nut Tree, Mae and Don were on their way to the city on the high and windy hill. Because "Bonanza" was so popular and the Cartwright's ranch was so near, a side trip had been mentioned. But Brandon was very young and Mark too busy to really be serious about such a trip.

Meeting up with Margarette and Don Hill, Mae coaxed, "Let's go to the pier."

Having gotten to the pier, not one of them could believe what they saw. At the back of the restaurant at which they had eaten many times were a half-dozen seals, awaiting their welfare handout from the garbage of the restaurant.

"That may be cute now," mourned Don K., "But every seal on the West Coast will learn about this and it won't be comical for the restaurant!"

That evening the foursome started their fun at the Top the Mark at Mark

Hopkins Hotel, for cocktails. Don Hill campaigned for this beginning of a proper English gentleman's night out. He swore this was a necessity.

With the dining room and bar rotating and gigantic, cottonball-shaped fog rolling up the Bay, their drinks were served. Again, Mae was the only teetotaller. She had ordered a San Francisco "Passion." Don Kipfer roared. "Your drink is easy to identify, Mae. It's huge and has fabulous colors. You've one-upped us all."

But when Don K. saw the bill, he was not as joyful. He complained, "All our alcoholic drinks are $3, Mae's drink is, dig it, $4.75!"

Mae suggested how they should spend the next day. "Margarette has never been to San Francisco. We must get truffles at the Pier, ride the cable cars, go to Big Sur redwoods, and also those just up northeast!"

Mae was always optimistic about how much a mere human could do in one day. Her plan turned out to be a really backbreaking day.

"Dinner tonight must be at the Tonga Room at the Fairmont Hotel," directed Mae.

"Why?" asked an exhausted Margarette.

Midway through dinner Margarette's puzzle was solved. Out floated the band on its bandstand into the large lake in the middle of the dining room. Lightning flashed, thunder shook the table and rain thundered down.

"My word," exclaimed a really surprised Margarette.

The next morning they met with the main group of about twenty-six RCAF officers and wives. All the men wore red caps, and the wives white caps, all emblazoned with "Canucks Unlimited" for easy identification.

The time by air seemed to pass rapidly. Mae summed up her impressions of Singapore. "Our Orchard Hotel is as luxurious as any in Las Vegas. I would like to meet Mr. Lee, Singapore's number one man. This is the most heavenly place I've ever been. Everyone is perfectly dressed. There is not even a gum wrapper anywhere to be seen. No drugs. No robbery. What a town!"

Mae did not get to personally meet Mr. Lee. But that evening, almost as if on schedule, Mr. Lee, with his bodyguards, passed within feet of the tour's tables in the restaurant. No one, not even Don K., for Mae's sake, had the gall to approach Singapore's leader.

So many things to see. The famous Raffles Hotel for a hot, spicy buffet and a Singapore Sling were among the best. Then while attending the famous play, *The Singapore Sling,* in the Raffles dining room, Mae, almost exploding, confided to Don, "I'm sure I can feel the presence of Maugham and Kipling."

However, when Mae rode in the three-wheeled pedicab, her instinct for self-preservation surfaced. By chance, she drew a wild Mongolian driver and she had to hold on for dear life. "Look at how large Mae's eyes are," observed Don K. "She's not a happy traveler."

In Singapore, at Don K.'s insistence, Mae bought a Singapore Airline hostess gown at The Top of the Hill. Don, watching the fitting, proclaimed, "Beautiful!"

"The RCAF officers and their wives are bonny," Mae whispered to Don K. And so these very RCAF officers and their wives, the Yanks, British, Australians, and New Zealanders came to the ceremony at the International Cemetery. Ministers came from Bangkok, as did Canadian High Commissioner Sean Brady.

Across Malaysia they visited rubber plantations. Even here, the people were attracted to Mae. She was invited to hack at the bark of one tree with a small machete. She drew sap! Next they examined cocoa bean pods on the tree.

That night at dinner, Don H. acted as their server for their table of eight at their Malaysian dinner. His efforts were applauded until he offered baked jellyfish. He found it necessary only to serve himself.

Don K. loved the ancient techniques of silver smithing, weaving, and stone sculpting. And even he was spellbound by the beauty of the buildings at Wat Doi Suthep.

In Thailand, in Ching Mai, they went again to the summer palace and the small craft towns thereabout. Don K. was absolutely surprised by the beautiful, modern Ching Mai Air Terminal.

"There is nothing recognizable of the old wooden building I came here to land at in 1969!" observed Mae.

"My objective in Chiang Mai," announced Don K., "is to see Tony Anonporn. But no one seems to understand me. Perhaps Tony wants to remain anonymous." Finally, a young woman smiled at Don K. "Ah, yes, Tony. He has a shop, the Anong Porn, just down the street."

Tony came down a beautiful flight of stairs from the second floor, dressed in a tailored, Thai silk outfit. He recognized Don K. immediately and invited both Mae and Don K. upstairs to have tea with himself and his beautiful Chinese wife. Don whispered to Mae, "Tony's so thin. On the other hand, he's terribly rich. I can guess he left the furniture manufacturing business. I don't want to know what he's doing now!"

Tony laughed and cagily revealed. "I knew you were in Chiang Mai, Don."

"How," asked Don K.?

"The owners of the silk shop in Pusan sent me a message. That honorable man said the girls there believe a white princess had been sent to visit them!"

But only to quickly the short, friendly visit had to end. It was obvious that both Tony and his wife found Mae fascinating. They seemed very reluctant to let her leave.

But of course time waits for no man or woman. On they went. When they reached the airport at Rangoon, Burma, Don K. told Mae, Don H. and Margarette, "Something's wrong, folks. There's not a single aircraft on the ramp!"

Mae turned white, "What can we do?"

"Nothing," advised Don K. "Let the tour director, John Harvey, take care of us."

A Burmese came out of the terminal to meet the group. He conducted them through an empty terminal to a second floor room. During the waiting time, before retiring upstairs, Don managed to purchase from the man a beautiful, wooden symbolic carving of a dog for one dollar! Upstairs, the RCAF tour director, John Harvey, went to meet with the officials. He came back after talking to a Burmese government representative.

"Folks, good and bad news. We've landed right smack in the middle of an insurrection here in Burma. We won't tour Rangoon. It's not safe. We'll bypass it and first go to Mandalay. We won't stay in the hotel downtown when we return. We'll stay at a better hotel, the Inya Lake outside Rangoon. Seems satisfactory. However, they won't move us anywhere until we come up with a carton of cigarettes!"

"My God," hissed Don K., "We've stopped smoking in the United States. Where in the world would we get a carton of cigarettes?"

Providentially, as Mae had often attributed to God, help was at hand! As all the tour people had noticed them secretly smoking, two Canadian women each came up with a carton of American cigarettes. "Praise the Lord," some enthusiastic voice approved and these two women were heroines the remainder of the tour.

So out of the terminal they all strolled, walking toward their bus. Here they ran into a gang of twelve teenagers who demanded cigarettes to allow them to get in the bus. John Harvey directed the men in the tour: "Give me all you men who feel up to it and we'll clear the way. You ladies pass down between us!" And soon the tour group was on its way!

The first cemetery the group visited was just outside of Rangoon. The huge, stone entrance way was modern, beautiful and breathtaking "The cemetery is so well taken care of," observed Don K., "that I can hardly believe it. It's certainly more beautiful, although not so memorable as Arlington."

As they moved slowly along, seemingly for hours, inspecting tombstones for names and ranks, Mae suddenly stopped. "Don, these are Yankees buried here! Two first lieutenants, three sergeants, and five enlisted men. Why?"

"No telling without searching the records, my dear. But from their ranks and deaths on the same day, I'd guess this was an aircrew. And to die so far from home for a cause I doubt they understood is sad. I'm glad I came to see this place."

When the tour group landed in Mandalay, and checked in at the hotel, they entered a whole new world. They were met by Yee Yee, who had relatives living in Florida. Again Mae drew most of Yee Yee's attention. She constantly wanted to touch Mae, obviously seeking her friendship.

They saw fields full of Brahma cows, goats that were mind-boggling, Buddhist white stone and gold temples, the Ava Bridge, and beautiful girls doing intricate embroidery.

As usual Mae was not only an inspiration for Yee Yee, but was like a goddess for the small street urchins of Mandalay. They came up to her, firmly grasped her wrist and in good English demanded, "I be your son! You take me with you. I hungry. Please, you take me your son!"

Strangely, these boys did not approach the other women. "Maybe," laughed Don K., noticing how well fed these young con men were, "they have their minds on your huge shoulder bag. Maybe their palaver is distraction."

Mae gave Don K. a hideous frown. "What a terrible thing to say to me!"

When Mae and Don K. saw the dugout canoes carrying produce on the Irrawaddy River, they both broke out into tears. Mae remembered for both of them: "My dad Tracy's favorite song, copyrighted by Oley Speaks in 1907, was about this faraway river and these exotic cities. How he could sing their words with such emotion!"

"I know," whispered Don K., and began in a not-too-glorious baritone. "On the road to Mandalay, where the light flotilla plays, I can feel the 'chunkin' paddles . . ."

And there, in one of the most beautiful temples in Burma, stood the world's largest bell, weighing ninety tons. Our female guide, Yee Yee, who resembled Mae, asked Mae to step forward. Again Mae the chosen one. "Mae, take this huge wooden ram. Hold it like this and give the bell a solid blow near its bottom rim!"

Don K. could tell Mae was more than a bit apprehensive. Here she was, halfway around the world from home, in a Buddhist temple, on the Irrawady River, about to arouse the Gods. Mae stepped forward and gave the mammoth bell a huge, huge, blow like it may never have received before!

"My word," commented Margarette! "That's my oldest sister!"

For now, unexpectedly, suddenly, seemingly both from outer space and deep within the earth came a rumble that not only hurt the human ear drum, but shook these observers earthly bodies!

"What a bell!" quote Don K.

The old walled city at Mandalay brought back memories for many of the Canadians on the tour. One group captain explained. "Few Americans, perhaps few people anywhere, knew the full extent of the Japanese expansion during World War II. Those Nipponese owned this walled city. Our 'Over the Hump' squadrons were, pushed back into India. But we lived to see the British crush and force these invading Japanese from Mandalay and from these very walls you see in front of you!"

"Now," murmured Don K., "I'm afraid we're in for some of the cruel downside of the modern Burmese government!"

"What are those children doing over there with what looks like a teeter-totter?" asked Mae.

"By Allah's beard," gasped Don K., "I suppose they're getting their technical training. They're lifting that heavy lever up and down, using its mallet head to turn rocks into sand for building material!" And Don K. went over under the tree where these beautiful handsome cherubs were working and gave them a hand.

"But look," marveled Margarette, "Mae's opened her huge shoulder bag. She's giving them each an American flag and they're hugging her. "What a picture!"

Next they viewed two men with three-foot-long wooden hammer handles with stone heads attached, endlessly pounding, from a standing position, a large leather sheet. "What on earth?" asked both Mae and Don K., of Yee Yee.

Their proud Burmese guide explained. "Those two are beating gold cuboids into thin golden sheets. See here," and she showed a sheet of gold so thin its thickness was immeasurable."

Mae winced, "*Shogun*, that is backbreaking work. In the United States no one would do that. They would go onto welfare first. That one man seems to be middle-aged. He has probably been pounding that leather cover for twenty years!"

Back on the Irrawaddy River, it was clear that water buffalo and men were the power of choice for moving the huge teak logs from the river to the shore. "These men," supposed Mae, "and the families, are probably living in the hovels we see along the river bank while the men who own the operation are dressed in fine silk and live in places like the Inya Lake Hotel!"

"Perhaps not so different," speculated Don K., "as the comparison between J. P. Morgan, Andrew Carnegie, and our fathers."

But by far the most degrading encounter was yet to come. Everyone was scheduled to go for a launch ride on the Irrawady River. Everyone, by this time had been violently alerted to the ordinary Burmese's poverty, and so had purchased hard candy, wrapped in cellophane, to give to the children in the villages. "Now, they say we're not stopping at any of the villages," complained Mae.

"Don't worry," replied Don K., "they'll take us close to shore and we can throw the candy to the kids!"

Not to be! The kids were kept back. Instead, some of the most beautiful young women in the world, many with babies roosting on their hips, swarmed the beach, some in the water with mud up to their knees, collecting this mana from heaven."

"Where is my God," murmured Mae. "Those girls are in filth up to their knees. And see how they treasure the candy we're throwing. There's probably not a single woman on this tour who would bother to peel the wrapping from a piece of this hard tack for the reward of eating it!"

Don K. had told Mae of his hope to see Pa'gan where the Burmese had established the world's largest collections of temples. It seemed like a miracle but the tour stopped briefly at Pa'gan so that Don K could always remark that "I've been to Pa'gan!"

There was just time for a quick stop at the Grand Market. Mae wanted a souvenir spoon and so far had failed. "This is my last chance, Houdini. Please hire one of the hundreds of guides idly hanging around this place." Done!

After stopping at a dozen shops, one lady nodded yes. She went to the back of her shop, lifted a floor board and *voila*—a beautiful, properly stamped, spoon with a sculptured Chinthe Lion on its top!

"Thanks to Buddha!" whispered Mae, nodding her head in satisfaction.

Back outside Rangoon, Mae critically inspected their Inya Lake Hotel. "Can you imagine this marvel after what we have just seen? The atrium is five stories tall, the length of the hotel. It has it own canals with arched bridges, shrubs, flowers, and chairs and long tables!"

But in spite of this luxury, Mae had a difficult time sleeping because of the small arms fire. She knew the sound well. The next morning she looked out their window, down at the lake. "Puskin, those look like dead, floating bodies in the lake to me!"

Don K. did not answer. He simply went to the window and closed the shade.

However, both Kipfers could not forget some of the most dazzlingly dressed and coiffured men and women they had ever witnessed promenading their hotel. "Don, could anyone wonder," gasped Mae, "why there is insurrection in Burma?"

But Rangoon was now under control. With control of the insurgents complete, the tour was able to bus to the Australian Club where a lawn party was being hosted by the Canadian Embassy!

Back in Bangkok, they were again in the world Asian leaders hoped the rest of the world would gauge Asia by. There were thousands of fantastically beautiful Buddhist temples. There postured reclining, sitting, and lying, beautiful Buddhas of immense size. One of their gorgeous eyes was perhaps three feet long. Wooden Persian cats and Thai elephants, the floating market with its unbelievable savory fruit, and all in welcome security.

Here the group met with representatives from London, Burma, Thailand, Australia, New Zealand, Canada and of course the contraband Kipfers from the United States, to honor the World War II war dead buried at Kanchanaburi War Cemetery (1939–1945). "After seeing how the average citizen must survive in Asia, it is certainly surprising that the cemeteries are so beautifully kept!" wondered Mae.

"Perhaps," theorized Don K., "some of the money for upkeep comes from some other source."

"Breathes there a man or woman who, because of the book and movie, have not heard of *The Bridge over the River Kwai?*" asked Mae.

"Hardly," agreed Don K. "But I want to see it for myself."

"The Japanese, so far from their island, constructed a railway from Thailand into Burma in 1942–1943 for their World War II operations. It crossed the Kwai River at Kanchanaburi. We saw Hollywood's version of that bridge. Now, by the grace of our God, we'll see the real thing for ourselves," said Don K.

Mae and Don K., and most of the others, walked across "The Bridge over the River Kwai" and back. Mae was skeptical and of course deeply disappointed. "That's not the bridge we saw in the movie. It's no different than a trestle over the Licking River back in Licking County, Ohio!" Don K. winced. "The old bridge was demolished. This one has been modified many times. Today it looks just like an insignificant railroad bridge over the Tuscarawas River in Ohio. Still, it was an important part of world history!"

The whole party motored up the river to visit another cemetery. "It is difficult to believe that 9,000 prisoners of the British Empire died building this bridge and rail line as prisoners of the Japanese!"

Back in Bangkok, everyone wanted to see the solid gold, sitting Buddha, which was so large it may be the largest piece of gold in the world. It weighed five and one-half tons. Even so, this Buddha would barely outdo the Emerald Buddha, which has its own devoted temple.

"Astounding," reflected Mae.

"I have seen it and while no one was looking, touched it!" pointed out Don K. "But I do not believe it. I will never believe it."

"Tell me you didn't touch it, Taiping," shivered Mae. "Even more remarkable" she concluded, "for years it was covered with plaster to hide it so that it looked like a standard stone Buddha. Only recently, by mistake, did someone discover the truth!"

Mae now quoted a 700-year-old Thai carving, which best summed up Thailand. 'The Thais are thriving. Fish are in the water. Rice is in the fields. The king does not tax. Any may trade gold and silver. And any may laugh and sing!'

Then the modern technology, which produced the aeroplane, made it possible for Mae's tour group to flit from one location to another, like Hong Kong's Kai Tak Airport. "Hong Kong," Mae announced. "Its history and modern-day ambiance make it difficult to comprehend and describe. But let's start with our hotel, the Imperial, right in the center of Hong Kong," suggested Mae.

"Where in the world is our bellhop taking us?" asked Don K.

"To the top floor, it seems," grimaced Mae.

When the bellhop opened the door to their room with a flourish and placed their luggage inside, Don K. snarled and joked with Mae. "For gosh sakes, Mae, I thought what this joker says is our room was one of the hotel's broom closets."

At breakfast, a Canadian military officer, Fred Tilston, a double-leg amputee and one of the most decorated soldiers in Canada, who wore the Victoria Cross, was asked how he liked his room. He told the group at our ten-person table. "It's the only room I've ever rented in which I could relax in my bed and without moving, brush my teeth in the bathroom!"

Talk about crowded! When Mae and Don K. attempted to leave their Imperial Hotel for a shopping tour they found that the sidewalk was so crowded that there was no way to move except with the crowd. "Try to work your way toward the street, Mae, and I'll push you."

"Thanks," groaned Mae.

But no matter how hard they tried, they overshot their crossover by half a block!

Don K. had just noticed something he supposed everyone else had chosen to ignore. He was hesitant, but decided Mae could handle such an inhumane sight. "That coolie is coming up from that sewerage manhole, hanging on to the huge knot in that gigantic rope, dressed in only a loin cloth, has just been down in the sewer acting like a human sewerage drain opener!"

"God save his soul. He isn't even wearing goggles," mourned Mae.

For lunch Mae and Don K. broke away from their group, and worked their way toward the harbor and the elegant Hilton Hotel and its second floor smashingly decorated dining room. The dining room was nearly empty. "My, the waiters are all in formal suits and we have three of them just for the two of us," observed Mae.

"And talk about a meal from soup to nuts. This is it. One of the most lavish we have ever enjoyed. And the price is little more than the tip back home."

No mind is nimble enough to understand China. Not even Confucius. When Mae and Don took a leisurely cruise in and around Hong Kong Harbor they were totally astounded. "This harbor is totally clogged with junks," shouted Mae. "How can anything move here? How can one get their junk out from the center of hundreds of other junks?"

"No way, José," observed Don K. "These people live aboard. And did you notice the clothesline-like ropes with dozens of dried stingrays pinned to them? Wouldn't you love to be invited for dinner?"

But that night the whole visit was saved at the gymnastics circus. "Such acrobatics," agreed Mae. "They certainly have no equal. Even a rare panda bear to ride a bicycle and help them perform."

The Canadian Group Captain John Harvey, their tour director, told the group, "I have arranged a special treat for the men on our tour, through our Canadian Embassy. As some of you may know, the Gurkha troops have been used for special purposes by the British Empire for centuries. A regiment of Gurkhas are paid to protect Hong Kong. Tomorrow, ladies, your men will see them in practice maneuvers in Kowloon."

When Don K. returned the next day, Mae asked, "Well, Kublai Khan, how did the war go?"

"I got to meet the Gurkha commander, Mae. What a thrill. He was not so tall, nor stout. But I saw in his eyes and his handshake that he was a no-nonsense man. And the Gurkhas maneuvers went off like clockwork."

During the day, Mae and the ladies shopped in Hong Kong on Nathan's Road and Queen's Road in Victoria. "There is no end of stores, Don. There must be thousands. Merchandise of every kind, from automobiles, suits, dresses, wristwatches, to pocket knives. Seemingly enough to supply the whole world!" roared Mae.

Sandwiched into all this feverish activity was an evening reception at the exquisite home of the Canadian ambassador.

To understand what overcrowding really means, one should visit Hong Kong's New Territories. Some condos hold 90,000 persons. Many of these may never fish, golf, walk through a pasture field, nor climb a tree. The human race, if it understands nothing else, understands full well how to multiply. Left uncontrolled one can see inevitable calamity!

And just as they were beginning to learn where various things were located in Hong Kong, off they flew to Shanghai aboard an A-3110 aircraft, flight CAAC 502.

On the Yangtze River, when the group arrived at Hongqiao St. Guest House, Mae was sharply aroused. "Don, we are not supposed to stay in such a luxurious guest house. If I'm not mistaken, this is where President and Mrs. Nixon stayed during their famous diplomatic trip to China from which we welcomed them home at Andrews AFB. And now we're here. The atrium is not only beautiful it's four stories tall and our room is a match for the best Hilton."

"Yes, my dear. The Chinese government certainly has found out that these Canadian officers we're traveling with were the men who flew the Hump and saved China! Our hotel is certainly not the Shanghai Hotel, into which we were scheduled."

"No matter the reason, I'll take the Hong Qiao Guesthouse," retorted Mae, "It's absolutely gorgeous."

The following day, China's window on their primary grade school system was opened for the tour to inspect. Mae, having been a primary school teacher was like a huge sponge. "Look at their beautiful rooms. Look at how well-fed and dressed they all are."

And when their teacher announced it was lunch time, the class was like a huge praying mantis preparing to strike. "See, one little girl is putting out the bowls and plates. Another is pouring the tea. And another is serving the rice. What precision. How many hours a day do the children attend school?" Mae asked of their teacher.

The teacher was very pretty, young, and seemingly quite intelligent. She also spoke English, "Well, they have formal studies from 0800 to 1500. But then they all go to optional classes until 1700. You will see them playing the violin or piano, working with a computer or painting."

Mae turned to Don and whispered. "Look out, United States, for these people are preparing to bury us."

Then, as per their schedule, the tour group was up and gone early. "Xian is an art center," explained the Chinese tour director, Chinese state tour director, and Chinese national tour director. Marco Polo believed Xian to be the world's largest and most extravagant city. Its museums date back more than 8,000 years!"

And so Mae was able to see, touch, and have explained to her, elephant tusk ivory carving, silk painting, marble sculpting, cloisonne and many other crafts. In the parks, wherever Mae went, thousands of Chinese gawked. In her white, red-lettered Canucks Limited cap, tailored London Fog raincoat, pastel trousers, white leather shoes, large leather shoulder bag, and matching scarfs, Mae was a beautiful sight never before seen in China, as she promenaded outside the Forbidden City!

Don K., on the other hand, was memorizing wooden carving techniques and stone-sculpting artistry. "Everywhere, my busy bee, the Chinese are working!"

"Bejing is certainly a beautiful city," observed Mae.

Yes," agreed Don K and the perfect place to introduce this group to their first traditional Chinese dinner. "Twelve people at their huge round table," counted Mae. "And the lazy susan-like a smaller round table in the center, which rotates so that anyone can turn the table and bring the dish he desires to his plate. No passing required round here!"

"Don H. and Don K. like their beer at every meal," announced Don K., "but the dozens of dishes, from vegetables to Peking duck, certainly startle our western palates."

That night the whole tour group went to the Shanghai docks through Shanghai's eleven million residents. "I never believed," Mae told Don K., "that I would ever be standing on the Shanghai docks with thousands of Chinese, near midnight, giving English lessons. The historical stories of the atrocities committed here on unsuspecting fellow human beings are simply stupefying," declared Mae. "And, Genghis Khan, these Chinese are students. And students that seem to love us," countered Mae. And Mae had good reasons to be smug. While the students seemed to bypass some in their group, they clustered around Mae. Somehow they felt her compassion.

"Mae, as you have already said, Bejing is a beautiful city. Of course, huge, beautiful, Chinese-style buildings. Gigantic stone-carved statues and animals. And who could describe the Forbidden City? And who could imagine the veneration given to Mao by the hoards of mourners who visit his death place each day?

"And in the street stalls, miniatures for sale of all these things. Bicycles by the thousands. But now for The WALL!"

And thus on to visit the Great Wall of China. "But Don K.," insisted Mae, "before we get to the most astonishing sight in China, let's exchange our knowledge of China at the time of the Wall's construction."

"Okay, my sweet historian. I know Huang Ti first unified China and was her first emperor. Yes, my dear, he codified the laws, standardized weights and measures, standardized the language, built national roads and canals, fixed the length of wagon axles and many other accomplishments. We have still not done many of these things in the western world!

"Perhaps commendable. And certainly the Great Wall is an engineering feat. And you know he did not believe in cremation. Actually he forced 700,000 men to work for thirty-six years to build his tomb, which has recently been excavated. It covered 500 acres. Thousands of life-sized terra cotta warriors, chariots and horses have been uncovered."

"You," agreed an astonished Don K., "my sweet researcher, have done your homework. But there is simply no way to prepare oneself for this spectacular engineering accomplishment."

"True, Thucydides, but what of the millions who spent their lives working here with only a bowl of rice per day as pay? What of the millions who lie buried within the Great Wall?"

"Forget the terror, *mon amie*. Look at what they created. The stones that make up the facing of the wall, the floor between its balusters, and the balusters themselves, generally six feet tall with evenly spaced cutouts for weapon firing are themselves works of art. We could carve these stones no more perfectly today."

"But look," pointed Mae, "the wall meanders beyond my eyesight in a course more crooked and up and down than that of a Texas diamondback rattler!"

"Only to true. This wall was built to protect the perfect civilization of China from the uncivilized hordes to the north. But, as in many places in China today, there were no power tools like we have in the West. Filling cavernous valleys and cutting down mountains was out of the question. So, their engineers followed the high ground. When Earth's plates heaved, there was no regularity to what resulted."

"Surely, my engineer companion, there is no real way to describe this sight!"

Just a short distance from the wall, when the tour stopped to see the life-sized armies, excavated, a part of Hunan's underground cemetery, the group had to go through an avenue of craft booths with very eager Chinese salespersons.

"Be very careful," admonished our Chinese guide. "These Chinese peasants are uneducated but they are very sharp bargainers."

"How shrewd can they be?" Don K. asked Mae. "I'm ready to buy some of their crafts."

Don K. soon found exactly what he wanted. "Look, Mae. Six miniature terra cotta soldiers and horses in each of their net bags." Don K. after much negotiating, got the salesperson from thirty luan down to twenty luan. He went back to the bus and his Chinese director. "How did I do?"

The Chinese director laughed. "Terrible!"

Back Don K. went. A dozen hawkers surrounded him. They sold him another bag of terra cotta figures, this time for ten luan. Back to the tour director. "How did I do?"

"Terrible!"

Having bought twice as many terra cotta figures as he intended, Don K. went looking for other items, but the hawkers surrounded him again. "Five luan, sir," they kept shouting. Finally, as he walked away, one persistent salesman groaned. "Two luan!"

"Sold," shouted Don K.

Back to the tour director. "How did I do?"

"Good!" grinned the young Chinese.

Don K. felt he needed to discuss a rather important matter with Mae. "Mae, I know you remember that I told you how interested I was in serving in China after I graduated from West Point.

"As a part of that dream, I researched a great deal of information about Chiang Kai-shek. I went so far as dating and making friends of two of his nieces. I have never really lost my interest in the Chiang family. Now I have a chance to go and visit one of the most important places in Chiang's life. What do you think? It is an extra side trip from our tour."

"You are not the only one who has had an interest in the Chiang family. Madam Chiang came often to our Adventist Hospital in Takoma Park. When we peons who had sprung from the Great Depression's stricken economy learned of one of the madam's habits, we were both impressed and awe-stricken. She slept only on silk bed clothes. And if you please, she demanded her bed clothing be changed each day. Yes, let's go to Black Horse Mountain."

Chiang Kai-shek, as do most politicians, was determined to destroy his Communist opposition. He used all his energy and power to that end. However, many of his Chinese supporters and much of the world, believed he should be fighting the Japanese invaders. Two of his fellow generals held Chiang prisoner at Black Horse Mountain and forced him to change his priorities!

Don K. and Mae stood looking at the three-sided building that looked much like an earth dugout back in Ohio. Its interior was not much larger than a comfortable room. Its furnishings were primitive.

Don K. whistled. "Perhaps what we are looking at does not really represent this place as it appeared in 1936. How could one of the world's most powerful men be housed here, even as a prisoner?"

Mae snickered. "I feel a bit relieved to learn the Chiangs had some uncomfortable moments in their privileged lives. You must admit that this building has been painted with brilliant colors!"

The most honored military guest on the tour, Fred Tilston, and his traveling companion, Grant Arbuckle, had left the main tour group, missing all the events until now in China, to savor again the hospitality of the world's fourth most elegant ranking hotel, The White Swan, in Guangzhou (Canton). "We are not scheduled to stay in this hotel, Queen Tzu Zia. We're on a bare-bones tour," Don reminded Mae.

"Maybe," laughed Don K, "the government discovered you were among their honored guests, Mae. Relax and enjoy!"

"My word. This hotel has thirty-two restaurants. A tour of the lobby is worth the price of this trip. Fred Tilston is right on," said Mae.

"Look at that three-masted sailing junk, six feet tall. It's carved from pure jade. Even its sails are jade. It must be worth millions of dollars. I have never imagined such a work of art," whispered Don K.

And after visiting the White Swan's surrounding gardens, Mae concluded, "The wealthy live well everywhere but those who live in the White Swan should be ashamed to hoard such beauty!"

The traditional Chinese dinner took on new meaning at the White Swan Hotel. The furniture was glorious, the table China, eye-boggling, and the food, including Peking duck, was top drawer. The female servers were dressed in expensive clothing with a western cut. They were young, beautiful, cultured, and educated as of course they had to be at the White Swan. But as with all their other wonderful experiences, the tour group had to depart the famous White Swan.

"One more stop, paisan," complained Mae, "And I hope it's the best."

"Guilin is purportedly the most beautiful city in China. Even I've heard of it," admitted Mae. "Artists from all over the world have come here to paint the Li River, the formidable rock formations, its junks, and its people."

The first day, the whole tour group left the Li Hotel, and under the control of their guide, Riang, went for a boat ride on the Li River. "The huge rock formations that look like huge loaves of bread set on end or castles hidden in the mountains, bordering the Li River are different from any other scenes on Earth," agreed Mae.

When they returned to their hotel, Mae badgered Don K. to take a walk along the Li River. Shortly, she pointed and demanded, "I must have my picture taken with that darling old man standing with an oar on that narrow bamboo floating dock. Look, he's wearing a Ho Chi Minh hat. His jacket and trousers are of black cotton. He's wearing sandals. Some type of furry skin cape hangs down his back. He has a thin beard and mustache. And look at his grin. He must be no more than five feet tall and weigh one hundred pounds. I'm a giant compared with him. What in the world is he doing?"

"Well, my pretty little maid, he's a fisherman!"

"How can that be? He has no pole, no hook, nor any bait."

"He's one of the most unusual fishermen in the world, and certainly one of the last. See that cormorant perched on the circular cane basket. He's well trained. The Chinaman places a wooden collar around the cormorant's neck so that he cannot swallow a fish. The fisherman has a long, thin line attached to the wooden collar. With a special clicking sound the old man sends the cormorant out to look for fish. When the cormorant catches one, it is brought back to the basket and deposits the fish!"

"Unbelievable," agreed Mae. "I would like to see that!"

"And so you shall, my sweet!"

With that, Don pulled a ten luan note from his wallet and flashed it up under the old fisherman's nose. Then Don made motions like a bird flying, diving catching a fish and flying back again toward the three. Money works wonders.

The old fisherman snapped on the collar and clicked his tongue. Off went the cormorant. He made one circle over the water, dove and returned with a small flopping fish.

Mae shook the old fisherman's hand. Don handed over the ten luan. Everyone laughed and departed, now friends.

After another scrumptious traditional Chinese dinner that night, Mae and Don strolled across the hotel's beautiful garden. "It's such a beautiful night, Marco, do you believe it would be safe to cross the river and shop at those stands along the other side of the river?"

"I don't know why not. They have such wonderful crafts." And then suddenly Mae realized Don was intently examining a large dragon carved from what seemed to be black granite in one of the stalls. "You seem to like that carving. The price is ridiculously low, why not?"

"It's one of the best I've ever seen. But it must weigh forty or fifty pounds. We have to carry this along with everything else we've bought!"

Mae could see that her hubbie really, really wanted this sculpture. "Well?!"

Don was about to violate a rule Billy Green had quoted for him in Brussels so many years ago: When you see something you really want, buy it. Tomorrow, when you go back to get it, it'll be gone!

Still, he found himself saying, "We can't do it." How was Don to know that he would mourn this decision the rest of his life and regret that such a sculpture did not rest, displayed in his own home.

Mae, always on the lookout for fascinating adventures, looked beyond their pathway and could see commercial stores nearby. "Don, Ann is a petti-point weaver. She has attempted to get certain Chinese patterns in the United States and has failed. She asked me to try and get several for her on our trip. Let's try it."

Mae and Don noticed strange glances from the store's staff when they entered the local Chinese store, but certainly that was to be expected. After a short search, Mae found exactly what she wanted. "Let's take them over to the counter and pay for them."

When Mae pulled out her Chinese tourist money, the saleswoman began screaming. Immediately, the whole staff surrounded them screaming and shaking their fingers. Scary. Don suggested, "Let's slowly leave without the patterns!"

Several salespersons followed them across the street. "What on earth?" demanded Mae.

Something to do with the money. Perhaps they are not allowed to accept tourist money. Perhaps it is for use in the national stores. At any rate, it was clear they were not happy with the shoppers!

As Mae and Don knew, their party was closely monitored by a Chinese guide from the tour company, one from the Chinese state, and one from Nationalist China, itself. Still, it was clear that the young Chinese they met saw advantages in learning English and Western ways. Their young Chinese state guide was constantly on the bus's communications system practicing his English by telling jokes. He began: "A young Chinese wife became in-fatuated with a male Western friend. Actually, she became pregnant by him. Naturally, she did not want her husband to know of this. However, the hus-band, seeing the blond-haired, blue-eyed baby, was not fooled. He told his embarrassed wife, "Do not tell me this baby is mine. Two Wongs cannot make a white!"

This same young man, realizing that the Chinese facial structure did not allow the Chinese to seem to laugh, while Japanese seemed to laugh all the time, showed his very white teeth and said, "You have noticed, we Chinese do not seem smile. This a great handicap in our business relations with West-erners. On the other hand, the Japanese seem to smile the time. We Chinese are going to hire the Japanese to teach us Chinese how to smile!"

"China is beginning to feel like home," Don K. said again in Hong Kong.

"Don't you get sucked in, Chiang." Mae demanded, in her most patriotic demeanor. "We're heading east!"

But that morning they had time for a short walk about the area. On a side street, Mae pointed to a sign that read, GENTRY TAILORS, 2ND FL. B. "Let's go up!" she said.

Seeing only a Chinese lady, Mae explained, "My maiden was Gentry. Is Mr. Gentry in? I'd like to speak with him."

"I'm sorry, but you'll have to come back tomorrow."

"I can't. I'm leaving for America at noon. Do you know where Mr. Gentry came from?" "I believe he came from England." And so the mystery as to how a Gentry got to China was left unsolved.

The Kipfers' trip home was uneventful.

David arrived from Miami 25 June 1988. Charlie from Bowie 27 June, and Mark from the Florida Panhandle 28 June. On 29 June they were deep sea fishing from Colonel Marlen Reber's yacht in sixty feet of saltwater in the Gulf. David yelled, "I can see hundreds of barracuda stacked up like cordwood, most of them over five feet long."

They had come for large grouper. Marlen cautioned, "When you catch a grouper, get him up fast or the barracuda will get him!"

When the four Kipfers returned to 825 Via Formia, Don, said, "Mae, everything was wrong. We didn't catch a grouper and the barracuda wouldn't even take our bait. David snagged a few barracuda scales with a treble hook!"

Still, all was not lost. Charlotte Harbor produced cobia, shark, manta rays, triple tail and trout in abundance. And at night, in the middle of Charlotte Harbor, they caught dozens of black tip and hammerhead sharks.

On 18 August, Mae and Don were again off to Ohio. Sentimentality, loyalty, and love drove Mae directly to Tracy's grave. Still, nothing could fill the void for her. Again picnics, reunions, and boating at Margarette's farm. Then off to Marysville to visit Aunt Glenda. But she had friends only there at the home.

"Don, Aunt Glenda is not the person you remember. True, she is perfectly groomed and made up, but her life may be traveling only with old memories."

Mae, Don, Anna, and Carolyn spent more time together than Mae had been able to do since she left home nearly forty years earlier. "Don, mother's amazing. She's always smiling. And wherever we go, she's always encouraging the people we're visiting, especially those older than herself."

"She hasn't changed. She's an honest broker. I believe she has passed those traits on to you!" added Don.

Hardly had Mae and Don returned to Punta Gorda when niece Betty Soldatis Hayes and her husband, Don, arrived for a few days. Boating in the harbor, chasing porpoises, swimming in the Kipfer pool and eating exceptionally good food is what the two Ohioans needed and sought. And that was precisely what they got.

On 15 September, the Punta Gorda Isles golf group was again off to Doral for another Alice in Wonderland vacation. Again the Kipfers were top-money winners!

No biography could contain all of Mae's activities. But from her past, her next-door neighbors from Horseshoe Drive in Surratsville, Maryland, Helen Forest, and Frank, a retired Washington, D.C., fire department captain, stopped by. It was as though almost thirty years had not separated them. Old stories had become icons.

It was a sign of historical time passage. The Heibers were throwing their fiftieth wedding anniversary party for several hundred people at BSCC. Mae had become an expert and leader in almost every field of endeavor. Now, Carole Lee asked Mae, "Mae, would you take the official photos for our anniversary?"

Mae didn't hesitate a heartbeat, "Of course,"

Mark, Carole, Brandon, and Stephanie arrived 24 November for Mae's traditional Thanksgiving dinner. She had also included Dick and Majel Anderson.

But after Thanksgiving Day, the real fun began. Mae laughed. "Out come the instruments. Don on clarinet, Mark on guitar, and Brandon on drums. Outside, Brandon in charge, down come the bananas. Into dramatic action goes the mouse trap. Bang go the coconuts impacting the ground. Catch that falling avocado. Eat that juicy papaya. Water the garden. Catch those fish from the dock, and in between, eat Mae's delicious formal meals, goodie snacks whenever you're hungry!"

"Amen," approved Don. "They're at Grandma's house. Somehow you don't seem like a grandma to me!"

Next, Dr. Mike Gentry and his family arrived. "On his a first visit he was a struggling student and there were so many houseguests he was faced to sleep on a fold-a-cot on the pool deck," Mae reminded Don. "Now Mike's a chiropractor. He's married and has a son. Never mind, they'll just love the feel of our maritime tropical life."

Trim-the-Tree and the BSCC Medicare Open came and went. It was time to launch for Columbia, Missouri, and Christmas with Dave and his family. "Of course, David, we must tour the university and see where you work," Mae encouraged her son.

So off they went to inspect the impressive ROTC digs. Don and Dave collected six by six timbers and did a little home building. Then they went out for a remembrance dinner. Then the package opening on Christmas morning.

Mae knew what Don and Dave were up to a day alone in the fields of Missouri, digging up Indian flint artifacts as they had nearly thirty years before. "Have fun," she said with a stiff upper lip as they departed.

When they returned, bushed, it was a different story. "I count eight perfect arrow tips and a dozen other broken flint implements," reported an experienced Mae. "You must have found the site of an Indian village," summed up a surprised wife and mother.

"Could be," said Don

Life is full of surprises, especially when one is suddenly immersed in a group of chief executives and their wives from nearly every state in the union and are basically uninformed of their backgrounds. Such was the case of Mae and Don's good friends, Harold and Shirley Wyatt.

The second Wyatt invitation for a New Year's Eve party was innocent enough, but, again, the experience was totally unexpected. First the some one hundred attendees were served a scrumptious dinner by professional help. Then everyone retired to the game hall, which rivaled anything in Las Vegas, albeit much smaller. Play money was issued to each attendee. Then the gambling began. Harold and Shirley each ran a game but there were half a dozen foxy young females running other games.

Everyone played. Some were laisser-faire; some were sober. All were hilarious. But everyone was having a marvelous time. At midnight, after an adios toast for 1988 and a hope for 1989, everyone counted his or her money. Now Harold had a table full of most desirable merchandise; liquors, whiskeys, dinner chits, and candy. Then Harold's raffle began. If you had lost money at gambling, of course, you could not bid beyond your means. If you had won at gambling you could attempt to outbid the others for your desired items. And so one year ended and another began!

On 23 January, Mae and Don received a call from Mark saying Carole was in the emergency room at their hospital and they needed help. Mae canceled all activities and they immediately launched for Panama City to care for Brandon and Stephanie until 4 February 1989. Therein, began trips to the beach, visits to the Pensacola zoo, trooping through the Pine Log State forest, picnics, softball, meals out.

Returning to Punta Gorda on 25 March, Mae won the Burnt Store Country Club's Ladies Alligator Classic golf tournament and then, Frances Hodson's Memorial, Mae's jury duty, tiling the bathroom, Karl Koonce's visit, Nokomis again with the Kaneys, catching a large triple tail, Dick Anderson's heart attack, peddling Don's Florida calendar, and Doral for golf!

On 30 May to 14 June Mae and Don went to Bowie, Maryland, to help grandson Richard graduate from high school at the Washington Redskins football stadium. And Don, always wood sculpting, presented Charlie and Jane with lamp bases carved as male and female mallard ducks. The graduation was impressive, but not nearly so much as Rich in his graduation cap and gown and John in his dress United States Naval Academy midshipman's uniform. And from Bowie, Mae and Don motored over to Newark, Ohio, for reunions at Mae's mother's house, visits to the American Indian museums, get-togethers with nephew Dr. Mike Gentry's family, nephew Kevin Bebout's family, brother Tracy Gentry Jr.'s family, nephew Bob White's family and clan gatherings at sister Margarette Bebout's farm. Picnics were rampant at Moundbuilder Park and golf matches popular at Granville's beautiful course. Then on the way home, they stopped in Fayetville, Georgia, for a visit with niece Barbara Childress and her family. Then, on south to Charlotte Harbor and Punta Gorda.

Mae had always known that Don was a fisherman. It was only natural that her three sons would also be fishermen. So it was no surprise on 17 July that Charlie went to Missouri to ride with David and his big Mako outboard boat to Bay Point at Panama City to enter a shark tournament with Mark and Don. The first day, all eight members of the Kipfer party went into the Gulf for Spanish mackerel. The fish were nearly a solid mass and easy prey for experienced fishermen. The next night Dave and the others went out for a practice shark run. When they returned, Don could not wait to report, "Mae, Charlie hung a shark so large it jerked him through the air, twenty-two feet from the front to the rear of Dave's boat. Only the fact that Charlie caught and braced his feet against the rear of the boat, and thus broke the eighty-pound test line, saved him from being drug into the Gulf." All the noncombatants, deserted on shore, were bug-eyed with wonder!

The following night the tournament began. "Mae, when Dave attempted to leave Bay Point harbor through the pass, the waves were more than eight feet tall and his boat was unmanageable. You know we three Kipfers. We are determined men. No one of us wanted to give up, regardless of the danger. Finally we realized our only option was to return to Mark's new home here at 188 Marlin Circle. Even turning the boat broadside to such high waves was very dangerous. We were fortunate that David is such a skillful skipper!" said Don.

Later, they learned that no other boat was able to brave the storm and that the tournament had to be cancelled.

Consolation was a dinner at Mark's favorite Japanese restaurant. It helped, but nothing could compensate these men for their loss.

Back in Punta Gorda, Mae and Don caught a twelve-pound triple tail;

Mac scored a tournament hole-in-one; they picked huge stalks of bananas; and Don completed more wood sculptures.

"It's a long way from Brussels, Belgium, to Clearwater, Florida, no matter how you measure it," calculated Don

"I don't care about that," shouted Mae. "It will be wonderful to see the Deets, Terrels, Vera, and all the others again." And what a gala celebration that EOAR reunion turned out to be.

Then the bell ringers' birthday party for Don with the Harold Millers and Ivan Wines in Punta Gorda was superb. And Thanksgiving at the Mae and Don Kipfers with Mark, Carole, Brandon, and Stephanie was an upbeat family affair. And of course Mae's Trim-the-Tree Christmas party for forty semiformal-clad people for cocktails, dinner, and entertainment was a social affair of the year.

On route from Punta Gorda to Panama City for Christmas at son Mark's home, Don explained, "At my home, when I was a boy, we all knew Christmas was a time for joy because of Christ's birth. But for the children, especially the two Kipfer kids, it was like a scene from fairyland! We went to bed upstairs on Christmas eve at the same time as always. But, of course, neither my sister nor I could sleep. We were listening for Santa's sleigh or the bells on his reindeer. Early in the morning we hurried down the second floor stairway, apprehensive that Santa might have forgotten us, to open the doorway into the rooms downstairs!"

"Voila! A huge Christmas tree decorated with colors and sights beyond belief. A miniature town set about the base of the tree. And beyond our wildest hopes, dozens of gaily wrapped presents. It was a brain-exploding experience, the like of which I have never felt again! Many fruity psychologists today believe such an extravaganza warps a child's mind. But from my distant vantage point and world wide experience, I say, 'Please, please, play it again!'"

Mae, an Adventist, was not so enthusiastic about so much material demonstration. "It was not that spectacular at my home," she said. "But our boys have benefited from your experience and their Christmases have been just grand. I wonder what we'll find in the way of tradition in Mark's home at 188 Marlin Circle.

Mae and Don's expectations were soon answered. The Christmas at Mark's home was certainly spectacular. A glorious traditional Christmas tree. Too many expensive presents. Tasty food to a fault. And happy riders. However, one thing was totally different, especially for Panama City. It snowed!

Mae coaxed, "Don, let's make a snowman!"

"OK, Eskimo woman."

And so everyone pitched into the fun. "First, roll some big, huge snow-balls for the body," directed Don.

"We'll need a hat," added Carole.

"And nuts for buttons," added Brandon.

"And a carambola for his nose," laughed Mark.

"And prunes for his eyes," declared Mae.

"And a red ribbon for his mouth," laughed Stephanie.

And so Frosty, the snowman, sharing a very rare appearance, capped a very Merry Christmas with the Kipfers in Panama City.

"Don," bubbled Mae, "I know you've been wood sculpting in every spare minute and volunteering for community shows all over South Florida. I'm really happy that your Dutch doors, see through carvings of each of us in the Garden of Eden, from black walnut received a judged blue ribbon for best carving at the big South Florida Wood Carvers Show and that they were subsequently featured in *Chip Chats*, the magazine of the National Woodcarvers."

"Thank you, my dear. But you know that's not why I carve. Still, it's nice to know that others find my work pleasing."

Don told Mae when they received notification of the death of her sister Carolyn on 1 February 1990, "I would remind you that my physics teacher, Miss Digel, daughter of a minister, told we students, physically speaking, the only difference between a living and dead body is a small charge of electricity. Now anatomically speaking, that may be true, but we both know there was much more to sweet caring Carolyn than that. Our religion speaks to our souls. And we both know your sister has gone to be with her heavenly Father."

Mae returned to Newark for Carolyn's funeral. Once again all the relatives assembled to reaffirm their mutual support.

Punta Gorda was always home base. Sandwiched in at Punta Gorda were a visit by the Mike Gentry family; house visits by the four Bob Whites; visits by Howard and Isabel Kanney from Massillon/Nokomis; and Tracy and Arlene Gentry Jr. from Newark.

On 9 April Mae and Don picked up their new 1990 Cadillac DeVille. Then David and Anne arrived for a ten-day visit. With David, fishing was all the entertainment needed. Hundreds of cobia, sharks, and trout were caught.

"Punta Gorda may be the best city in the world in which to live," Don told Mae, "but if you venture out into the rest of the world occasionally, you'll appreciate it even more."

"Yes, Socrates!" And with this pointed hint, Mae knew they would be breaking camp!

So on 21 May, amid such mixed feelings, along with Margarette and Don Hill, the Kipfers were in flight to England and Ireland. "My father, Tracy," reminisced Mae, "loved to hear Irish tenors sing. Heres hoping."

Ireland

They had barely landed In London and checked in when Don H. proposed. "When I was stationed here we RCAF types used to hang out at a place called the Captain's Cabin, Let's see if it still exists. "It did, and of course they had to tip a pint, one of sarsaparilla. "Not bad for a bunch of young military rowdies," graded Mae.

"Sometimes, Don told the foursome, warmly inspecting his roundabouts in London, "repetitions are not all bad." And so their foursome visited again Westminister, Big Ben, changing of the guard, Stonehenge, Bath, and the Viking tower at Waterford.

Then off to Ireland to Molly Dick's at Youghal, and to hang upside down, high above death dealing sharp rocks to kiss the Blarney Stone. "Look at the peat bogs," pointed Mae. "And there's the sign I've been waiting to see, Ring of Kerry!"

"That's all well and good, Mae," agreed Don H., with a determined grin, "But I'm looking forward to having a few pints at the Limerick Hotel!"

At the Gresham Hotel in Dublin, Don K. had his first chance to experience Irish lasses in an upbeat environment. "Do not misinterpret my analysis, my pretty little maid," Don K. explained to Mae, "but these young women who work here in the hotel make clear to me the words of the song, "When Irish Eyes are Smiling."

"I'm glad," snarled Mae, in mock anger, "that I'm here to protect you."

But it would be totally unfair not to include the tours fantastic night at Galloway Bay! "Yes," Mae had agreed, "in Ireland we've heard many Irish tenors, but tonight we are to have a real Irish party, under tents on Galloway Bay. Now we'll hear real Irish music!"

Under the tents, tables were set for eighteen people. Each couple received a quart of wine. "It has turned out," said Don H. to Don K., "that you and I are the only two who drink wine! Do you think we can oblige?"

"We can try," gloated Don K. The night was filled with Tracy Gentry Sr.'s songs. Mae questioned Don K., "What did you think of these Irish tenors, Tara?"

Don K showed Mae a totally relaxed and pleased countenance, "My dear, they were the best I've ever heard!"

"Dublin, Dublin, Dublin," moaned Don K. "So many happy and sad stories it has to tell."

'Yes, you romantic," Mae agreed, "especially while you're standing there with your arm around the waist of the wonderful statue of Sweet Molly Malone!"

But quickly they passed from Ireland to Scotland.

"I believe we both agree," said Mae nodding her head, "that Scotland seems more like home than any other country."

"True," nodded Don K.

Neither were prepared for Gretna Green, to which young English under-age kids trudged to get married. Mae and Don kissed at Gretna Green's famous Kissing Gate, but when they entered the famous 1710 Blacksmith Shop where all the marriages took place, the tour director, their good friend, Valerie, their own tour director, pulled them aside and said, "Mae and Don, we're going to have a wedding here today! Mae looked around. "I don't see a bride or groom!"

Valerie replied, "You, Mae, are the bride." And taking Don K. by the arm, she announced, "And here is your groom. Now we need a maid of honor and a best man!"

"That's easy," replied Mae. "Margarette, my sister was in truth my maid of honor at West Point. There she stands."

"And there that staunch Canadian fellow, is Don Hill, He'll do as a best man for me," added Don K.

And so, with Mae and Don K., in London Fog coats, Don K. and Don H. in British bowlers, Mae in bridal finery and Margarette tending the floral bouquet, the Scottish female justice of the peace conducted the marriage ceremony over the Old Anvil in the Blacksmith Shop at Gretna Green. When the ceremony was complete the minister raised her heavy blacksmith's hammer and struck the anvil a punishing blow. With the sound of the impact still ringing in everyone's ears, the justice of the peace concluded, "You are now properly married," and then she unobtrusively slipped Don K. the formal, official contract!

"Edinburgh Castle deserved a week of exploration. One afternoon was not enough," complained Mae. "I could have spent that much time listening to the Scotsmen in their kilts playing on our way to the top of the hill."

Don K. laughed and teased his beautiful wife, "Sweet and lovely, are you sure you wouldn't like to spend some more time admiring those handsome Scotsmen's legs bulging under their kilts?" Mae gave Don K. a ferocious blow with her fist to his solarplexis.

But tours are rush, rush, rush. And so back to England to rush through many of the spots where time prevented Mae from lingering; The Hotel Piccadilly, York Minster; Coventry; Shakespeare's birthplace; Penn's Hall; Anne Hathaway's Cottage; Churchill's grave at Blacton; Blenheim Palace;

Mayfair; and the Tara Hotel. What a vacation!

After they returned home on 8 July, Bill and Marylou Blosser arrived for a visit. "Marylou," announced Mae, "you're going to see Charlotte County; Edison's home; the Peace River Wildlife Center, Ponce de Leon Park, Fishermen's Village, and Punta Gorda, itself." And so the Blossers did see it all.

The 7th to 9th of August, David and Anne were on hand to celebrate David's birthday. Immediately, on 9 through 21 August, Mae and Don were off to Bowie, Maryland, Newark, and Massillon, Ohio. In Bowie, Mae and Don went to Swan's Harbor to see Charlie's new retreat. Mae was astonished. "This is no log cabin, my dear one. It's a beautiful four-bedroom estate with a huge Maryland stone fireplace!"

Checking the estate over, she glanced out the window and saw Don and Don Jr., carrying bushels of shells for cover around the flower beds. Such a beautiful spot and such a luxurious home, but Mae knew she and Don did not need all the work that Charlie and Jane faced.

In Newark and Massillon it was another trip down memory lane.

On 20 September one of life's tragedies befell all the family members. Mae's mother, the Gentry clan's matriarch, sweet Anna Kathyrn Glaunsiner Gentry died. Both Mae and Don returned to Newark to mourn with most of Newark's citizens.

It was at the memorial service that Don realized that Mae was not just remembered for her influence upon the rest of the world, but even more so in her own hometown from which she had been absent more than forty years. Don later told Don Jr., "A dozen handsome, silver-haired men came by, hugged and buzzed your mother. They all said something to the effect of, "Oh, Miss Gentry, you haven't changed. You're as beautiful as ever. The year I spent in your classroom changed my life. Again I thank you." And of course, Mae smiled at these successful men.

Almost to prove the old adage that time passes irrevocably generation after generation, on 6 October 1990 Kathyrn Mae Kipfer was born to Anne and David Kipfer.

Before departing to see Kathyrn in Columbia, Missouri, Mae and Don could not miss Thanksgiving with the Andersons at St. Augustine Ponce de Leon Country Club where they could enjoy a masterful meal and play golf; provide the Bebouts, Hills and the Gannons a canal boat cruise of the Christmas lights; participate in the club's Christmas Parade of Lights with the Andersons; and of course another hole-in-one for Mae at Burnt Store Country Club.

The city of Columbia and the University of Missouri were like returning to the military for Mae and Don. David was in uniform, his breast full of ribbons and he sported senior pilot's wings. There were visits to the armory, and to basketball games in the awesome university gymnasium.

For Don, Christmas was the best of all the American traditions. But beyond that, Kathyrn Mae captivated both Mae and Don's hearts. Mae told Don, "She's just two-months old, but so smart and Don, she just loves you, When you sweet talk her she just smiles at you and gurgles!"

New Year's Eve is not only a closeout of the old year, but beginning of the new. So it was special to have Mark, Carole, Brandon, and Stephanie come from Panama City to Punta Gorda to celebrate.

Kevin Bebout and his family were visiting Margarette in Alligator Park, so that New Year's Eve captured a goodly share of the family.

"It should be noted," agreed Mae, "that we gave sweet Stephanie a realistic Barbie automobile that was fast and powerful enough so that she could knock you down, sir!"

"Yes, I'll never forget that bump. But she'll be queen of her neighborhood. It will completely change her personality," said Don.

Carole found interest in Don's three-million-year-old nautilus agate dug from the mountains of North Africa and polished like a precious stone. "Wow," was her appraisal.

1991 was a year notable for golf achievements. On 30 January Mae won the Alligator Classic, 6-5 on the 19th hole. On 29 March, Don won his flight in the BSCC Championship, after thirteen years of encouragement from Mae. On 24 April, Mae won the President's Cup, gross, 87, 85, 88. On 30 October, Mae also won the President's Cup for the new season, this time for net scores, 69, 65,72 (67 net average, superior like the professional golfer she is). And on 2 April 1991, as team captain and cocaptain, Mae and Majel announced that the BSCC Ladies golf team were the Southwest Florida Ladies Golf Association Champions!

Perhaps the biographers and the readers suspect that the beautiful, vivacious, energetic Edna Mae Gentry Kipfer was slowing down at this point in her life. Guess again. Look at February's schedule, 1st typical 0930 bridge at Mid Barrys, 1900 dessert at Millers; 3rd, 0900 golf with Thrashers, 1900 Bridge Bebout/Hills; 4th, 0800 Golf Team Saint Andrews, 1900 Bridge at Heibers; 5th, Vote, 1800 Dinner and bridge at Ruth Greens; 6th, Mae BSCC golf; 7th couples golf 1500, Bridge 1845; 8th, BSCC 1800 Howells and Lobseres party; 9th, Golf 1304 Cianellas, visit Wines; 10th, 130 (Couples Golf, 1900 bridge Bebout Hills; 11th, BSCC annual meeting; 12th fishing; 1900 dinner with Andersons; 13th, 0900 golf, 1530 golf board; 14th, 1500 couples golf, 1700-1900 cocktails at Cianellas; 15th, Rotunda team play;

16th 0900 Aetna Challenge with Bebout/Hill; 18th fishing .19th, Dinner at Bebout/Hills, Tracy Gentrys arrive ; 20th, 0900 golf; 21st Tracy/Arlene cruise with Mae and Don on Charlotte Harbor, 1500 Couples golf; 23rdm BSCC cocktail, dinner with Vavalos; 24th, Couples golf 1051 with Gannons, 1800 BSCC dinner; 25th, 1800 cocktails, dinner and dancing with Rebers, Louises and Whittemores; 27th, golf, Joyce and Dick Rand cocktails and dinner BSCC 1800; 28th couples golf, bridge 1830.

Upon seeing this schedule, Mae's aunt Vada told Don, "No one could carry out such a schedule!"

"Wrong," replied Don. "Edna Mae Gentry Kipfer can!"

June and July were furious. It was miraculous! Mae dipped with her landing net more than two dozen four-pound spade fish from the Charlotte Harbor water at its artificial reef. "I could have dipped a thousand," laughed Mae, as Don pulled in Spanish mackerel.

Papaya were plentiful and weighed more than eight pounds each. When Mae picked her self-grown, succulent, sugar-sweet pineapples, she had to boast, "What a thrill it was to have your very own pink grapefruit, papaya, and pineapple for breakfast.

From Panama City through Lafayette, Louisiana, they stopped at Don's Seafood Restaurant to reminisce about meals there years ago. Then on to San Antonio for the EOAR reunion. Mae told Don it's wonderful to see and talk with the Wichers, Terrels, Woodyard Johnsons, Boveries, Vera and all the others again."

"Yes, that's true, and what amazing things they've done with their lives," he said.

Prior to the conventions commencement, they were off again to Randolph AFB, the Alamo, the Cowboy Museum, and a restaurant on the San Antonio River.

Everyone from EOAR was happy and looked much like they did twenty years earlier. Mae made sure she and Don circulated and visited with each attendee. She whispered to Don, "Store the memories, Tech Ops, they will have to last for some time!"

By 6 December Mae and Don had returned to Punta Gorda, then back-tracked to Panama City to serve as substitute parents for Brandon and Stephanie while their father and mother were in Acapulco vacationing.

By this time Brandon was intrigued by his pet snakes and creating Dagwood sandwiches. "Let's go to the Marianna Carverns," laughed Mae.

"And off to the woods for some tree climbing," added Brandon. "And, let's visit the Old Turpentine still."

Of course, they had to attend Stephanies' choir at Beach School. "And how could we pass up the playground at Tyndall AFB," asked Mae. But soon the rested, invigorated parents, returned and the grateful grandparents departed.

Christmases are always grand when they bring families together. David, Anne, and Kathyrn made the Christmas of 1991 merry and bright. Kathyrn could help hang the stockings, investigate the presents under the tree and eagerly await the arrival of Santa Claus.

"Are you sure, Paul Bunyan, that you want to saddle David with helping you fell that fifteen-foot-tall century plant that he brought us as a foot-tall sprout from Texas, during Christmas vacation?" asked Mae mournfully.

David had brought the foot-high century plant from San Antonio years before. Now the plant, itself, was fifteen feet tall, not only filling their front yard but dominating their upbeat neighborhood.

"Since blooming, its flower is a tall as our house, Mae. It's a hazard."

"Everyone stops to look at it," agreed Mae.

"It's got to go!" So Don rented a huge chain saw and David applied the muscle. Roger Nelson carried a truck load of heavy leaves away to his country ranch. When David was nearly finished with the sawing, juice flying everywhere, he announced, "I have to quit, folks. I feel strange all over. My skin hurts and I'm a little dizzy!"

So David went indoors and Don finished cleaning up. "I think I'm getting tipsy from the tequila juice. Look, it's running down the yard." And many neighbors who had dropped to watch the mayhem, had the same reaction.

"What are you going to do with that tall, thick post like center that's left?" questioned Mae.

"That is something I thought I would never see. It's a hardwood center to a cactus. It really looks like something alive, standing there!"

"What are you going to do with it?"

"It's from Texas, my dear. I'm carving a Texas road runner from it!"

Months later, when the carving had been completed, and the roadrunner was running on their lanai Mae and Don were sitting in their family room after dark, reading. Mae almost screamed, "Look, Don, there's a huge black beetle coming over the doors into our family room. What in the world is it?"

Don examined the horned beetle. "My word. You remember I told you they put a worm in the bottom of every good bottle tequila? This is a worm that's grown up. I just looked at the roadrunner carving and there's a large, neat hole where this beast exited!"

"What a story," laughed Mae.

But other events were unfolding. "It's too bad," complained Mae "but really wonderful things in life seem to be torn asunder and discarded. Our trip to Venice, home of the Barnum & Bailey circus will be one of the great treats in Kathyrn's life. The circus makes up here, and tries out their performances that will play over the United States."

"I understand your concern. It is unfortunate! This will be the circuses' last stand here in Venice. The Venice city fathers have declined, according to the paper, to pay $5,000 to repair a railroad spur the circus must have to provide transportation "What a terrible loss. The people of Venice cannot really understand what they are doing!"

Polynesia

But the circus move was a problem even Mae could not solve. So the Don Kipfers were about to move onward, this time to a far, far away place. "I agree with Gauguin, and Michener," admitted Don. "The islands of the Pacific are places where one can feel alive. I'm raring!"

"I know you, you wahine beach boy! You love not only Hawaii, prize of the Sandwich Islands, but the terrifying music and dances of Tahiti and Michener's description of trial marriages on Bora Bora. Did you bring your ukulele?"

"I'll never admit that, Leloni."

What a way to begin a vacation. Just checking into the Royal Hawaiian Hotel gives me the shivers," admitted Don. But the next morning on the seaside lanai of the Rainbow Hilton, eating papaya and banana bread, Don K. lost most of his reserve, especially when Mae murmured, "This, my dear, is what I remember best about Hawaii." And Margarette smiled, looked at Don H. and agreed, "Mae's right!"

"But today," reminded Mae, "we go to Pearl Harbor and the Polynesian Village for a preview of our cruise."

After the very sobering tour of the sunken ships at Pearl Harbor, Don explained, "I had just come off the night shift at 0700 at Republic Steel in Massillon. In came the foreman and announced, 'The Japanese have just attack Pearl Harbor.' Almost unanimously, twenty voices screamed, 'Where's Pearl Harbor?' When that was made clear, such a scream of indignation shook the room that I knew the Japanese would pay dearly for their treachery!

"Now, here today, more than fifty years later, I'm seeing it again for myself. Back then, in that washroom, and many others like it, the Japanese fate was sealed. The philosophers insure us that times change! And that is surely true, especially concerning patriotism and love of country. A large portion of the young men in our Republic Steel shop, without even knowing where Pearl Harbor was located, went out to volunteer and sign up to take care of the dirty Japs! God. help them!"

"The Polynesian Village and Show," explained Mae, "gives one a chance to see, feel, and hear at one spot, life in the South Pacific. It is a show, here in outdoor, maritime tropical Hawaii that is guaranteed to reach the heart of the most hardened person." But the four interlopers took advantage of their pre-tour stay in Hawaii to visit Waimea Canyon, Kawai Beach, the Kawai Grotto, Haleakalat (Maui), Lahaina (Mauai), The needle (Maui), walked across the hot lava beds, and stood against the stupendous Hawaiian water falls. Now they rushed to board the "Love Boat."

"The television series, called the 'Love Boat,' based upon the cruise ship, the *Pacific Princess*, had not begun to prepare me for this experience," laughed Mae. "No one, not even King Kamehameha, can rate such lavish treatment as we're enjoying. Frankly, it's indescribable."

Evenings aboard the ship were formal and Mae declared, "I know that on each trip I declare this but, the food is the best I've ever tasted. Their on-board shows are as good as any I've seen on Broadway!"

"Mae," cautioned Don K, "it takes eighteen laps around the boat deck to make one mile. You have to walk five miles to get a Love Boat shirt!"

"Never mind, Beach Boy. Watch, I'm up to it," hissed Mae.

When the Love Boat docked at Moorea, Bora Bora, both Don K. and Don H. ran to the island's only car rental shop. "It's a good thing we hurried," Don K. reported. "They only have one car for rent."

Second priority was viewing Bora Bora's lagoon. "Never, never," roared Mae, "have I ever seen such beautiful colors. Pastel blues, greens, and shinning whites and yellows. I love the water birds and also the multicolored fish in the transparent water."

And when Mae and Margarette went wading, Don K. added, "Even Michener could not imagine such a sight."

"There are coconut palms covering all the flat areas but as soon as there is any elevation they are replaced with grass that makes the hills beautifully green," observed Mae.

"Stop!" shouted Don H., startling Don K. "There's a stand where we can wet our whistles." Then smiling, the rotund proprietor served cold beer, then explained the pens they had seen at almost every lonely home. "We keep our coconut crabs in there!" smiled the proud barman.

When Don K. went to examine these crabs, he came back all animated. "You know those gigantic crabs climb up, knock a coconut down and with their claws tear it open. They are huge and I imagine quite dangerous!" He turned to the grinning man from Bora Bora. "Do you eat these crabs?"

"You bet your life we do!"

The American women grimaced.

Don K. missed very little about the character of the people he met. He realized the Bora Bora man had been ogling Mae. "Sir, come back tonight and we'll let you try our roasted coconut crabs." Don K. understood the invitation. "Nice of you, but we are very short on time."

Halfway around Bora Bora, Don K. pulled over. "Those four young women are about as beautiful as you might ever happen to see," appraised Don K. "Right out of Michener."

"Those tempting trouble makers are selling those saris hanging on that rope strung from tree to tree. But I don't really need a sari, mon ami."

Nonetheless, over to the rental car, the smiling darlings came. "They're going to work on Don K.," anticipated Mae. "Sir, you need several of these saris as presents for your wife and her friend. See how nice they look." The girls emphasized that the outfits showed yards of hip skin.

"Yes, girls, I see," approved Don K., obviously with considerable appreciation. "I'll take two." He then handed the beautiful silk saris over to Mae and, with a devious laugh, added, "I bought those just for you, dear!"

And as they traveled beyond this they found that Polynesian Tahiti was more than advertised. "The girls, and fellows, too, are simply beautiful," concluded Mae, "and so talented. Sofitel Maeva beach, with its huge stone carvings of Polynesian gods, simply adds to the mystique of the environment and the succulent Polynesian food." And at this journey's end, they enjoyed the flight back home.

There, they swung again into action, attending the wedding of grand niece Holly Childress to Brad Spicer, and visits again with Howard and Isabel Kaney in Nokomis. On 18 April, Letha and Walter Ritter, Isabel and Howard Kaney had lunch with Mae and Don at their beautiful Burnt Store Country Club. "This is not the most happy occasion for any of us," said Mae. "You all remember I was the governess for Franklin and Helen all those years ago. Now we must go to Venice for Franklin's memorial."

On the way to Venice, Don gave his own memorial for Mae to hear: "Franklin was one of the best men our country has ever turned out. Almost too handsome for a man. A college graduate and a lawyer with a wonderful personality. He should have been the chief justice of the Supreme Court. What events conspire to frustrate what surely should have happened. Perhaps too much family money. Perhaps lack of sheer determination."

Mae remained silent.

In Venice clans assembled and everyone paid their solemn respect to Franklin. "Unfortunately," moaned Don, "funerals are for the living. The dead are on their own!"

Back in Punta Gorda, life kept whizzing by. Mae wanted a picture with one of her prized papayas, "I know it's not a monstrous Mexican papaya, but it weighs more than eight pounds! Not bad."

When the cat's away, the mice will play," quoted Mae. The weather forecasters were either on vacation or sleeping, for down the Kipfers' canal, like a hundred-mile-an-hour locomotive, came a hurricane that no one expected, that became known as the no-name storm. "Harold Miller, our next door neighbor," Mae told Margarette by phone, "lost his davits into the canal and his huge, new cruiser, with all its electronic equipment, is lying on its side in the canal, covered with saltwater!"

Don could tell what Margarette was saying even though he was not on the phone, for Mae replied to her sister. "We were lucky. We just lost the small corner of our lot and one slab of seawall."

On 29 June Vera Alexandre, Don's secretary from Brussels appeared at the Kipfer quarters in Punta Gorda. Off they went to Sanibel Island to help Ruth and Bill Woodyard and all of their many offspring celebrate their fiftieth wedding anniversary. "Well, Bill," laughed Don, "it's been a long, hard road, eh?"

"Not long enough and actually a pretty pleasant road, I'd like to do it again!"

Mae added, "For Ruth and I one of the high points in our marriage was launching in a U.S. jet airliner from Cairo, Egypt, with Lawrence of Arabia playing on the loudspeaker and landing during the coup in Athens. We really didn't know how much danger we were in!"

Then 19 July Mae and Don left for Columbia, Missouri, to mind the fort while Laura Anne Kipfer made her appearance. "Gosh," gloated Mae, "Kathyrn really is a beautiful child. And so smart for being only twenty-one months old." Mae and Don took her everywhere. The parks, the flower gardens, the ice cream parlors, and to local farms.

Mae could hardly restrain herself, "Don, I believe you are in love with Kathyrn."

Don had shown and explained every detail of her home to Kathyrn. "Mae, she's right in line after you. Do you hear her point and say, 'Over here, under here, up here, beside here'?"

"True, Capote. But don't forget we really came to welcome the newly arrived Laura Anne to our family."

"True, my dear, I haven't forgotten. We've seen as much of her as waking hours will permit, in the hospital and home here at David's. And what a fine-looking baby she is."

After a quick visit to Mark and his family while passing through Panama City, they were back home to welcome the Zanas and Bob's sister Lillian for a visit with the Kipfers in Punta Gorda. These were the same people, Bob, a dentist, and Helen Mae's cousin whom Mae had known and lived near since she was a child. Later she told Don, "I'm very proud to be able to entertain my friends and relatives in such a wonderful home."

"My dear, all these people come here to see you, and to be invigorated not to see the house. But the house you've earned and deserve," said Don.

Russel Moyer was a grown man, dating the women of Massillon as the teenage Don was learning from his cousin's courting techniques. "I can still remember watching Russ press a crease in his trousers before a date," revealed Don.

"I remember staying with Russ and his family in Tampa when the boys were small," recalled Mae.

Now, Ronnie and Russ were coming for a short house visit. Breakfast on the lanai with palms and saltwater, enjoying fresh cut fruit, lunch with crispy baked fish and salad, and dinner at Burnt Store Country Club. They all toured Punta Gorda and then both Don and Russ played the organ. Don whispered to Mae. "I didn't know Russ could play the organ. Gosh, he can do anything."

"Russ, I remember hunting and fishing with you and my dad so many times," recalled Don. "It is wonderful to have such memories."

"Yes, you're correct, Don. Uncle Charlie was my model. He was a great athlete and sportsman." And so their visit ended on a welcome sentiment.

Again Mae won the President's Cup. Net 66, 73, and 75! "Great golf, sweetie," congratulated Don.

Once again Mark, Carole, Brandon and Stephanie were in Punta Gorda for Christmas and New Year. Kevin Bebout and family were at Margarette's. Don Hill's son, Wayne, Judy, and Colin filled out the party. So there was a total of eighteen persons to enjoy family activities and say hello to 1993.

"Our guests are beginning to stack up," Don commented.

"I love it," squealed Mae. "The Ruffners, Rhonda, Len, Leigh, Stacey, and Matt are so congenial. Their kids, Mark's two and Kevin's get along so wonderfully."

Egypt

But so much domestic tranquility gave way to another exotic tour. Mae and Don had both been to Egypt, but not south (or up) the Nile River, to its interior. Now was their opportunity. "What will we find there?" questioned Mae.

"Many surprises, I'm sure, my pretty little maid. We've both read oodles about Egypt, but no one can put an exotic place on paper!"

After Mae and Don K, Margarette and Don H. landed in Cairo and made their way by cab to their gorgeous Semi Ramis Hotel, Mae observed. "Look at the herds of camels in the streets. Whatever for?"

Don at first tried to ignore the question, but then softened his reply. "Do you see any camel saddles? Draw your own conclusions."

"Please don't tell me they're going to eat these noble animals!" begged Mae.

The cab driver turned his head and gave them a glance that said, "*Stupidos!*"

In Cairo, the tour group, with Margarette and Don H., went to a papyrus factory where fabulous Egyptian artists were plying their ancient crafts. "We must have one of an Egyptian prince and princess," demanded Mae. "The artist says he will put our names right under each figure in gold Egyptian hieroglyphics."

"So be it, Allah," concurred Don. Then examining the young Egyptian's work, Don chortled, "Unbelievable. With their code, I can actually read the names!"

Of course, camel riding was a necessity, as was another visit to the Great Pyramids. And one's education concerning ancient Egypt was improved one thousand percent by attending the nightly authentic light shows. And in Cairo, itself, again, to see the Mena House, the tower, the huge lions at the Nile el Taric bridge, the city bazaar (Khanel-Kanlili).

Then they began that part of their trip they were anxious to experience. Their arrival at Aswan and visit to the enormous Aswan Dam, highlighted so often in news about the Russian undertaking, was really impressive. And their arrival at AEU Simbel was just as impressive. It was simply just a gorgeous air terminal. "The enormous stone carvings of Ramses II here at the Abu Simbel and and the Temple of Queen Nefertari are beyond belief," gasped Mae.

"Many people in our world doubt that the United States ever landed on the moon," reminded Don K. "And though I've read romantic tales and scientific journals concerning these places we are now seeing, I really rather thought of them only possible as mythical. No more!"

"By boat to the Philae Temple," read Margarette in her guide book. "Yes," agreed Mae, "and then to the Ptdemais Temple at Kom Ombo!"

"Can this be?" gasped Don K. "All my life I've heard about what we westerners viewed as the excesses of the Agha Khan, who made his religious subjects pay a tax of his weight in gold and diamonds each year."

"You can be sure," added Don H., "that he kept his body weight at its max!"

"Now, by felucca boat, we're sailing to see his palace and mausoleum," warned Mae.

"What a view," concluded Mae. "The blue Nile bordered by green trees, and covered with a blue sky. The Agha didn't seem to have many worries!"

But on the luxurious *Queen of Sheba*, a four-stories tall tour boat, it was a different scene on shore. Fields were green with rich crops. Women were fully clothed from head to toe.

The top deck of the *Queen of Sheba* was a huge swimming pool. Beautiful women were swimming lazily. The tour boat, with no Nile docks, was moored to stakes pounded in the Nile's dikes. The Arab men, standing on shore, their eyes at a level with the ship's pool, fully garbed, their tongues reaching nearly to their knees, ogled these perfect infidel ladies, which no Arab Muslim man ever hoped to see.

Mae managed to get ashore along one of the irrigated fields, to have a little interchange with a real Egyptian. "I got a picture of that beautiful little Arab girl with her adorable white-haired donkey that looked like a giant rabbit. I was overcome her beauty. I gave her a good sum of money."

"Good for you," agreed Don K., "but I saw your face changed to anger when she walked behind the dike and handed her money to that huge Egyptian man!"

Then on to Edfu and the Temple of Horus, once the most powerful God in Egypt. Don K., for a reason unknown to the others, was particularly taken by Horus. He told Mae, "I'm going to carve a sculpture of Horus."

"Next," reported Mae, "is our stop at Luxor. Upon seeing it, she declared, "Luxor and its wondrous bazaar are themselves worth our trip!"

"Still, when you report to your neighbors and relatives don't forget the enormous crocodiles that we've seen lying along the banks of the Nile. In one gulp, they could swallow a person. They are a part of Egypt, also," added Don K.

Next they were off to the locks at Esna. Then the fantastically large temple of the ram-head god Khmem. "Who could fantasize Luxor," asked Mae. "Our largest U.S. buildings, and works, like the Statue Liberty, are simply puny when compared with the temples and stone carvings at 'The Valley of the Kings' or 'The Valley of the Queens.' No narrative, no pictures, no television, coverage can describe this place, established by mere man, thousands of years ago. One simply must meet it eyeball to eyeball."

"Now, you've said it all," agreed Don K. "I learned one lesson I never knew, my dear," summarized Don K.

"My dear, I thought you knew everything."

"Hardly. Really, with all the different factors who have ruled here, from Asia, Europe, and Africa itself, it's very difficult to sort out who an Egyptian really is. But it's clear to me that black people, whom the Egyptians call Nubians, ruled Egypt during its most progressive periods. Of all the literature I've read about Egypt, this was never even hinted about to me!"

As a sort of farewell, the tour staff took them to the Pharaonic Village and offered them their last Egyptian dinner at Felfela restaurant. "What a wonderful way to close out our tour! I will never again be the same female you married, Abdula," crooned Mae.

"Sweetie, if you make any improvement, I will not be able to keep up with you!"

Missouri

Back in Punta Gorda, stability reigned. A welcome-home visit from son Mark and on the 15th of March, a wonderful visit from the Zanas. Soon to arrive were Tracy Jr. and Arlene. Sandwiched between these events was Mae's thirty-two-pound, forty-two-inch cobia and Don's 100-pound five-and-a-half-foot tarpon caught off Fishermen's Village.

Nothing can be more glorious for grandparents than another grandchild. So off to Columbia, Missouri, on 30 June to help David, Anne, Kathyrn, and Laura greet the arrival of David Banks Kipfer. Mae and Don entertained the girls by swimming, gardening, picking huge, juicy sweet blackberries, visiting every play park in Columbia, cavorting in the city's flower gardens, and visiting local farms again. Finally, that long-awaited day arrived, on 2 July 1993. "I can see from the jolly, jolly smile on your face, grandpa, that this is one of the very best days in your life!" said Kathyrn.

"Just a minute, my darling granddaughters, Kathyrn and Laura, you were not here to see your grandfather laugh and dance on the days you were born!"

By the 7th of July, Anne was up and around. Everyone went to Rocheport and Les Bourgeois Vineyards and had lunch and sipped wine. "I have seen many floods," explained Mae, "but the Missouri has exceeded any I have ever imagined. It's beyond its song 'Along the Wide Missouri'."

"There are houses and barns floating downstream. And from this high vantage point it's wider than many great seas!" she added.

For the proud, new mother, everyone went to Alexander's Restaurant where one could select their own steak and cook it themselves to their very own specifications on the huge central charcoal grill. "A restaurant that exceeds its advertisement," agreed Mae.

Home to Punta Gorda and Mae's pineapple-picking season. Then a visit by the Bill and Mary Lou Blossers and a revisit to the famous Tin City in Naples. Before the Blossers departed the four had to inspect and approve the foundations for David's new home in Punta Gorda at 5630 Almar Drive. "Home is the fisherman, home from the sea," quoted Mae. "How wonderful to have at least one son and his family reunited with us after so many years of separation. But David, the fisherman, is back to the sea!"

"Off again," beamed Mae. "We've passed through Charlotte, South Carolina, so many times. It's so historic. We've never stopped. This time we're stopping to see what makes it tick!"

"My learned historian, after you have traveled Europe, Asia, Africa, North and South America, Australia and New Zealand, the white man's cities in the United States seem so contemporary. Still, what history there is, can be found in Charleston," hypothesized Don.

"How about the circular Congregational church we visited among the old cranes on the second floor of the East Bay Trading company? And can you discount the authenticity of the women selling basic wares at the Old City wharves?"

"I don't want to cross sabres with you, sweet thing. You've made your point," retreated a chagrined husband.

"But this trip was intended for other purposes," reminded Mae. So off to Bowie and Swan's Harbor.

As they drove into Charlie's country log home, Mae remarked, "Here, anyone can see the beauty of God's nature at Swan's Harbor. And it will be fun to attend Jane's craft show in Cambridge."

Back in Bowie, Don was surprised. "I knew of all the national awards Charlie had received from Sears, but I was certainly impressed with Charlie's Sears and Roebuck Home Improvement Office in his home. He's some salesman. Best in the Eastern United States almost every year, He has his own computer, faxes, Internet, and subcontractors. What an operation."

But Mae and Don had another surprise in store. Charlie told them Sears had eliminated their Home Improvement Division, but had offered him a management position instead. "I always wanted my own store so I declined the offer and now I have my own store in Cambridge, called the Rainbow Waterworks. I want you to see it!"

"My," said Mae, "what a beautiful, impressive store." And inside Don was almost floored, "Surely it's impressive, Charlie. Show rooms, classrooms and Rainbow equipment of all sorts. We both wish you success."

Then on to Mae's aunt Vada's in Silver Springs for roast beef and Yorkshire pudding and updates. Then on to Uncle Dorsey's and Aunt Florence's in Zelinople. Knowing Uncle Dorsey might not live much longer, Mae asked him, "Is there any thing you would like to see or do while Don and I are here to help?"

"Yes," grinned Dorsey, full of ideas. "I'd like to play my coronet for you one more time, Mae Mae," and he did. "Next, I'd like to take one last ride around Zelinople to see my old spots," and they did.

"Is there nothing else, Uncle Dorsey?" Mae asked, knowing the answer from previous experience.

Mae's uncle's face lighted up. He grinned, and for a moment, he looked just like he had fifty-years earlier. "Yes, Mae Mae, I'd to go up on the hill and get an ice cream cone." And they did!

"Nothing much startlingly new has happened in Newark for a long time," moaned Mae. "But after this trip that can never be said again. Friends of ours, the Longabergers, have totally taken over Newark and made it their home. We're going with Bud and Arlene to see their 'Basket' World!"

On 18 August, Mae and Don visited the World's largest basket. "It is forty-eight-feet long and twenty-three-feet high. It's made from the wood of ten maple trees!" marveled Mae.

"It's authentic, all right," added Don. "See the two swinging handles."

And as a lark, back went the Kipfers to Ye Old Mill in Mount Vernon and enjoyed sundaes where once grain was ground in that mill for central Ohio.

In Massillon, their objective was the reunion of the old log schoolhouse students at Myers. It was nostalgic for Don to again see his birthplace. "It is just excruciating to see again 'that old gang of mine'," shouted Don. "Raymond McFarren, who cracked my mother's kitchen window with his BB gun, which for some unknown reason, my father never replaced, Bud Flounders, who got caught up in socialism. Phyllis and Natalia Brown, who were sisters." And a visit to Myers Church's graveyard where Hanah Baldwin's stone showed her birth as 1846 and her death as 1925. A woman, whom Don sometimes in his dreams seemed to remember, and information Mae had not known before.

Back again to home base in Punta Gorda. David and family came in 8 September 1992 to check the progress of their home at 5630 Almar Drive and to parade their intelligent, beautiful, offspring. As always, fishing was big. "My gosh," roared Mae, "a fifty-one-pound cobia and a twelve-pound triple tail. Some catching, men!"

Again golfing was featured in November. Mae, Margarette, Don K. and Don H. entered the much-advertised Couples Member Guest Tournament at Burnt Store Country Club. When the results were announced, Mae jumped with joy. "Folks, we've won first. Maybe, just maybe, my hubby's 77 helped."

Then on the 17th Mae won her third President's Cup. "You're becoming more experienced, Mae, and steadily better," congratulated Don.

Being a military pilot is not the piece of cake that faces the high flying, highly paid civilian captain. One must plan his own flights, obtain his own weather and train his own crew. His flights are always operational and neither he nor his wife knows whether he will return at day's end. So it was with both fond and hectic memories that David Lawrence Kipfer departed the USAF on 24 January 1994 after serving twenty years as a senior and command pilot and squadron commander. Like all other retiring military pilots, he had mixed emotions. He fully realized that return to civilian life had its ups and downs also! And so on 2 February 1994, Dave, Anne, Kathyrn, Laura, David arrived in Punta Gorda to begin a new life. "Goodness, we are so happy to have all of you in Punta Gorda," greeted a bubbling Mae. "I know your beautiful, eleven-room house on the canal just next to Alligator Creek is ready, but you should stay with us to rest a few days and let us pamper you before digging right in," coaxed Mae. But on 4 February the Dave Kipfers moved to 5630 Almar.

Fishing

"My," exclaimed Mae, "Dave, you and your Dad scored so soon. A 150-pound, six-foot tarpon right off Fishermen's Village. Who caught it?"

Dave looked a little sheepish at Mae. "Pop. It took him fifty-six minutes. That tarpon ran and reared like a stallion. It pulled our boat nearly a mile!"

"Sure, Mae," added Don. "I fought it, but it was Dave who gaffed it and pulled it aboard. I could never have done it alone!"

On 27 April, Mae took a call from Dave at 5630 just as she and Don had gone to sleep. "Mom, do you and Pop want to see a huge snook? I mean a HUGE snook! Come on over."

Mae didn't consult with Don. "We'll be there in ten minutes," she said.

"Dave was right," agreed Mae, looking at five-year-old Kathyrn standing next to and being dwarfed by the snook her daddy was holding vertically.

"Did you catch it from your dock, Dave," asked Don.

"Yes, yes. It fought like a demon. It weighs twenty-six pounds and it's forty-two inches long."

Don looked at the snook, then at Kathyrn, and finally at Mae. "Now, that's what I call a fish! Dave's trying to beat all my records!"

On 9 June, one day after Mae and Don's wedding anniversary, Hammond Banks, Anne's father arrived from Virginia to see his only grandchildren. "What beautiful, smart, well-behaved grandchildren I have," pronounced Banks.

Banks had been a distributor of fishing equipment and was eager to go fishing with Don and Dave. "But I soon found out," Don told Mae later, "that Banks was really a freshwater fisherman. He preferred the light equipment and catching trout, of which we always have by the thousands. I think perhaps fighting the huge sharks that turn Dave and I on were just a bit to much for him. He seemed a little apprehensive when we pulled those huge sharks aboard!"

"We'll have Banks here for dinner. And Zito's would be nice," recommended Mae.

"And unfortunately, before one can catch their breath, Banks will have returned home," added Don.

Perhaps Mae cared so much for golf and bridge because they both required considerable intellect. When you won, at either endeavor, you felt good. On 4 August, perhaps as a pre-holiday present for Mae, on the way home from their club, Don congratulated his bride. "First-place couple of sixty in the golf tournament and first-place couple of forty at the party bridge. A pretty good day, sweetheart!"

"Thank you for your help, big boy!"

A strange thing occurred at one point in Punta Gorda. The Heibers, Hamners, and Harms, all from Caterpillar bought condos on the canal leading from Punta Gorda Isles past Fishermen's village into Charlotte Harbor. "Now," exclaimed Mae, "the Heibers are celebrating their fiftieth wedding anniversary at our club and this gala affair will have guests from all over out country. Carole Lee Heiber had asked me to be the official photographer!"

"My dear, your fame has spread. All the marvelous photos from your Trim-the-Tree-Party, which you handed out to everyone were remarkable. But your phots of my sculptures are the best I've ever seen. The Heibers could not hire anyone who could do better."

On Father's Day, 19 June, Mae joked, "You men. But Dave's gift to you of that huge bull shark's head mounted on its black walnut plaque was special. Its jaws were large enough to swallow a small child whole!"

"Halloween was a grand time for us kids in Massillon," Don told Mae. "We collected corn for weeks to dry and throw at house windows. We soaped windows. We used our tic-tacs to make noise on wooded siding. We had a ratcheted saw blade with a crank to really raise Cain. The older boys put farmers' spring wagons on the top of the church."

"Pretty destructive, if you ask me," complained Mae.

"Yup, but now our grandchildren are having fun, too. A preschool party with Miss Jill at the Punta Gorda Library. And the house-to-house trick-or-treating on Via Formia.

On 10 December, Mae and Don received the expected, but unwelcome word that Russel Moyer had died. Mae tried to console Don. "Mae, he was the last of a generation that made the transition from homesteaders to full-blown Americans."

"We always had a wonderful time full of fun with him and Ronnie when we stayed with them in Tampa," remembered Mae.

"He was a college graduate, you know. The second in his family. He was more handsome than Gregory Peck. He was taller than other Moyers—six feet. He had the largest chest of any man I ever knew. Perhaps that was his Dutch ancestry. He never really had any formal athletic training but he was a great natural athlete. He hunted squirrels, rabbits, and pheasants with me and my dad. Here, in Tampa, he was a contractor and helped design and build many of Tampa's modern public buildings. His death robs me of a portion of my own life."

And so off went Mae and Don to Tampa for a funeral that neither one wanted to occur. Then Don, along with other members of the family, acted as a pallbearer for a burial viewed by family and neighbors and many other Tampa friends.

And there is no better way to start a new year than with a success. But the past is history and new history is yet to be made. Mae told Don, "In spite of the philosophy, doesn't it hurt so good to again win first in couples golf and second in couples bridge on the same day?"

"Amen to that, my fellow competitor."

Grandchildren

"By, the way," mentioned Mae. "All the multitudes of wonderful wood sculptures you've completed have been appreciated by everyone who received one. But those six, foot-long insects you carved are the favorite of your grandchildren."

On 4th of March, it so happened that Mae was looking after grandson David. "Let's go to the antic auto show in Laishley Park, Don."

"OK." It was a great hit. Mae commented. "David sure liked all the old autos. But I never expected that the reporter speaking to you would take your picture. You two are celebrities." But again these Florida natives, officially known as the Kipfers, were getting restless.

"I'll admit we've been about everywhere, Mr. Tour Director, but for some reason you've always short-circuited Bermuda. Is there any reason?"

Don knew what was coming. "Right. Bermuda has historically been an important stop, especially in the sailing days; even for aircraft. But I suppose I never wanted to see an English look-alike when we could go to England and see the real thing," Don teased. "Is there some reason you're asking?"

Mae was aggravated now. He was supposed to understand. "Paisan, you know there is. I want to see for myself. And Margarette and Don Hill want to go, also!"

So on 22 April 1995 in the year of our Lord, Don and Mae were securely settled on the good ship *Meridan* of the Celebrity Cruise Line. "Of course, the food is wonderful, like most cruises," admitted Don.

"And I was really proud of you when you won the on deck putting contest among the hundred of contestants. The holes were well hidden and bunkered and the ship was rolling. It was great."

"Perhaps. But the ship awarded prizes to all the winners of so many other nonsensical games that required no skill whatsoever. I received only a handshake!"

"Poor boy," sympathized Mae.

They visited the town hall at Saint George. Don K. and Don H. lifted a few pints at the Robin Hood Pub. All four had to try the wooden head and hand locks at the Butterfield Bank. "I suspect," laughed Mae, "that you will also have to have steak and kidney pie at the Robin Hood Restaurant, along with we two merry maids, Don Kipfer."

"If they cook it, I'll have it," replied Don K.

But it was on the local bus trips, rubbing elbows with the white and black English that the Kipfers learned most about Bermuda. "That English woman on the bus told me more about Bermuda than I ever wished to know," revealed Mae.

"But I'm sure everyone on our tour noticed. About half the help is white, half black, even in the conservative, ritzy banks. The black people, male and female, are dressed to perfection, perfectly made up, and so kind and helpful. It surely is an example for the United States," added Mae, always being optimistic.

"Only too true, my saint. But for that to happen, there must be huge changes in attitudes in both our white and black races. It's a monumental task that we may never live to see!"

The morning after Mae and Don arrived back in Punta Gorda, they were awakened by their doorbell ringing. There stood Don's classmate from West Point, Jim Frazer, who with his wife, Nelda, had been along on the Bermuda cruise, with a framed picture in his hand. He roared with laughter, "Don, I wanted to make up for the oversight by the *Meridan* crew when you won the putting contest!"

Jim held out as a gift, a beautiful print he had made on his computer. It showed a putting green on board a ship with many onlookers and a beautiful girl presenting a loving cup to Don. The caption at the bottom of the print read: "To the World's Greatest Putter."

Both men, Mae noticed, had a huge laugh. Don shook Jim's hand and told him, "Thanks, classmate. Only one West Pointer can appreciate another!"

Mae was not only a worldwide ambassador for the proud citizens of the United States, a diplomat, a teacher, a sports woman, an international executive, but arguably the world's best grandmother. She helped at each of her grandchildren's births. She helped teach then to walk and talk. She made sure they were strong swimmers. She taught them about nature and nature's animals. She made sure they were exposed to every aspect of life that would be valuable to them in their lifetimes. Now, back in Punta Gorda in her capacity as a Red Cross swimming instructor, she awarded the first Pollywog Red Cross Badge to Kathyrn.

Mae and Don and their three grandchildren visited the Punta Gorda pioneer's field day, watched their friend Ann Ashworth operate her weaving machine and celebrated Cracker Days. Everyone went to see Grandpa Don's public displays of woodcarving. The grandchildren helped Mae harvest stalks of bananas, large papaya, pineapples, oranges, grapefruit, starfruit, and macadamia nuts.

Dave hooked a seven-foot alligator, which had been cruising his canal, stalking his family, just off his back yard dock, and called the county's professional hunter to remove it.

The three grandchildren again dressed in their spook costumes and stalked the Via Formia in quest of huge bags of Halloween candy. "What hauls," appraised Mae. "You all will be sick."

"No, no, Grandma. We not get sick," said the novice spook, young David.

And so with a preschool library Christmas party, a Trim-the-Tree-party at the senior Kipfers, Christmas at son Dave's, and New Year's Eve with sister Margarette and Don Hill, Mae concluded, "A wonderful year, señor."

1996 began at son Dave's home with a New Year's Day party. But the New Year's activity switched to Mae supervising her grandchildren, harvesting bushels of grapefruit and oranges, and then a visit by Mae, Don, and Kathyrn to Myaka River State Park. "Now that we're fully rested," laughed Mae, "we're ready for houseguests!"

Don had many honors, Mae knew, during and after his military service, but on one of grandson David Bank's visits to 825 Via Formia, out of a clear blue sky, David announced to Mae, "I'm Pap Paw's boy!"

"That," agreed Don, is the best achievement award I have ever or will ever receive!" Way back in 1953 Don proposed to Mae, "Our family is growing and we're making so many long trips we need a large, dependable auto. How about a Cadillac?"

Mae almost laughed herself into hysterics. "Lover, you've got to be kidding. Honestly, do we look like millionaires?"

"We will when we get into our new Cadillac, sweetie pie!"

Now, more than four decades later, they were driving away from Val Wards with another new Cadillac. "They keep getting better," humored Mae.

On Leap Year, 29 February 1996, the Kipfers celebrated by again winning first at couples golf and first at couples bridge at Burnt Store Country Club. "Hooray, whoopee," cheered Mae.

Don shook his head. "Whoa, excited one. You know our luck can't go on forever, chickadee."

"Why not, may I ask?" retorted a confident wife. Now began Mae's favorite activity; entertaining houseguests. First Marylou and Bill Blosser; Lillian and Roger McNeiley; next Don's cousin Betty and her husband Bill Schnitzer; then the Ohioans Arlene and Tracy Gentry and Tammy Brownlee—all this rounded off by a visit from Tom and Betty Powell. It seemed no one wanted to be left out. As a pleasant surprise, Doctor Mike, Patsy, Justin and Valerie arrived.

Mae shook her head, "Don, don't tell me again, for I know all about you Kipfers' Irish traditions on St. Patrick's Day. Your mother always had a grand party that day for your Grandmother Kipfer, your aunt Mary, and your sister. All those blarney relatives born on that revered saint's day. It was not that important at my house. "But now the Cronins, across the canal, those rabid Irish, are just as energized. Their party's huge. And John believes in washing all the hors d'oeuvers and food down with plenty of Irish whiskey!" It was a time of Old Sod remembrances, Irish jokes and community disturbing Irish laughter.

The men's member-guest golf tournament at Burnt Store Country Club was a huge affair. Don K. and Don H. were entered. Don K. felt they played their best, especially Don H., who pared two of the par five holes. It turned out they placed fourth. "Pretty darned good for us, Don H.!"

It is no surprise to me that you've been selected as a Distinguished Citizen of Massillon," glowed Mae. "But I can hardly believe Massillon is devoting a whole week of celebration to you, offering to pay your transportation, your hotel expenses, and most of your meals. And lucky me, mine also!"

But, of course, Don was excited and there was no doubt that the Kipfers would accept the invitation and would fully participate, in all the festivities! Upon arrival in Massillon, they were met by a nice lady, Jo Annen, the selection committee chair, and checked into the best motel in West Canton, Ohio. "Nice," approved Mae.

On their first meeting in Massillon, they were introduced to Peter Boron, a renowned scientist, and John McVay, coach and athletic director extraordinaire, Don's co-distinguished citizens.

"It's nice to see all my relatives again, Mae, although I regret that all the Kipfers are gone, especially my parents. How my mother and dad would have enjoyed this celebration!"

But a visit to the Kaney home and to dinner at the Massillon Club dispensed such thoughts.

"It was nice of Verna and Warren to take us to that fine restaurant devoted to the 356th fighter Group," added Don. "And I really enjoyed walking along Main Street and Tremont Avenue again and visiting the new city hall."

"Of all the activities in Massillon, I liked the talks Don gave at Massillon's Washington High, at the Chamber of Commerce, the Lion's Club, and the alumina gathering the most," bragged Mae

"I could not believe it when I received a folder of professional photographs prepared by Pep Paulson (our one-time high school football team's mascot, Obie the tiger) that covered the whole week's activities!" admitted Don.

"Sure, but the huge formal accolade from the Ohio House of Representatives signed by Jo Ann Davidson, speaker; gold seal of formal recognition by the Ohio Senate signed by Stanley J. Aronoff, president; and the formal proclamation from the town of Massillon, signed by Mayor Francis R. Cicchinelli, whose father was a close friend of yours, certainly were honors anyone could be justly proud of."

"Yes, it is certainly a moral booster to have such recognition. I know my accomplishments were submitted by my long-ago close friend, Phyllis Brown. She is the person who felt that recognition was deserved and necessary!"

"But best of all," Mae enthusiastically pointed out, "of all those awards, the silver-leafed photograph of you as a full colonel in uniform, which will hang in the Hall of Fame in Massillon forever, is the most important. It shows that you:

    a. Were an Air Force full colonel, with command pilot, command missileer wings.

    b. Your many assignments, including those to Canada, Vietnam and Thailand.

    c. That you received two Legions of Merit, the Bronze Star, and fifteen other medals.

    d. Are president of MaeDon, an oil painter, a published novelist, and nationally recognized wood sculptor."

"From such a heady trip, my patooti, it's difficult to get back down to earth," Don admitted.

And so again home and exciting activities. Mae's additional duties consisted of BSCC publicity chairperson and required frequent faxing. Kathyrn began tae kwon do. On two days in successive weeks, Dave and Don caught, according to Mae's reckoning, "one twelve-pound triple tail, one fifteen-pound triple tail, four blacktip sharks more than four-feet long, and a thirty-pound cobia!

Dave finally realized that the extended night hours with the U.S. Post Office were counterproductive for his family, and began teaching high school math in Moorehaven.

When the E. O. Starks first moved into their new house across the canal from the Kipfers, Mae recorded this conversation: "What did you do in your other life, Starky?"

Starky replied directly to Mae, but Don's ears were also receiving the same conversation. "I started out as a chemist for Eli Lilly, but then went into cabinet making. We sold Indiana black walnut cabinets all over the world."

Don could not believe what his neighbor was telling him and Mae. "My great Uncle, E. B. Kipfer was sales manager for Eli Lilly for twenty-two years. Did you happen to know him?"

Mae thought Starky was going to faint. She was sure she saw his knees go wobbly. All the color left Starky's face. "Did I know him? I worked directly with him at Eli Lilly. I'll tell you a short story. One day he and Eli came screaming up the front drive of the company building in Eli's car. Apparently they had experienced all kinds of trouble on the way in. Eli was so mad I heard him shout, 'If anyone would give me a plugged wooden nickel for this car, they could have it!' E. B. reached into his pocket and handed over a nickel."

Mae entered this part of the conversation. "Did Mr. Lilly make good on his promise?"

"I really couldn't say for sure," laughed E. O., "but I noticed E. B. began driving that car right after Eli's offer!"

Now, after the grandchildren's trick and treat, Trim-the-Tree, and Christmas at Dave's home were over, Mae was entertaining again. Now it was the Starks, E. O. and Julia with Glen, Judy, and Carol on the twenty-sixth at Mae's home for cookies and coffee.

Then back to other activities. "Mae," laughed Don, "we've done better but a second in couples golf and a third in couples bridge isn't a bad way to begin the New Year."

"That may be your opinion," grinned Mae, "but, paisan, you're going to have to do better!"

On 27 January Mae and Don motored up to visit brother Tracy and Arlene at their new home in Bradenton. "They seem very happy with their living arrangements," concluded Mae. "I believe they'll stay there."

Then Mae and. Don prepared for a visit by Jacques and Pat Gelinas. "Whenever I visit with Pat and Jacques, it brings back wonderful memories of Ottawa and McClellan AFB. What heady times those were," reminisced Mae.

"Don't fret, my pretty little maid. You are having just as much influence today as ever. Not only on the adults but on your grandchildren. What opportunities they are benefitting from. Such activities as dining at Burnt Store Country Club teaches them values."

Almost to fulfill Don's prophecy, there were rapidly visits with the grandchildren to the Seafood Festival and the Parade of Ponce de Leon Conquistadors in their replica of Ponce's old sailing ship. "And look," screamed Kathyrn, Laura and David, "the Conquistadores are throwing out golden doubloons to the crowd!" And off all three of them dashed to collect their share.

But naturally, the adult activities continued. Mae and Don won first place in the prestigious Burnt Store Country Club Guys and Dolls tournament. Then another second in golf and a first at bridge on the same day. "Not to shabby," acknowledged Mae.

Kathyrn, Laura, and David were not only good students in academics and sports but also very good at art. Kathyrn was featured her first time on 27 April 1997 as a winner at the Punta Gorda Art Guild show. "Just like their father and grandfather," said Mae.

"What do you want most now, after such flattery, my dear friend?" added Don. "And, what are we doing here at Laura's and David's graduation from preschool, may I ask?" he whispered.

"You are correct in wondering where the time has disappeared to, great oracle," said Mae. "It seems like just yesterday that David arrived here, unable to roll from his back to his stomach! Now, they're graduating from preschool. And soon we'll be going to Kathryn's graduation from kindergarten! What I want is a continuous upward trend!"

Mae did not often brag about her husband's accomplishments in public. No one knew better than her that such activity could be counterproductive in the United States! But just this once she could not resist. "Of course, Don has sculpted wood scenes all over the United States, but this one is something special. He got permission to use a Florida state-protected live oak felled by the developer of The Breakers Restaurant. I watched the woodsman saw out an eight-foot section of the trunk and bring it to our garage."

Invariably her audience would ask, "What did Don carve?"

"A seven-and-one-half-foot-tall, two thousand pound 'Liberty,'" whistled Mae!

Having seen the photos, they would say, "The face looks like you, Mae. What are you going to do with it?"

"Well Burnt Store Country Club will have it for awhile. The expo gift shop wants it for a display. The SunBank will get a chance. And then it's going to the Charlotte County Cultural Center."

There was a short break in the routine in Punta Gorda, so it was time to hit the road and rekindle old times. "First," said Mae, "we're going to see Mary Lou and Bill in Port Orange. She told me we're dining at Norwood's Seafood in New Smyrna Beach."

Then, having had such a good time with the Blossers, the Kipfers were off to the Ponce de Leon golf resort at Saint Augustine to play with the Tartaskys. As they departed northward again, Don concluded, "The Tartaskys are so nice, and so much fun to play golf with. And, I enjoyed touring the Old Saint Augustine fort with them again.

Mae and Don stopped at Andrews AFB to take care of some official business and decided to stay overnight in the VIP quarters. "Why not again enjoy the good life? We earned it and God knows, we've never taken advantage of any of the perks to which we're entitled," pointed out Mae.

Then on to Bowie to visit with Charlie and Jane. "Let's hit restaurants," proposed Mae. "We can visit just as well there." So look out, Surfside 7 and Adam's Ribs, and after a splendid visit with Mae's aunt Vada in Silver Springs, it was a straight shot south again.

Some retirees found retired life boring. Not so with Mae and Don. Life was filled to overflowing and moving much to fast.

"A second in golf and a first in bridge," smiled Mae. "And also followed by a first in golf and a third in bridge. How about Dave being hired as a math and science teacher at Port Charlotte Middle School and both Kathyrn and Laura are at Sallie Jones Elementary School," reminded Mae.

"November 1 has always been a special day for me, since it my birthday. But since Anne's father Banks Hammond died on the very same day, it will always be a little clouded," admitted Don.

"Don's birthday," Mae told Bea and Don Nichols, has always been perfect because you two shared it with us at the Bell Ringers."

Mae told son Dave afterward, "It was such fun because Don Nichols had worked for Don at Andrews AFB nearly thirty years earlier and both couples had socialized together. Don N. had been Don's number one man to administer Rome Air Development Center and among the many technical activities he helped with he had been the lead on a study to evaluate a Technical

Agency at Kennedy Space Center. And as a sort of joke, Bea Nichols always gave Don K. a quickpick on the Florida Lottery for a birthday present!"

Then on 17 December one of life's tragedies struck the tight-knit Kipfer family. "Beloved son Charlie," Mae was told by Don, before she could reach her phone, "has had a massive heart attack and is in Doctor's Hospital. We've got to go to Bowie immediately!"

"Hello, Jane," interrupted Mae, her nurse's training springing forward to confront the occasion, "what's Charlie's prognosis?"

"It's serious. They can't do an angioplasty. They're going to have to do a bypass. I could use some help."

Mae had never declined a plea for help from anyone during her whole life. And neither had Don. And never had they faced such a terrifying emergency. But Mae told Don, "You're close to pneumonia. You've been warned by Doctor Tadalan to take care of yourself. No cold, no outdoor activity. If you go to the cold north you could die. We can't go. Jane has two full-grown men, John and Richard, living with her and they are each capable of independently running a household. There is no way we could help Charlie. He is in the hands of surgeons who would, not in any case, tolerate us interfering. Perhaps we could not even see him, and with your near pneumonia, you should not even be visiting the hospital. John and Richard will just have to wash their own dishes and dirty clothes."

Fortunately, in answer to prayers to God, Charlie survived the bypass surgery and very slowly returned to a near normal status. Mae, reasoned Don, is one active person to keep up with. Out of compassion, he asked her, "Are you sure you want to cook for, entertain, and update the Bebout/Hills, Wayne and Colin Hill, the Trent Thomases and Kevin, Grace Bebouts, Dave, Anne, Kathyrn, and the Eric Bebouts on New Year's Day?"

Mae rolled her head back and laughed. "Why would you ask? They're my relatives. We'll have a ball! And of course, if our museum isn't enough for entertainment, there's euchre and Chinese dominoes."

Then after this hectic month, Mae and Don saw January out by each winning first at golf on their gender days. "My dear, Florida has special hidden perks," Don told Mae, "like my first stone crab dinner at Longboat Key on 24 February with the Pat and Jacques Gelinas!"

"How did you like it, Neptune?' probed Mae.

"Wonderful. Wonderful. But it was Jacques' turn to finance the meal, and that bib, which said: MOORE'S STONE CRAB RESTAURANT, on its front, cost Jacques a small fortune!"

On 28 February the Tracy Gentry's, Bebout Hills, and Dave Kipfers were back for lunch at Mae's 'Fine Dining." Another Irish bash at the Cronins' and then another first place at bridge. Everyone in the Kipfer family really loves Charlotte County.

"The Florida International Air Show is one of the grandest in the United States," agreed Mae. "Especially, the three grandchildren liked it when that paratrooper came over, after jumping from ten thousand feet and gave them each a pencil!"

In April, Don began tennis lessons for all three grandchildren. During free play, Don and David played Kathyrn and Laura. Laura, a macho athlete, who knew her sports, complained bitterly, "Grandpa, that's not fair. You and David will win!"

Don told Mae, "Laura's growing up!"

On sixteenth of May, Mae and Don went to Books-A-Million for an auspicious occasion. "Unbelievable," admitted Mae. "Kathyrn's here showing her artwork and autographing copies of it! Her winning entry is a fine drawing of her dad, mother, herself, her sister and brother. It's a tribute to her feeling for her family."

"And what a beauty she, herself is!" admired her grandfather.

Then afterward, Mae said, "Let's take our grandchildren to the party at the Old Punta Gorda Train Station. There will be plenty to do there."

"OK," agreed Don, "but we're also going to the Frontier Days at Laishley Park, right on the Charlotte Harbor." So after the train station, off they went to Laishley Park. There, they all enjoyed the watermelon-spitting contest, racing on stilts, riding the miniature train, sack racing and a chance to weave under the watchful eye of their weaving expert and friend, Ann Ashworth.

On 31 May, Dave held a special, early fiftieth wedding, anniversary for Mae and Don. "Congratulations, Mom and Pop," smiled Dave. "You've made it."

"Yes," agreed Don "It has been a more fabulous trip than I could describe. I only wish I could do it again!"

On 4 June 1998 David Lauran Kipfer, draped in a blue gown and topped with a student's cap, graduated with honors from Miss Sylvia's Pre-School class.

But unknown to Mae and Don, despite the fact that they both saw their son and his wife at least once a week, the seeds of trouble were stirring in Anne and Dave's marriage. When Mae learned of this she was heartbroken. "Both Anne and Dave are highly educated. They are both intelligent and handsome. They live in what might be correctly called a mansion. They have three of the most beautiful, talented, and well-beloved children one could wish for. What else could one want" What else on this Earth is there!?"

"We may never know!" admitted Don.

This was just their first blow. The tornado was yet to strike. Don had proposed months earlier, "We've always had such a close-knit family. Because we all live so far apart and have different lifestyles, we've seemed to grow further apart. I've got a proposition that may help to bring us back together."

"Go, man, go," encouraged Mae .

"Why not arrange for everyone to take a cruise of the Caribbean? No work; meals together; lavish entertainment. Everyone can mix as much as they please. What do you think, matriarch?"

"Brilliant, Christopher. But getting seventeen independent thinkers, who all have different schedules, together at one point and one time will be tough, but we can do it!"

Don had reported to Mae in December. "The plan for the cruise is complete," guaranteed her hubbie. "I've made all the arrangements. "I've checked it out with Charlie, Mark, and Dave. All are ecstatic. Looks like a go."

But then came Charlie's heart attack on the 17th of December. "All that planning is of no use. He definitely cannot go cruising," declared Don.

Then strike number two. Mark's wife's father has been diagnosed with terminal cancer and could die any day. "You know how strongly she feels about her father. I'm sure she will not leave him."

Then for a third, and fatal blow to the cruise plan, Mae added. "Dave's new job, vital for his family, calls for him to administer student final exams during the period we would be gone. Looks like traveling is off for us, Pancho!"

Europe II

"Not so fast, my sweet optimist," cautioned Don. "We are the ones having the anniversary. We are the ones who have trod the world together. We are the ones who faced the ups and downs together for fifty years. We have walked the walk! We're going back to Europe!"

"Whoopee," agreed Mae.

"This time, my dear, sweet wife, we're going on a tour. There will be no detailed planning, no reservations to confirm, no scouting out the most important things to see, and no cooking. We're going as wealthy people of leisure!"

"Thank you, Wooden!"

And so these two world travelers from America's Midwest found themselves on their fiftieth wedding anniversary at the Novotel in London, England, just off Hyde Park. "Again we're seeing the Parliament, Big Ben ,the changing of the guards and the Hammersmith," announced Mae.

"This trip is to be a review of our fifty years of travel. But the fabulous box of candy and the yellow roses Dave sent are contemporary," pointed out Don.

"True, these presents certainly represent thoughtfulness and are fully appreciated. How could he arrange that?" wondered Mae.

"He's a retired Air Force officer. He can do anything," smirked Don.

Then across the English Channel to that wonderful Grand Place with its Gothic town hall, the Hotel DeVille. "And Don, you'll soon be eating at your favorite restaurant nearby, the one and only Chez Leon's."

"I really enjoyed our reunion dinner with Guy and Michelle Smeet, my Belgian secretary, and with Chris Falque, my interpreter when she took us to the spooky bar!"

In Amsterdam, Don, knowing better than any tour what Mae hoped to experience again in this wonderful town told her, "We're not scheduled with the tour to eat at a real Indonesian restaurant. We certainly cannot miss that. Let's peel off!"

"Wonderful idea." And as they walked by themselves along the street of restaurants, Mae was first to point. "There, that's a real Indonesian restaurant. They advertise Guangdong Cuisine!"

And as they ate, surrounded by the Indonesian ambiance, looking out on the Dutch street traffic, Mae could hardly contain herself. "A la, sweet treat. Thirty-two courses!" Then out of the Low Lands east to Germany. "Ah ha," whispered Mae. "Another cruise on the Rhine River."

"True," and on they progressed to the Marvelous Red Walled Castle. They stopped in the storied Heideberg and then in Rhineland everyone marveled at a wine barrel, the size of a railroad tunnel. When the tour stopped near Triberg in the Black Forest at a gorgeous half-timbered guest and souvenir shop, Don bounded out of their bus before anyone else even stood up. "See," he told a wondering wife who saw many things but perhaps not what her husband intended under that huge, beautiful clock set against the inn's wall. "Hornberger Glock-en-Spiel. Manuel Hornberger was the relative for whom my father was taken from grade school to labor on his huge farm. Can you believe that?"

"I've seen so many things in our fifty years together, that I am seldom surprised, miene herr," replied Mae.

At Triberg, Germany, Mae and Don saw a wood carving of the "Last Supper." "It's the same size and color as the one you carved, sweetie. And at first glance they might seem identical. But yours is better!"

Switzerland, the country where the apple shooter, William Tell shot the apple off his son's head with a bow and hunting arrow! Also the home of the Rhine Falls, Trout, and Lucerne. In Lucerne, Don suggested, "Let's break off from the tour," and they enjoyed Swan's Lake, yodeling, Alpine horn blowing, a folklore party, and the Tower Wall. "Voila!" reacted Mae.

The tour went over the Arlberg Pass and headed for Italy. "Let's get out and throw a few snowballs," lobbied Mae. She did not fool Don for a moment, for he fully understood her intentions. Still he was not fast enough to duck and Mae made a direct hit on her fast-maneuvering husband.

And almost before anyone could settle, they were over Brenner Pass and into Italy. "And again," smiled Mae, "we're back in Venice at the Grand Hotel. Could anyone even imagine the Byzantine Basilica or the million of souls who have passed through it? Or the clock tower on the Giudecca canal? Or Saint Mark's Square, itself?"

"Frankly," said artist and engineer Don, "I was fascinated by the very artistic glass blowing!"

And on their tour to Rome, the tour director stopped momentarily at Assisi to inspect the Basilica of Saint Frances. "I remember Charlie Skouras, your West Point classmate, retired from the Army and made the movie, *Saint Francis of Assisi*," Mae recalled.

"True enough. I went to see the movie, totally because Charlie had made it. It was one of the best I have ever seen. However, there was little pornography in the film and so it did not fare well at the box office!"

Mae kept pointing out to Don road signs that had "a six-legged dog with a caution underneath, which says *Agip*." "I'm glad I'm not driving," said the shrewd one.

And in Rome at the Jolly Midas Hotel, Mae and Don both threw three coins into the fountain. They again went to the Colosseum, Piazza Venezia, the medieval tower clock at San Gimignano, Pizza del Campas at Sienna, Gallery of Arts in Florence, Michaelangelo's *David*, the Santa Maria del Fiore, the Gate of Paradise, and the Ponte Vecchio shops.

The leaning Tower of Pisa, sixteen feet out of perpendicular, was a welcome repeat, as was Monaco. But this time Mae and Don were sad to visit the grave of Princess Grace. "What a beautiful, gracious person," exclaimed Mae.

"I agree with that," said Don. "But I remember a much younger Grace Kelly, when she was a starlet in New York City and came to our formal dances on Saturday night at West Point. You do remember those?"

Ignoring this side comment, Mae shouted, "Paree, Paree!" and giggled. Again the Champs Elysees, the Arc of Triumphe, Sofitel Porte de Sevres, onion soup, Lacostes, Place de Concord, Montmartre, Notre Dame, and la Nouvelle Cabaret!"

"What a wonderful way to celebrate fifty years as a world traveler," said

Mae as they flew homeward.

"Nothing could be better," agreed Don.

Conclusion.

In Punta Gorda there were the hilarious birthday parties on 2 July for David's fifth and on 23 July for Laura's sixth. Mae had been an accomplished athlete all her life. By fourteen she had all the badges obtainable from the Red Cross swimming program. In Punta Gorda she had presented her credentials to the local administration and, as a result, had officially trained Kathyrn, Laura, and David in all the delicacies of proper swimming. On his fifth birthday Mae told David to stand and come straight to center. "David Kipfer, in recognition of your swimming accomplishments, I award you the Red Cross pollywog badge." All present clapped.

There are many advantages to living in a small town. In September, Mae and Don, took the grandchildren to the Punta Gorda's Adventure Museum to enjoy a new display. Who should be there but the oft-quoted, and famous historian, U.S. Cleveland. Don walked up to the historian and presented him with a copy of Don's novelette, *Punta Gorda*. "Now, kids," Don advised Kathryn, Laura, and David, "for historical evidence, come over here and have your picture taken with Mr. Cleveland." And so it was done.

And so another chockful year was helped on its way by a huge Mae's Trim-the-Tree-Party, Christmas at Dave's home where David received a real live miniature jeep from Grandma and Grandpa Kipfer, and New Year's at Dave's home on a warm, tropical night on the banks of his beautiful, saltwater canal.

"How can you top that?" asked Mae.

"Mae," purred Don, pulling Mae to him, embarrassing her warmly and giving her a passionate kiss, "when I was a boy I never expected to live to see the twenty-first century. Now we have just one more year to go," commented Don.

"Don, your mother always said, it's 'abominable to get old because all your friends are gone.' Still, I intend to go happily on. True, the people we have come to love in the past quarter century are rapidly leaving us, but we are making more friends," countered Mae.

Thus began another crammed year. "Don and Laura picked bushels of oranges, climbed to the top of the rocket in Gilchrist Park, and took a tennis lesson," Mae told Dave.

"On 8th of January Kathyrn and Laura took art lessons from Don," Mae announced to Anne.

"On 16 January David built a space port on Mae's lanai from boxes, cars, and space ships," Mae reported to Don. Don carefully inspected the creation. David waited anxiously for his grandfather's reaction

"Very good, David. Realistic. As good as I could do!"

On 23 January, Dave, Kathyrn, Laura, and David picked a record nine-pound turnip that they had raised in their very own garden. "I must have a picture of that," declared Mae. Then off they went to the Shell Creek Antique Air Show.

"Your past always comes back to jog your memory," philosophized Don. Les Schaub appeared one day out of nowhere. "He worked with you at Wright Field in the Armament Laboratory in 1952 and again in Baltimore and at Andrews AFB in the Systems Command Headquarters. He looks good," evaluated Mae.

"He's doing OK, but he misses Ronnie. You recall, Ronnie died," reminded Don.

"Mae's still winning at team play and all the other golfing events," Don told one of their old-time golf partners, now unable to play, but like all the others, interested in Mae's abilities.

"Laura's off to dance classes. Mae and I won third in couples golf and third in bridge. Kathyrn's featured in her school's talent show," Don told a near-normal Charlie, when he called.

Again the Kipfers enjoyed entertaining the Gelanas, and then, one of Don's favorite cousins, the Betty and Bill Snitzers.

"All of our grandchildren are good soccer players," noted Mae. You saw that for yourself, today, Don. You got to cheer as their team won, two to one and David scored one goal," Mae repeated.

On the 8th of March, four huge Ohio black walnut planks, 12 x 5 x 36 inches arrived from Warren Wefler. "It's good, Mae, to have a millionaire for a friend, eh what?" Ana Mae laughed at the joke.

"And those thirteen big farms Warren owns will never miss those few planks!"

On 13 March Tracy and Arlene arrived. Cronins held their St. Patrick's Ball at 1700 and duplicate bridge was at Gulicks at 1930. "A rather full day," Mae mentioned to Don.

On the 18th Mae and Don won first in couples golf. And the next night the President's Ball at a ten-person table. "Gosh, we're busy," smirked Mae.

"Those grandkids are something," raved Don, shaking his head. "David's 'Student of the Month,' and Kathyrn's art is on display again at the Visual Arts Center!"

Mae was a conscientious Christian all her life. Her academic courses all through school, including college had contained religious studies. Don had been a Sunday school superintendent, deacon, and Sunday men's Sunday school teacher before he was seventeen. Mae brooked no nonsense on this special subject. "Our grandchildren must taste the joy of being a Christian. It's sunrise service for us all on this Easter. Shoney's for breakfast afterwards."

On the 21st, at Heibers' home, and two tables of bridge, Don won first. There was a near revolt. Everyone shouted, "Don't tell us you never win," they all laughed. On the 27th, everyone went again to the Florida International Air Show. "What a blowout," laughed Mae.

Mae always sought improvement. In Canada she had taught her own sons to cook and bake when they were four, five, and six years old. "Today," Don pointed out, "no one can do better at cooking and baking." And so it was no surprise when Don saw David, Laura, and Kathyrn, four, five, and seven, working like beavers over their delicious hot cross buns in Mae's kitchen. "Bravo," bragged Don, pretending to steal one as they came out of the oven.

Back again to the Florida Frontier Days for all the games and for Pirate Days. "Grandma," laughed sweet Kathyrn, "we liked that."

On 8th of May, Mae and Don won first at duplicate bridge. "It was certainly time again that we showed some skill!" agreed Don.

Mae understood all the messages when Don asked his grandchildren. "Kids, if you spend all your money, how much will you ever have left?" After hearing the axiom so many times the chorus was always, "NONE!"

Thus Mae opened a savings account for each grandchild in the Nations Bank. "They earn money for good school work and special achievements," Mae explained to Don.

Don almost became spasmodic. "One of these days Kathyrn will be a thousandier."

As a follow up to these incentives, Laura, in the first grade, received, best in computer study, first in physical education, and most improved. "Are you sure we can bank roll your incentive program, my dear," pretended Don.

"Oh, yes," replied Mae. "I do not spend all the money I get!"

On 10 July, Jane and Charlie arrived in Punta Gorda by air and again Mae and Don invited, "We'll do what ever you like, Charlie."

Charlie simply blurted out that plenty of fishing and a good Thanksgiving dinner in July, would do! And so Mae immediately began preparing a full-blown feast!

Then on 25 July Marylou and Bill arrived. Off to Bokeelia on Pine Island for lunch, dinner for eight at Mae's, the following day to Burnt Store Country Club for lunch, and the SouthTrust Bank for picture taking with *Liberty*. "Everything's squeezed in," laughed Marylou.

On 18 August, *Liberty* was transported to the Charlotte County Cultural Center. Mae filled in: "The manager says thirty thousand people a year visit his center. A good place for *Liberty.*"

On 24 October, Mae was packed and ready. "Las Vegas again, boy. Getting together with EOAR will be fun but watch your money!"

So once again a glorious reunion with the Warrens, Bill Woodyard, Vera Alexandre, Michelle Smeets, Bob Lamb, and all the others. Breakfast at the Desert Inn, the Circus Circus, the New Frontier, Treasure Island, and the Venetian. "Oh, my," gasped Mae. And when Don stepped out into the atrium, he saw real Venetian gondolas. When he looked up he told Mae, "Nature has blessed Las Vegas, at least in one way. What a glorious sky!"

Mae burst out in roaring laughter, "You must have eaten to much breakfast, lover. That ain't sky, boy! That's a painted canopy!"

"No point in wasting a trip West when we can hop across the mountains and see Jacquelyn and Ron Martin in San Juan Capistrano," suggested Mae.

And so there they were, high on a cliff above the Wild Pacific in Jacquelyn's backyard patio looking out at Santa Catilina!

"Can you believe, Copernicus, herself not so sure, that those huge earth movers are topping the 'mountain' just across from us to put in a housing development," Mae gushed out in utter amazement. "They are literally changing the skyline."

"What a project!" added Don.

Mae was fascinated and continued to appraise this engineering miracle. "But what is that object I see way out in the Pacific?"

Jacquelyn, by now accustomed to the activity just across the valley from her house roared with glee. "That, my beautiful cousin, is Santa Catalina Island! The mountain that blocked our view is gone. We can see it twenty-four hours a day, now. Whoopee!"

Again they went back to the Mission and watched the beautiful young Hispanic girls dance in the court and wondered at the Mission's spectacular bells. And then, when it was to soon time to leave, Don returned with Mae, a year older, to beautiful Punta Gorda.

"Your schedule for the last several weeks of this century looks like you didn't schedule time to sleep, my dear!" wondered Don. "Could anyone imagine undergoing such torture?"

"Buck up, Gargantua. Enjoy yourself."

"Start with Santa and Kathyrn, Laura and David at Fishermen's Village; soccer games and trophy presentations for all three grandchildren; Don's belated birthday party with the Don and Bea Nichols at Holiday Inn; Thanksgiving dinner at Mae's Inn; a huge Mae's Trim-the-Tree party, with Ann

Ashworth and Dave Kipfer winning the blind boggle; golf and lunch with Dave at BSCC; on 5 December Kathyrn's Master of Ceremonies performance at Sallie Jones; Kathyrn in the Swingsations at Gilchrist Park; Kathyrn helping Mae bake springerly cookies; the private family Trim-the-Tree-Party at Mae's for Dave, Shawn, Kathyrn, Laura, David and Anna Kate; the boat ride for all the Kipfers through miles of spectacularly lighted canals in Punta Gorda Isles; the Christmas morning opening of hundreds of presents at Dave's 5630 Almar Drive; the viewing of Kathyrn's bedroom walls with paintings side to side and top to bottom by her father Dave with indescribably beautiful underwater scenes; a visit by Louise Grow on 31 December from Newark, whose father was in business with Mae's father Tracy, and whose son George and his wife, Linda, accompanied Louise.

No sooner than the Grows left, Mae and Don took their grandchildren to Fishermen's Village to see and thoroughly explore a live, operating replica of Columbus' ship, the *Nina*.

As they left Fishermen's Village, David proposed, "Grandma, how about stopping off at your house for some of your delicious Christmas desserts, before we go home?"

How could a grandmother resist such a request? As they sat on Mae's lanai, looking out at the saltwater through her tropically landscaped back yard, Kathyrn asked another question, "Grandmother, Daddy says you were a great athlete when you were young. You know we are soccer players and study tae kwan do. We'd like to know what you did."

Mae was silent for a long time. The kids wondered if she was really going to tell them anything. Finally, she spoke, "Well, children, it'll probably be a little boring, but if you want, I'll tell you."

Everyone clapped. They all smiled and relaxed on the stuffed lanai chairs ready to listen. Mae began, "When I was about Kathyrn's age, I lived across Twenty-first Street in Newark, Ohio, from three boy cousins. One was about my age and the other two were older. Sometimes two of my other cousins, Eber and Helen Updike would join us. We would run endurance races."

"What," asked David, "is an endurance race?"

"We'd run at top speed around the large side yard until you could not run anymore and fell down, exhausted. I always won!"

"Wow," said Laura, shaking her head, imaging how she would have felt. At Woodrow Wilson Junior High School I ran track, played basketball, softball, and soccer. I earned my Red Cross instructor lifesaving diplomas and taught many swimming classes, at Newark's municipal pool."

"In high school, at Mount Vernon Academy in Academia, I played basketball and volleyball and coached and referred both. I did the same thing at

Sligo Academy in Takoma Park, near Washington, D.C."

Don interrupted, "Kids, I believe I should take over from here. I have kept a record of your grandmother's records and I will use those to bring you up to date." He looked each grandchild in the eye before continuing. "Your grandmother was busy the next several years raising your dad and his two brothers. But when we went to Ottawa, Canada, she showed many Canadian men how a Yankee woman could ice skate, ice ski, bowl, and play tennis.

"When our family returned from Canada to live in Linthicum, Maryland, and your father and his two brothers were in school, your grandmother finally had time to get serious about golf. I hope all of you appreciate her marvelous record!"

1956–1957 Fort Mead Maryland. 9 Hole Golf Club Champion.

1958 AAFB, Maryland. Bowling, High game 208

1959 AAFB, Maryland 9 hole golf champion

1960 AAFB Maryland 9 hole golf champion

1961–1965 Maxwell AFB, Alabama Consistant place, 18 hole

1965–1968 Brussels Belgium 2nd place, Ladies Austrian downhill giant salom.

1969–1970 Maxwell AFB 18 hole, 4th Flt Golf Champion Mae's Moppet's Bowling team, 1st

1971–1974 Andrews AFB, MD Consistant winner, 18 hole golf Bowling Team, first place

1975–1978 McClellan AFB, State Representative, Lawrence Links California. Women's Golf Team Base Champion, 18 hole Golf Base Champion all four years

1976 MCClellan AFB Bowling high series, 502

1978 Burnt Store CC Ladies Golf Team member

1979 Burnt Store CC Ladies Golf Team member, tournament chairman

1980 Burnt Store CC Team member, handicap chairman

1981 Burnt Store CC Member Golf Team, 18 Hole Ladies Golf Assoc. president. Established first 18 hole Ladies Constitution and Bylaws, golf team member

1982 Burnt Store CC president, BSCC Ladies Golf Assoc. member, Golf Team

1983 Burnt Store CC Ladies Golf Team member

1984 Burnt Store CC Golf Team member, Club Alligator Classic champion, Club Ladies Champion, BSCC nominating committee

1985 Burnt Store CC BSCC Club Champion, Golf Team member

1986 Burnt Store CC BSCC Club Champion, Golf Team member

1987 Burnt Store CC Won Four day Couples Championship, Doral. Hole-

In -One BSCC # 17, Champion Alligator Classic, Champion Swatfest. Golf Team member

1988 Burnt Store CC Golf Team member

1989 Burnt Store CC Medicare runnerup, Golf Team member

1990 Burnt Store CC Hole-in-one, Golf Team Captain, West Central Florida Golf Team Champions

1991 Burnt Store CC Vice President WCFWGA, Champion, Alligator Classic, Champion President's Cup First Couples Member-Guest BSCC

1992 Burnt Store CC Golf Team member

1993 Burnt Store CC President WCFWGA, Golf Team member

1994 Burnt Store CC Golf Team member, four firsts at Couples golf

1995 Burnt Store CC 1st Presidents cup A Flight, Team member 3 Firsts BSCC Couples Golf

1996 Burnt Store CC Golf Team Member, 5 firsts Couples Golf, 1st Memorial Day Couples

1997 Burnt Store CC BCSS 1st Place Guys and Dolls. 3 First in Couples, Golf Team member

1998 Burnt Store CC 1st Annual Salvation Army. 4 Firsts Couples Golf, member Golf Team

1999 Burnt Store CC Team Fun Day 1st Place team, 1st Labor Day couples, 4 first couples, Golf team Member.

When Don had finished his list, he made an additional comment: "What I have told you are just the most important accomplishments your grandmother has made. If you count all the tournaments during her twenty-two years here in Punta Gorda in which she has placed as a single, a double, or a member of a four-person team you would have more than three thousands wins!"

Mae had three really animated grandchildren. Kathyrn shouted, "Wow!" Laura added, "Wonderful!" And David concluded, "That's my grandmother!"

After this historical review, they all went to Dave's house for a huge New Year's Eve celebration.

Safe again in their Via Formia retreat after a riotous New Year's Eve Party, Mae kissed Don and. declared, "My dear, we made it!"

After breakfast on New Year's morning, Don took Mae by the arm, kissed her and led her over to a plush couch. Always wary of her aging husband's motives, Mae looked at him in surprise for he had never acted in such a formal manner with her ever before. "What's up, governor?"

"Mae you know that all the expert historians call our generations 'The Greatest.' More than anyone I have ever known you deserve that accolade.

Of course, I have walked every step with you and no one knows what you have accomplished better than I do. When I met you as a fourteen-year-old governess in Newark, Ohio, and knew that I would marry you one day, I could not in my wildest dreams believe that you could accomplish the unbelievable feats I have witnessed!

"To make any complete record I suppose I must go back to your sports accomplishments, to your coaching and refereeing, especially in track, basketball and swimming. You gave young kids a chance they otherwise never would have gotten. Rising from such a meager financial base, your skill in getting and paying for an education at the private Academy at Mount Vernon and at Takoma Parks Missionary College was a hopeful beacon for all the poor kids in Ohio. Who else could pull off such an impossible feat?

"Your good looks and friendly attitude bolstered the self-esteem of many drags at West Point. And for the record, it should show that you were the first young woman to wear a cadet gray, tailored uniform to an Army-Navy game.

"You were a rallying point for the younger West Point wives in their first assignment at Randolph Field, especially since you had been a teacher and had nursing training and they we mostly all pregnant and had to send their husbands off to dangerous flight training each morning.

"None of the NATO pilot trainees will ever forget the angel who rescued them from deep depression at Goodfellow AFB. Who can guess what those men have accomplished?

"At the USAF Institute of Technology at Wright Field you took the total responsibility for raising three infant sons under three years old. You personally, without any help, clothed them, attended their toilet, got up at night and tended to their frequent childhood ills. All so your husband could devote full time to his master's degree studies in the first automatic control class in the country. In addition, you helped out at the base nursery, the Officers Wives Club and made an unmistakable impression on my full colonel advisor.

"When I reported into the Armament Laboratory at Wright Field as a brand-new captain, and found myself in charge of a section of three other engineers, senior NCOs, and a secretary, you immediately assumed the role of a commander's wife. You met the younger incoming wives, arranged for their off-base housing and made yourself available for consultations.

"When we were reassigned as a result of a request from the Canadian government, to Ottawa, Canada, you took off on a course that seemed predestined. You joined the U.S. Embassy Officer Wives Club and also the RCAF Officers Wives Club. You drove all the American wives about Ottawa in snow, ice, and cold of winter. You were the guiding direction for the parents of De Roy Kennedy school in the organization of their elementary school's PTO.

"You held huge cocktail parties for fifty or more RCAF officers and their ladies on a monthly basis. Always with good humor and a smile.

"When you arrived in Canada you saw signs on places that sold alcoholic beverages saying, 'Women' on one door and 'Men' on another. You said, 'Canucks, that must go!' And, for your farewell party at the Ottawa RCAF Officers Mess, our invitation read, 'Captain and Mrs. Kipfer.' It was the first time a female had entered the mess. It was to honor the respect the Canadians had for you.

"Back home in Baltimore and Andrews AFB, you had plenty to do raising five, six, and seven-year-old sons. However, you increased your influence by taking up the sport of golf and winning tournament after tournament, at Fort Mead and Andrews AFB. Again you helped with the Officers Wives Club projects.

"So beautiful, so kind, never a grumpy moment, you found yourself as the head of the Andrews AFB Officers Wives Club Hostess Committee. Soon you were the official hostess for General Foulois, the first chief of staff of the Air Corp. Then you were hostess for the first seven astronauts wives when ever they were in Washington, D.C.

"At the Air University you continued to excel at golf and to assist as a temporary teacher at Bellingrath Elementary School. With three sons involved in track and football there were plenty of cuts and bruises to mend. And again, your shoulder was used by many a young wife with depression problems. Your frequent parties at your home helped raise the moral of the whole Warfare Systems School.

"In Brussels, Belgium, at the European Office of Aerospace Research you hit a new level of accomplishment. Now, as Technical Operations for Europe, Asia, and Africa, I was busy. Not only did you have to arrange for family trips to all Europe's fun places, but to help entertain visitors to Brussels. Perhaps one of your most fun responsibilities but also one carrying the most responsibility was guiding the trip arranged by the Dakaks of Jerusalem for the wives of the thirty American executives wives through Greece, the Middle East and Egypt. Could anyone believe you would have to dodge the six-day war and a coup attempt in Greece?

"But even more trying was the return trip on the USS *United States* to the Montgomery home for you and David. Such a close-knit family. Husband off to Vietnam, two sons off to college. But you held it all together! My trip to Vietnam was hell, but after I had survived, it was an experience I would never trade for anything.

"On your own trip to visit me in Vietnam and Thailand you didn't miss an opportunity. You certainly impressed the senior member of SEATO!

"When I returned from Vietnam, a walking skeleton, covered with ribbons and medals, of all the people in the world, you were the only one to come and meet me. Shame on my fellow citizens! You knew you were back in the thick of government operations, when we were off to Roslyn, Virginia and then to Andrews AFB where I was director of electronics, avionics and weapons in the director of laboratories. Back for you to winning on the Golf course and work with the Officers Wives Club. You had dozens of wives of officers on my staff to consider and thousands in the field. Now you were busy advising younger wives and orchestrating more parties. Your influence on our country was immeasurable.

"And our final military assignment to McClellan AFB where I was responsible for worldwide logistics of all Air Force Ground electronics, the A-10 aircraft, and the Space Shuttle. Now it was necessary for you to have many personal consultations with wives of staff personnel. Small parties were held at your quarters but you were the official hostess with the mostest for huge official parties held at the Officers Club. It was at McClellan that you took up tennis again and played on the base team. You were on three different bowling teams. Each of the four years we were at McClellan you were the Ladies Base Golf Champion.

"Departing the Air Force, and its daily exposure to danger, life in Punta Gorda, Florida, seemed like heaven. Your retirement home, much grander than you had planned, with a boat at your dock and access to the Gulf of Mexico and a new Cadillac made life seem bonny.

"You soon had us entering and winning golf tournaments at BSCC. And soon also winning at party and duplicate bridge. But although you relished the constant flow of friends and relatives as houseguests, golf was your challenge. You and I, you as single, you with a doubles partner, and you as a team member during the twenty-two years in Punta Gorda, have won or placed in more than three thousand tournaments!

"You've won the BSCC President's Cup, the BSCC Alligator Classic, the BSCC Club Championship, the Swatfest, BSCC Medicare Open runner-up, The WCFLGA Women's Team Championship (Team Captain) numerous invitationals, the BSCC Couples Member Guest, among many others.

"You've served as tournament chairman, birdie chairman, team cocaptain, team captain, president of the BSCC Ladies Golf Association, treasurer of the SW Florida Ladies Golf Assoc. and as its president. You put in place a constitution that put the Ladies of Burnt Store in conformance with the USGA. You insisted that the captain of the golf team select the best qualified golfers for team members. You met all the new BSCC members and encouraged them to join the Ladies Golf Association and to play in their tournaments.

"You have remained with me all these years. You have given your sons the family base and education they deserve." As Don caught his breath, he again pulled his beautiful, talented, even-tempered wife to him and kissed her. "My dear, you have simply torn the twentieth century to shreds. Your grandfather told me those many years ago, 'Mae is a princess.' Your mother told me, 'Mae is an angel.' But I know, having shared every step of your path with you, watching you radiate America's personal freedom, and having witnessed the constructive effect you've had on the Old Earth's people, that you are indeed, "An American Princess!"

Don felt Mae shudder. Then she smiled and looked up at him with her sweet, audacious smile, saying, "*Mon ami*, if you think my performance in the twentieth century was good, watch me in the next one"

About the Author

Colonel Donald Charles Kipfer is of English-German descent. He was born in rural Ohio during the Roaring Twenties.

Colonel Kipfer nurtured his appreciation of America's natural wonders by working as a farmhand and in the steel mills. He entered the military as an aviation cadet during World War II, graduated from West Point, and serviced his country as a pilot, scientist, and engineer during three world conflicts. His extensive travels have proved conclusively to the author of *American Princess* that the American political system is one of modern man's greatest accomplishments.

Colonel Kipfer resides in Punta Gorda, Florida, with his wife, Edna Mae Gentry Kipfer, an American princess.

Printed in the United States
1186200005B/43-204